THE LANGUAGE GAME

www.penguin.co.uk

THE LANGUAGE GAME

How Improvisation Created Language
and Changed the World

MORTEN H. CHRISTIANSEN
AND NICK CHATER

BANTAM PRESS

TRANSWORLD PUBLISHERS
Penguin Random House, One Embassy Gardens,
8 Viaduct Gardens, London SW11 7BW
www.penguin.co.uk

Transworld is part of the Penguin Random House group of companies
whose addresses can be found at global.penguinrandomhouse.com

First published in Great Britain in 2022 by Bantam Press
an imprint of Transworld Publishers

A CIP catalogue record for this book
is available from the British Library.

ISBNs 9781787633483 (hb)
9781787633490 (tpb)

Typeset in 11/16pt ITC New Veljovic Pro by Jouve (UK), Milton Keynes.
Printed and bound in Great Britain by Clays Ltd, Elcograf S.p.A.

The authorized representative in the EEA is Penguin Random House Ireland,
Morrison Chambers, 32 Nassau Street, Dublin D02 YH68.

Penguin Random House is committed to a sustainable future
for our business, our readers and our planet. This book is made
from Forest Stewardship Council® certified paper.

To our families

CONTENTS

PREFACE

THE ACCIDENTAL INVENTION
THAT CHANGED THE WORLD

Language is essential to what it means to be human, yet we rarely give it a second thought. We discover just how central it is to every aspect of our lives only when it fails us – whether in a foreign city or following a stroke. Imagine the cataclysmic impact of a mystery virus that deprived us of language: modern civilization would rapidly give way to anarchy; citizens would be lost in an informational vacuum, unable to coordinate, bargain or reason with each other. Or consider an evolutionary scenario in which our ancestors never developed language. Without the ability to transmit information and skills easily from person to person, to share ideas, form plans or make promises, it is hard to imagine we could have developed the cultural and technological sophistication of contemporary hunter-gatherers, let alone more complex societies. Having a large, humanlike brain is not enough. We need look no further than our nearest primate cousins – the bonobos, chimpanzees, gorillas and orangutans – for an idea of how limited our society would be *without* language. The gulf between ape communities and human society in the areas of culture and technology may not result only from language.[1] But, as we will see, the human invention of language is probably the key factor from which most of the other differences flow.

Even though language is deeply rooted in everything we do, it is profoundly puzzling. How can mere noises or gestures convey meaning at all? What are the patterns in the sounds, words and meanings of which language is composed, and where do they come from? Why is understanding how a language works such an immense challenge for armies of professional language scientists when each new generation of children can easily master their native tongue by the age of four? What is it about the human brain that makes language possible? Why don't we all speak the same language? Why can't chimps talk? Can machines understand language?

Progress towards answering these and many other questions has been blocked by the fundamental misconception that the rough-and-tumble of everyday language is a pale shadow of an ideal language, where words have clear meanings and are put together following well-defined grammatical rules. But this traditional story has things exactly backward. Real languages are not slightly mangled variants of a purer, more orderly linguistic system. Instead, actual language is always a matter of improvisation, of finding an effective way to meet the communicative demands of the moment. Humans are playful, metaphorical, creative communicators whose words only gradually come to have more stable meanings. And the relatively stable regularities of grammar are not the starting point. They are the *result* of countless generations of communicative interaction, through which linguistic patterns become ever more entrenched. We shall see that the apparent impurity, disorder and ill-discipline of contemporary speech does not represent a ragged instantiation of some perfect ideal. Instead, the bricolage of language, its bafflingly complex, interacting and overlapping patterns, is a product of its history – the myriad conversations that have incrementally and inadvertently created today's sophisticated linguistic systems. The spontaneous emergence of linguistic order is a story as remarkable as the emergence of life itself.

Language, we suggest, is like a game of charades – a limitless collection of loosely connected games, each shaped by the demands of the situation and the shared history of the players. Like charades, language is continually 'invented' in the moment and reinvented each time we play again. Ludwig Wittgenstein, arguably the most influential philosopher of the twentieth century, saw meaning as arising from how we use language in communicative games. A cry of 'Hammer!' could be an instruction to start hammering or to pass a hammer. It might be a warning that a hammer is falling from a nearby roof, a reminder to buy a hammer or not to forget to bring one, and so on. The possibilities are limited only by our imagination. What counts as a hammer, or hammering, will depend on which 'language game' we happen to be playing. When putting up a tent, a hammer can be a mallet or a convenient stone; if we're demolishing a house, a sledgehammer is a good hammer, but if we want to carefully shape metal jewellery, we'd want a delicate 'chasing hammer' instead. For Wittgenstein, it makes no sense to ask what 'hammer' means independent of its use in a particular communicative game. The meaning of a word comes from how we use it in conversation.[2]

From this perspective, learning a language is like learning to be part of a series of endless, community-wide games of charades, where each new game builds on those that have gone before. Each new generation of language learners is not starting from scratch but joining a tradition of linguistic games that have been in progress from before anyone can remember. To join in the game, the child, or the second-language-learning adult, needs to jump into a linguistic game and start playing.

This is how they gradually master specific communicative challenges, one by one. Learning a language is learning to become a skilful charades player. To play language games successfully, we need to be adept at dealing with the back-and-forth of everyday human interactions – we don't need to learn an abstract system of grammatical patterns. We talk without knowing the rules of our language just as we play tennis without knowing the laws of physics, or sing without knowing music theory. In this very real sense, we speak, and do so skilfully and effectively, without *knowing* our language at all.[3]

In this book, we outline a revolutionary perspective that overhauls almost everything we thought we knew about language. We shall see how the game of charades, where linguistic communication is banned, paradoxically reveals deep insights into how language works. We'll explain how our brain is able to improvise linguistic 'moves' at an astonishingly rapid rate, how we create meaning 'in the moment', and how the rich and complex patterns in language emerge from the accumulation of layers of past games rather than from an innate genetic blueprint or language instinct. We'll see how languages are in continual flux, how people without a common tongue can create language from scratch surprisingly rapidly, and why it's likely that language has been independently reinvented countless times. Language games can develop in many directions, and it is this open-ended process that has led to the amazing diversity of languages across the world. And the creation of language is not only important in itself – it also changed the nature of evolution. It is what makes human culture possible, with its laws, religions, arts, sciences, economics and politics. We'll find, too, that the improvised inventiveness of human language is why real humanlike communication is so incredibly difficult for artificial intelligence to mimic. This in turn has profound implications for whether computers will really be able to outsmart us in the near future.

We'll argue that language is perhaps humanity's greatest accomplishment. Yet it is not a product of individual design or brilliant foresight; it is the result of a uniquely human ability to play successive communicative games. In our daily interactions, all we ever aim to do is to construct a solution to the conversational challenge of the moment. But over time, systems of communication begin to emerge through multitudes of conversational encounters. Humanity's most important invention turns out to be unplanned, a side-effect, a collective accident.

◉

This is a book about how language emerges gradually, one communicative interaction at a time. And the ideas in this book have themselves emerged gradually, one conversation at a time, in the thirty years that we, the authors, have been working together on language. The two of us met at the University of Edinburgh, where we received our PhDs at the Centre for Cognitive Science (now part of the School of Informatics). Our scepticism concerning the then-dominant view of language as being governed by abstract mathematical principles that might be encoded in our genes was one of the many things that drew us together. We, like many others, wanted to explore ways in which the rule-like nature of language might arise as a side-effect of more fundamental principles.

Many memorable conversations have followed, such as the fascinating discussion we had with philosopher Andy Clark (at a bar where Nick, looking potentially under-age and having left his passport in the car, couldn't initially have a drink) that ranged from why scissors fit our hands and why popular tunes are so easy to sing, to how language has evolved. Another time, when we took a memorable post-conference stroll in Vancouver's Stanley Park, with the sun sparkling on the ocean, we realized that the complex interlocking patterns in language may be the product of construction (like building the Eiffel Tower using different kinds of Lego blocks) rather than of reduction (like chiselling it from a single block of raw marble) – a change of viewpoint that completely shifted our understanding of how languages are learned and how they change. Later, we started to see deep links between patterns in language at different timescales: the fleeting flow of speech, the years it takes a child to learn language, and the centuries and millennia over which languages themselves form and change. Other pieces of the puzzle gradually fell into place as we pondered these and related ideas in subsequent meetings.

The centre of gravity in the study of language has shifted dramatically over the past three decades, and it has been a wonderful experience for us both to be part of that change. Yet the received wisdom about language passed on to the general public and to the many researchers outside our field remains stuck somewhere in the mindset of the mid-1990s or earlier. Since then, and to some extent before that point, a new picture has been forming about how language works. The astonishing mental gymnastics that allow us to talk with each other, and the piecemeal process by which languages are learned, have fundamentally shaped language as we know it today. Humans have collectively and inadvertently created language, which has allowed us to dominate the planet and, quite literally, change the course of evolution. The story of language is the story of humanity; the new understanding of language that we outline in this book radically revises our conception of ourselves.

1

LANGUAGE AS CHARADES

The term *'language-game'* is meant to bring into promin-
ence the fact that the *speaking* of language is part of an
activity, or of a form of life.

LUDWIG WITTGENSTEIN,
Philosophical Investigations (1953)

After days of heavy squalls, Captain Cook and the crew of HMS
Endeavour were finally able to drop anchor at two o'clock in the
afternoon on 16 January 1769. They moored in the Bay of Good
Success on Tierra del Fuego at the very south-eastern tip of South
America, hoping to replenish their supplies of fresh water and
wood before attempting the two-month voyage across the empty
South Pacific Ocean to Tahiti, where they would observe the
transit of Venus. After dinner, Cook, along with the botanist
Joseph Banks and the Swedish naturalist Dr Daniel Solander, led
a party of men ashore to search for water and, as Cook strikingly
put it, 'to speak with the Natives'.

Once ashore, they were met by a group of about thirty to

forty indigenous people, most likely a band of Haush hunter-gatherers, who appeared at the end of a sandy beach and then retreated. Banks and Solander broke away from the rest of Cook's men and advanced a hundred yards or so. Two of the Haush people stepped forward about fifty yards in the direction of the Europeans, displayed small sticks and then threw them aside. Cook's party interpreted this as indicating that the natives had peaceful intentions, and they were right. The gifts that Cook's men offered to the Haush were, according to Banks, 'receivd with many uncouth signs of friendship'. Three of the Haush even came aboard the ship, where they ate bread and beef (though apparently not very enthusiastically) but refused rum and brandy, gesturing that it burned their throats. Banks noted: 'After having been aboard about 2 hours they expressd a desire of going ashore and a boat was orderd to carry them.'[1]

What is perhaps most astonishing about this encounter is that it was possible at all. The Haush and the Europeans could hardly have been more different from one another (see figure 1.1). For example, the clothing that each group wore would have seemed equally strange and unusual to the other. Whereas the Europeans wore the shirts, waistcoats, jackets, breeches and hats typical of their period, the Haush – both women and men – wore cloaks made from the skins of seals or guanacos (a wild descendant of the domestic llama) thrown over their shoulders and reaching down to their knees. Also, as Cook remarked, 'the Women wear a peice of skin over their privey parts but the Men observe no such decency'. The Haush lived in beehive-shaped huts made from sticks and covered with branches and grass, with an opening on one side facing a fire. For food, the women collected various kinds of shellfish and the men hunted seals with bows and arrows. The Europeans found no signs of government, religion

Figure 1.1. Drawing by the Scottish landscape artist Alexander Buchan showing the *Endeavour* crew refilling their water barrels and interacting with the Haush on the shores of the Bay of Good Success on Tierra del Fuego.

or even boats. Given all of these differences, how could Cook confidently set out to 'speak with' the local people? How could a ship of European explorers and an isolated hunter-gatherer community successfully exchange gifts and food? And how could the Haush indicate a desire to go ashore at the end of their visit aboard the *Endeavour*?

Without a common language, communication between the two groups would seem all but impossible. Indeed, the young Scottish botanical illustrator Sydney Parkinson, who died later on this voyage after contracting dysentery in Java, noted that the language of the Haush was 'unintelligible to every one of us'.

Cook's party spoke English and Swedish, and could no doubt between them manage a little Latin, French and German. Although these languages might seem various enough, they all belong to the same language family, known as 'Indo-European', and have much in common. They have similar inventories of sounds, parts of speech (nouns, verbs, adjectives, adverbs and so on), as well as interlinked grammars, vocabularies and even literary traditions. Indeed, we only need to go back about five thousand years to find a common ancestor of all the languages that the crew of the *Endeavour* would have spoken.

Little is known of the Haush language. It may not have had more than a few hundred speakers at any time, and was not written down before the last of them died around 1920. Banks describes the language as 'guttural especialy in some particular words which they seem to express much as an Englishman when he hawks to clear his throat'. Further clues about how distant Haush is from Indo-European languages can be gleaned from its better-studied neighbour Ona, a fellow member of the wider Chonan language family. Ona has just three vowels, and many of its twenty-three consonants are utterly unfamiliar to the European ear. Instead of the variety of familiar parts of speech in Indo-European languages, Ona has just two: nouns and verbs. And whereas in English the standard word order is subject–verb–object (e.g. *John eats porridge*), in Ona, and most likely in Haush also, this order is reversed to object–verb–subject (*porridge eats John*).[2]

Communication between the Europeans and the Haush, then, might seem unachievable. Not only did they have no common language, they also possessed hugely different life experiences, traditions and knowledge of the world. Neither side could be sure whether a drink would be interpreted as a beverage or a poison (recall that the Haush handed back the glasses of spirits largely undrunk), what would be valued as a gift or what might function as a weapon. Yet communication and cooperation were both anticipated and achieved. The drive to communicate was somehow able to reach across what would appear to be an unbridgeable gulf.

Consider the two men from each group advancing, no doubt with some trepidation, towards each other across the beach. There is a message here: we are deliberately making ourselves vulnerable and unready to attack because we wish to have a friendly interaction. Note how the Haush displayed and then cast aside their sticks – thus conveying that they had weapons but had no intention of using them – to demonstrate that their intentions were peaceful. The two sides were playing a game of high-stakes cross-cultural and cross-linguistic charades with pantomime actions taking the place of speech.

Although the two sides had no common language, both were doubtless aware that the others *had* a verbal means of communication, albeit one they could not understand. Banks presupposed as much when remarking on his difficulties picking up on the Haush language: 'During our stay among them I could learn but two of their words, *Nalleca* which signified beads . . . and *oouda* which signified water.' Banks's assumption was justified. Human societies exhibit a great variety of technological, agricultural and economic complexity, but no group of humans anywhere in the world has ever been encountered without a language. Indeed, as we shall see later, when no common language exists between groups of people, a new linguistic system is rapidly cobbled together.

REDISCOVERING CHARADES AT THE MAX PLANCK INSTITUTE

The Max Planck Institute for Psycholinguistics is housed in an elegant modernist building in a forest at the edge of Radboud University in Nijmegen, Netherlands. Its teams of researchers span disparate approaches to understanding human language, bringing together anthropologists working on non-Western languages, cognitive neuroscientists studying the brain mechanisms of language, geneticists linking language and genes, developmental psychologists studying how children learn language, and linguists exploring the links between language and thought. The institute is also extraordinarily welcoming to visitors, as we know from our experience there.

At night, the institute empties, but visitors remain, talking with one another in the open spaces overlooking the woodland as the light fades. On one such evening in June 2011, the two of us were idly chatting about the game of charades. We mused on how strange it is that people can communicate at all through unfamiliar combinations of gestures and wild overacting. We noted how shared knowledge is so incredibly helpful (trying to convey the title of a film of which one's audience has never heard is always a challenge), and how each fleeting gesture (say, a wave of the hand indicating a king or the sea) can be reused on the next turn, or even the next day. Crucially, we considered how rapidly these gestures become simplified and stripped down. If you play charades with the same people for any length of time, the clues become ever more patterned. Partial and conflicting conventions start to emerge. In short, a communicative system begins to form.

In that moment, we realized we had stumbled upon a new hypothesis about how languages begin. Faced with the immediate challenge of communication, Cook's crew and the Haush created signs and symbols in the moment. Humans with a message to convey, but without any linguistic resources at hand, will improvise an ad hoc communicative solution – whether through sounds, gestures or facial expressions. And in doing so, they inadvertently create a resource for future exchanges, to be reused and modified as required. Similarly, in a past game of charades in Nick's family, bringing the fingertips of both hands together, arching them to resemble a church steeple, and then moving the steepled hands horizontally in a wavy motion to mimic the bow of a ship bobbing up and down on the ocean came to signify Columbus sailing to the Americas. In later games, this gesture was available to help pick out 'Columbus' himself, 'the Americas', 'ships' – and, with suitable mimes for descent and disaster, 'the *Titanic*'.

But can the charade-like interactions between Cook's crew and the Haush really be seen as the possible beginning of a language? Although the two groups had some success communicating with one another, enabling them to establish friendly relations, share food and visit each other, there were many things they couldn't 'talk' about. There were no recitations of poetry, exchanges of gossip or even just idle chats. Of course, the *Endeavour* only spent five days anchored in the Bay of Good Success, so there wasn't much time for Cook's crew and the Haush to improve their charades-like communications, let alone learn each other's languages (apart from the couple of words that Banks picked up). With more time, however, the interactions between the two groups could very well have evolved into something more closely resembling a language.

At numerous times in human history, groups of people with very different languages have been thrown together by circumstance (frequently in colonial contexts) and have needed to communicate. This is, in essence, the situation of Cook's crew and the Haush, but stretched out over many years and unfortunately often with disastrous consequences for the indigenous people.[3] In these extended cases, a simplified linguistic system, known as a pidgin, typically emerged, with a small vocabulary and little grammar. Initially, such pidgin languages have a limited functionality, primarily allowing people to communicate instrumentally (about what to do and how) and referentially (about where and with what tools). As in the encounter on the Tierra del Fuego, poems, gossip and small talk are largely absent from early pidgins. But with more time, and repeated learning and use, pidgins can evolve into a richer so-called creole language, with an enlarged vocabulary and more complex grammar. For example, Haitian Creole emerged in the eighteenth century from a mix of colonial French and the languages of enslaved West African people, and now it has more than ten million speakers. In these more mature, fully fledged languages, the whole panoply of language use emerges, from poetic declarations of love and despair to idle gossip about your neighbours and mundane chit-chat about the weather.[4]

LINGUISTIC CHARADES

Given that charades involves getting a point across via gesticulation, typically using one's hands, it may seem that the idea of language as charades would not apply to spoken language. After all, spoken language, or vocalization of any kind, is typically not allowed in the game of charades. Does the language-from-charades story mean that human languages of all kinds can be traced back to some form of sign language? Among others, Michael Tomasello, an influential primatologist and developmental psychologist at Duke University in North Carolina, suspects that this may be the case.

Tomasello offers a compelling thought experiment.[5] He asks us to imagine two groups of young children, happily growing up on separate, isolated islands without any outside language input and without any adults around (leaving aside questions about how this might actually occur). On one of the two islands, children can only use gestures to communicate (no vocalizations), whereas on the other island they can only use vocalizations (no gestures). Let's call these islands Gesture Island and Vocalization Island, respectively. Would either of the two island populations be able to come up with a useful system of communication? Tomasello argues that only the children on Gesture Island would have a chance of evolving language-like communication. Gestures can be used not only to draw attention to objects but also in an 'iconic' manner to represent things, such as when the steepling of the hands is used in Nick's family to denote Columbus's ship. The children on Vocalization Island would be left with mere imitations of emotional expressions like *ha-ha* or *waah*, animal sounds like *woof* or *meow*, and other onomatopoeic expressions like *beep* or *vroom*. Vocalizations, he says, simply don't have the iconic powers to signal meaning in general: it is easy to imagine making a gesture for 'stirring the pot' that others would have no problem figuring out, but coming up with a vocalization to signify the same action seems impossible.

Tomasello's reasoning has considerable empirical backing – though not, thank goodness, because evil language scientists have actually raised populations of babies in isolation from language and human contact. Indeed, we know from the ominously named 'deprivation' studies with non-human primates that such an experiment would provide little insight into the origin of language. The now infamous experiments in the 1970s by the comparative psychologist Harry Harlow, at the University of Wisconsin, Madison, showed that when rhesus macaque monkeys were brought up in isolation – often with cloth or wire 'surrogate' mothers, and sometimes in a dark isolation chamber worryingly called 'the pit of despair' – their behaviour ended up severely disturbed.[6] Likewise, isolating human babies from other members of their species would very likely have deleterious consequences beyond language development. So no reputable language scientist would carry out what in linguistics circles has come to be referred to as the 'forbidden experiment'.[7]

However, since the late 1970s a real-life version of Tomasello's thought experiment has been unfolding in two schools for deaf children in Managua, the capital of Nicaragua.[8] The children were taught lip-reading and spoken Spanish, but with little success. The deaf students remained communicatively isolated from the surrounding hearing community and even from their teachers. The children did interact with their families using so-called home signs – simple, idiosyncratic gestural systems that deaf children often develop to communicate with their hearing families in the absence of an established sign language.[9] So when thrown together in the deaf schools, these children were in a situation very much like that of the children on Tomasello's Gesture Island. Although the students can vocalize, it doesn't do them any good because the other children are unable to hear them. Their primary means of communication is their hands.

In line with Tomasello's reasoning, what is now known as Nicaraguan Sign Language gradually emerged, becoming increasingly complex with each new generation of deaf children entering the schools. For example, students in the first generation used a variety of signs for 'horse', with one person pantomiming holding the reins and moving them up and down as if riding a horse (see figure 1.2).[10] Another signer first used one hand to depict a human riding a horse by spreading the index finger and the middle finger of one hand, placing them on top of the other hand (held flat as for a handshake), and then followed it with a pantomime of holding the reins of a horse and slapping its haunches. A third student also used the depiction of the human atop a horse but then followed it with a gesture showing the horse's tail swinging. And a fourth student used just the sign depicting the human straddling a horse. By the third generation, the sign for 'horse' had been

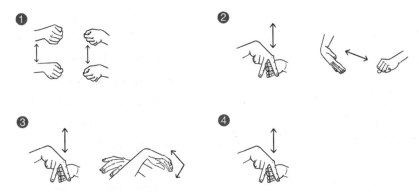

Figure 1.2. Four different signs for 'horse' used by the first generation of Nicaraguan Sign Language users: (1) pantomiming holding the reins of a horse, hands going up and down; (2) depicting a human straddling a horse, followed by a pantomime of holding the reins (left hand) and slapping its haunches (right hand); (3) the same sign for a human atop a horse followed by a gesture showing the horse's tail swinging (right hand); and (4) the human straddling a horse sign on its own. By the third generation, the single sign for 'horse' in image 4 was used by all the students. (Drawings by Sunita Christiansen.)

conventionalized into a single sign: the depiction of a human straddling a horse. Similarly, gestures that started out merely as iconic mimicry over time became conventionalized into more abstract symbols, transforming themselves into signs. The emergence of Nicaraguan Sign Language is charades writ large.[11]

But what about vocalizations? Is Tomasello right to think that, unlike gestures, they cannot easily represent meaning iconically before becoming conventionalized and eventually turning into vocal symbols? Enter Marcus Perlman, a psychologist at the University of Birmingham. He was curious to know whether Tomasello's intuitions about the limitations of vocalization were correct, so he put them to the test. In a series of clever experiments, Perlman invited people to play *vocal* charades, without using any words or gestures.[12]

To figure out whether it's possible to use vocalizations to convey the meaning of different kinds of concepts, a contest was held with $1,000 in prize money. Entrants in the Vocal Iconicity Challenge had to submit sounds made by the human vocal apparatus to convey a diverse set of meanings, ranging from nouns, such as **knife**, **water** and **tiger**, and verbs, such as **cook**, **hunt** and **cut**, to adjectives, such as **bad**, **big** and **dull**, and more grammatically specialized concepts such as **one**, **many** and **this**. The entries included many fascinating vocalizations, such as a 'glob-glob-glob' sound for **water**, a low growl for **tiger**, a whooshing sound for **knife**, and multiple reduplications thereof for **cut** to indicate that the knife was used as a tool for cutting (see figure 1.3 for examples). Another contender used 'va' to signify **one**, repeating it three times to represent **many**, 'va va va', conveying that the concept of **many** can be understood simply as multiple **one**s. The vocalizations in each entry were evaluated by asking naive listeners, with no knowledge of the competition,

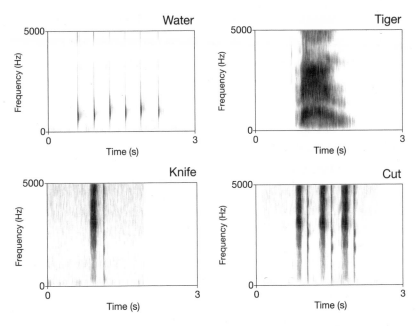

Figure 1.3. Visualizations of four entries from Perlman's study using spectrograms that show the combination of different frequencies (vertical axis) in each sound across time (horizontal axis): the darker the bands look, the louder they sound – and the narrower a sound appears horizontally, the shorter its duration. Top left: 'glob' is repeated six times to indicate **water**. Top right: a low, broad-spectrum growl denotes **tiger**. Bottom left: a single 'whoosh' represents **knife**. Bottom right: the 'whoosh' from **knife** is repeated three times to suggest **cutting**. (Spectrograms by Marcus Perlman.)

to guess their meaning. The prizewinner reached an impressive 57 per cent correct guesses (whereas random guessing would have resulted in only about 10 per cent accuracy).

It was not just English-speakers in the United States who could understand these vocalizations. In an ingenious follow-up study, Perlman and colleagues conducted a web survey asking native speakers of more than twenty different languages, as dissimilar as Albanian, Zulu, Amharic, Thai and Danish, to guess the intended meaning of the vocalizations. The results were stunning: people from all over the world were able to guess the meaning of these vocalizations. Perlman went one step further and tested non-literate populations in remote field locations in the Amazon jungle in Brazil and the Vanuatu archipelago in the South Pacific – again with the same results. Even the inhabitants of these isolated places readily guessed the intended meaning of the prizewinning vocalizations.

Although these results are impressive, the best entries were carefully crafted over days, perhaps weeks, by teams of academics studying language evolution and related topics. Fortunately, though, Perlman's other studies have shown that you don't need an advanced degree to improvise meaningful vocalizations. In fact, vocalizations produced by Chinese children to convey a range of meanings were correctly interpreted by English-speakers, including those created by congenitally deaf children whose native language was Standard Chinese Sign Language. So it seems that people in general are quite good at coming up with vocalizations on the fly that can be interpreted by others – though the accuracy of their guesses tended to be considerably lower than for the contest entries. But as soon as we're allowed to interact with one another, in essence to play vocal charades, accuracy goes back up again. If you pair people up and ask them to take turns communicating the meaning of different concepts to each other using only their voices, and then get them to do this over multiple rounds, the sounds they produce become more fine-tuned and easier to interpret, just as in the emergence of Nicaraguan Sign Language.

Perlman's innovative work revealed that Tomasello's intuitions about the bleak prospects for communication on Vocalization Island may be misleading. We don't yet have a direct comparison between improvised gestures and improvised sounds – but it seems that the human voice is capable of creating multifaceted sound patterns that can carry the kind of rich iconic meaning needed to get communication off the ground. Repeated communicative attempts using vocalizations can then lead to more abstract expressions, which may eventually turn into words.

Without a time machine, the answer to the question of whether language originated in gestures, vocalizations – or, quite plausibly, some combination of the two (such as a repeated cutting action synchronized with whooshing sounds) will likely be forever shrouded in the mists of time. Indeed, it is conceivable that language may have been invented independently multiple times by separate groups of people, quite possibly with different relative emphases on gestures and vocalizations – but in all cases, emerging from repeated charades-like interactions.

Language is a clumsy, chaotic product of the demands of the moment. Yet the improvisations we concoct to solve each new communicative challenge are shaped by how we solved previous challenges, which then informs how we cobble together the solution to the next. The systematic patterns of language, to the degree that there is a system at all, arise through the accumulation of overlapping, interlocking and interfering patterns, each driven by the urgent demands of the communicative task at hand. They are the products of countless impromptu exchanges in which we struggle to get across, well enough for our purposes, whatever it is we hope to convey. And so, collectively, we build a language, entirely by accident.

MESSAGE IN A BOTTLE

Viewing language as charades, a collaborative game of improvisations, is not merely a minor twist on existing ideas about language but requires a paradigmatic shift in perspective, one that completely uproots a good deal of a century's worth of thinking about the nature of communication. Current theories of how we communicate come in many shapes and forms, but common to most of them is the so-called transmission model of communication. A sender encodes a message and transmits it over a channel to a receiver, who decodes it into its original form. This transmission view of communication is beautifully encapsulated by the work of the American mathematician and electrical engineer Claude Elwood Shannon, growing out of his classified work on cryptography during the Second World War.[13]

Shannon was interested in communication from an engineering perspective: how information can be accurately transferred from a sender to a receiver (see figure 1.4), whether senders and receivers are people, computers, phones or satellites. A specific message originates in an information source and is then encoded by a sender into a signal that is transmitted to a receiver across a 'channel', which may be affected by noise. The receiver at the destination decodes the message from the signal by reversing the process used to encode it. So, when making a call on a mobile phone, you're the information source, the phone is the sender, the digital cellular network is the channel over which the signal is transmitted; the person you're calling is the destination, and their phone the receiver. Noise introduced along the way brings about the all too familiar problem of poor mobile reception, prompting cries such as 'I can't hear you. You're breaking up!'

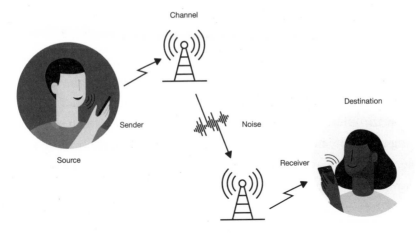

Figure 1.4. An illustration of the Shannon model of communication using a mobile phone call as an example. In this model, a message from an information source (person on the left) is encoded into a signal (by a mobile phone) and transmitted across a channel (mobile network) – subject to potential noise – and decoded by the receiver (mobile phone) into the intended message at the destination (the person on the right). (Figure by Sunita Christiansen.)

Shannon's theory of transmitting information across a communication channel provided the bedrock for today's interconnected world, from streaming videos on your smartphone to communicating with spacecraft at the edge of the solar system, and earned him the moniker 'father of information theory'. And it didn't take long for psychology to take notice, which helped propel the so-called cognitive revolution in the mid-1950s and the rise of the computer metaphor for the mind – the idea that the brain is analogous to a computer and that thinking is a kind of information processing.[14] Understanding the computational underpinnings of the mind became an interdisciplinary endeavour, uniting psychology, philosophy, computer science, linguistics, neuroscience and anthropology under the banner of cognitive science.[15] This

approach to studying the mind subsequently yielded many important insights into cognition and language, but it also carried
with it some fundamental theoretical limitations, of which the
most important for our purposes is that it ignores the fundamentally proactive nature of our brains.[16]

From an information theory perspective, linguistic communication can be seen as the process of transmitting a sequence of
symbols from a sender to a receiver. Indeed, long before Shannon, the Swiss linguist Ferdinand de Saussure – one of the
founders of twentieth-century linguistics – described a speech
'circuit', in which the message is encoded by the speaker and
decoded by the listener (figure 1.5).[17] It is therefore not surprising
that Shannon's ideas also ended up being applied to language,
providing a computational basis for our linguistic interactions.
The solution is elegant: conversation is viewed as the process of
sending packets of information back and forth between inter-
locutors, rather like two computers exchanging data over the
internet. As a sender, you use your vocabulary and grammar to
transform what you want to say into an utterance that you can
speak or sign. As a receiver, you apply this very same knowledge
of language 'in reverse' to extract the original information from
the spoken or signed utterance. A conversation, then, involves
taking turns being a sender and a receiver, alternating between
encoding and decoding information transmitted across the linguistic channel.

Paradoxically, though, an often ignored assumption of Shannon's theory is that meaning plays no role in it at all. Information
theory is all about engineering, aiming to solve the problem of
transferring a message in the presence of noise. For Shannon,
'semantic aspects of communication are irrelevant to the engineering problem'.[18] It doesn't matter whether the message is a

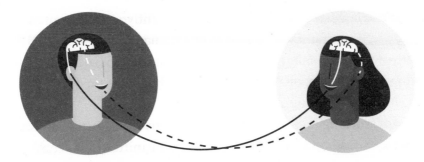

Figure 1.5. A modern rendition of Saussure's speech circuit in which a message originates in the brain of a speaker and then is encoded into a speech signal that reaches the listener's brain via their ears and is decoded into the intended message. (Figure by Sunita Christiansen.)

recipe, a poem, an encrypted file, a digitized picture or a stream of random noise. This idea works perfectly fine in an engineering context, where the exact same processes can *by design* be run when encoding a message and then in reverse when decoding it. But the same cannot be said for human communication, where meaning is paramount.

Consider, once more, the encounter between Cook's men and the Haush. They spoke such radically different languages and had such completely different life experiences that, according to the information transmission model, communication between them should have been all but impossible. They lacked an identical shared basis for the encoding and decoding of messages. Yet they were able to make themselves understood to one another to a reasonable degree. The problem with the transmission view of communication is that it is fundamentally passive: the receiver idly waits for the signal to arrive, then springs into action to decode the message once it appears. The signal therefore ends up carrying an incredibly heavy burden because it *alone* must convey all the communicative content across the conversational void between people. But when we think of language as charades, we realize that the communicative burden lies not just with a gesture or a sound but also with the creative ingenuity of the players – the signal, considered in isolation, is hopelessly ambiguous and uninterpretable.[19]

Even so, one might object that charades (however well practised) and language differ in one fundamental respect. Charades provides a set of clues for the audience to solve: What are we to make of the Haush throwing aside their sticks, or how should we 'read' the steepled hands diving downward as a sinking ship? But language, we tend to imagine, doesn't merely give clues. It somehow bottles meaning word by word and sends it across the ether to be uncorked and combined by the recipient (according to some unclear recipe). Language seemingly *transmits* thoughts directly from the mind of the speaker to the mind of the hearer, with no interpretation or creativity required from either sender or receiver. But these intuitions are a distraction: to understand how communication really works, we must free ourselves of this message-in-a-bottle viewpoint. It fails to deal with the richness, vagueness and playfulness of everyday speech, not to mention poetry, rhetoric, metaphor, jokes and banter. Meaning can't be distilled, let alone bottled.

Take, for example, the phrases **opening the door** and **walking through the door**. The familiar word **door** surely means the same in both phrases, right? But on reflection, the opposite is true. When we open a door, we physically shift a typically solid rectangular panel (the door) on its hinges. But walking through a door does not involve penetrating this same solid panel in some ghostly way. In **walking through the door**, **door** refers to the **doorway**, not the solid panel itself. The same ambiguity arises when we talk about **smashing a hand through the window** or **waving a hand out of the window**. The **window** is at one moment a pane of breakable glass and at another an airy aperture. With a house window, **breaking the window** might refer to breaking a specific pane or the entire window, or to damaging the frame around the glass or even the panels into which the window is set. And notice that with a car window, **breaking the window** has a further ambiguity still: breaking the glass or breaking the mechanism that causes the glass to slide up and down. Or consider the question **'What do you think of this paper?'**, asked while waving a copy of the distinctively pink *Financial Times*. Here, **paper** can refer to the literal salmon-coloured sheets of material, the particular (and perhaps especially battered) copy of the paper, today's edition, the *Financial Times* as a title, or even the news organization that creates it (as in **'That's the paper Mary works for'**). The possibilities are literally endless. And this is just what we should expect if we see language as charades. All we can ever do is gesture, suggest and conjure clues, hoping that our audience can discern the direction in which we are hoping to lead them in the light of everything they know about us and the world.

The language-as-charades metaphor suggests that language does not involve sending bottled messages from one head to another using a fixed code. Instead, we must see language, whether spoken or signed, as a rich, analogical, metaphorical and potentially highly creative means of conveying clues to one another, which can require any amount of ingenuity and even playfulness to interpret. And the interpretation of these clues does not depend merely on the words themselves but also draws on what was said before, what we know about the topic at hand and what we know about each other – just as deciphering the clues in a murder mystery depends on knowing the characters involved, their backstories, and what they were doing before and after the time of death. When we play the same communicative game, perhaps with the same person, the meaning of these clues may become ever more conventionalized (in a way similar to the emergence of a single sign for 'horse' in Nicaraguan Sign Language). Yet conventionalization is only ever partial, and meaning is always richly dependent on the current moment. Our brains are so good at the rich and flexible interpretation of linguistic clues that we are often entirely oblivious to the fact that we are doing any interpretation at all. We have the illusion that meaning is somehow 'transparently' transmitted by the words themselves. But on the contrary: meaning is in the eye of the beholder.

COLLABORATIVE LANGUAGE GAMES

'For sale. Baby shoes. Never worn.'[20] The terse prose of this mournful six-word story, mimicking a classified ad that offers a new pair of baby shoes for sale, evokes strong emotions in most readers. It's hard not to concoct some sort of narrative around it. We might imagine the devastated parents, having lost their baby perhaps due to a miscarriage, birth complications or cot death, selling the shoes they had lovingly purchased in happy anticipation of the birth of their child. In our mind's eye, we can see the bereaved parents standing at the cemetery, watching with tears streaming down their cheeks as a tiny coffin is lowered into the ground. We can empathize with the anguish they might feel in letting go of those shoes, perhaps because they are of humble means and need the money, or because the shoes remind them that they will never hear the joyful pitter-patter of their baby's tiny feet in their home. And we can envisage the sense of loss and despair that will haunt them for years to come, perhaps even breaking up their marriage. But, of course, none of these narrative details are in the six-word story – they are constructed by our minds, from what we know about parents, babies and grief.

The six-word story about the baby shoes is an extreme example of what has been called 'flash fiction', a genre of exceptionally short fictional works, each of which aims to bring an entire narrative to mind using as few words as possible. These thumbnail stories illustrate just how much we as readers contribute to the interpretation of what is written. From just a few words, a detailed narrative springs to mind. But the same principle is at work for language of all kinds: meaning is not transmitted like a message in a bottle but has to be constructed collaboratively by the participants in a conversation. The words that we utter or sign are only clues to the intended meaning. To fully understand what someone is saying, we need to construct an interpretation based on the linguistic clues and what we know about the world, what we know of each other and what was said before.[21] This constructive process is at the heart of how language functions. It works well most of the time; but, of course, sometimes our constructions can go awry and need to be fixed collaboratively. Just as in charades, we need to be 'in tune' with those we're conversing with, to reach a common understanding. We need to read each other's minds, at least to a decent degree, to play the language game successfully.

When we're talking with one another, the words, phrases and sentences we utter are merely the tip of what we will refer to as the *communication iceberg* (figure 1.6). Much of the work in the language sciences has concentrated on this visible part. But for language to work at all – for us to make sense of what is said – we also need the hidden, submerged part of the communication iceberg.[22] What allows us to spin a detailed narrative from the six words in the baby shoes story is a common set of cultural norms,

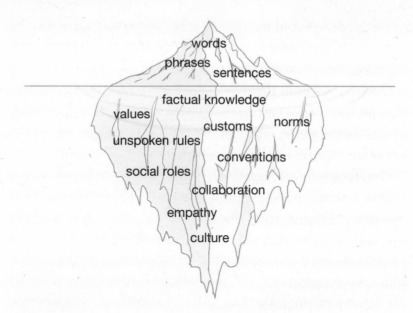

Figure 1.6. The communication iceberg, showing the hidden, submerged part that embodies the cultural, social, emotional and factual knowledge and skills that keep the visible linguistic tip afloat. (Figure by Sunita Christiansen.)

customs, values, conventions and expectations combined with an understanding of unspoken rules, social roles and relationships, as well as knowledge about the world and how it works. We need all our cultural, social and factual knowledge, along with fundamental interpersonal skills, to keep the linguistic tip of the communication iceberg afloat. Without it, our ability to communicate through language would sink into unintelligibility.

This perspective on language also has practical implications: whether it's a mechanic describing what's wrong with your car, a physician explaining the treatment needed for an illness or a scientist expounding their most recent groundbreaking results, we can all become better communicators if we pay closer attention to the hidden part of the communication iceberg. This is not a matter of haphazardly second-guessing what the other person is thinking. Successful communication requires empathy – we need to place ourselves in the shoes of others and see the world from their perspective (as best we can). The more we focus on how other people see the world, rather than just on what we want to say, the better our chances of being understood.

Conversations are, indeed, collaborative projects, where the goal is mutual understanding of what is being discussed, as elegantly demonstrated in a study by the acclaimed Stanford psycholinguist Herb Clark.[23] Pairs of participants were seated at either end of a six-foot-long table and asked to assemble simple Lego models given a prototype. One person was assigned the role of the 'builder' and had to recreate the model from scratch, using a bunch of Lego blocks, by following the instructions of the other person, the 'director'. Only the director was given the target Lego prototype. For half of the pairs, a barrier was placed across the middle of the table, preventing the director from seeing what the builder was doing, whereas the other half had clear sight of each other. If successful dialogue is simply a matter of passively sending messages back and forth, irrespective of the conversational context, there should be little difference between the two groups: the director can simply tell the builder the exact order of steps needed to combine the bricks into the finished model.

But this is not what happened. Where the director was unable to monitor what the builder was doing, it took the pairs more than twice as long to complete the task, and they used almost twice as many words to discuss how to complete the replicas. The barrier was not only a visual obstacle but also a conversational hurdle, reducing the speed and efficiency of communication considerably compared to the other, unencumbered group. And when there was no interaction at all – when the director recorded spoken instructions that were later played back to the builder – the results were even worse, with many replica errors. The takeaway message is that conversations are like charades, collaborative games of give-and-take, where we need to be sensitive to the perspective of others, what they know and don't know, so we can give them the right clues.

Further support for the importance of such perspective-taking comes from the use of improvisational theatre, or 'improv', to improve science communication. Improv is a mode of dramatic performance, often with comedic elements, where the acting and dialogue are not scripted but created collaboratively by the actors in real time. In a sense, it can be thought of as a kind of serial charades, with an improvised continuous storyline. For improv to work, the actors need to be in tune to 'feed off' each other's ideas and improvisations. Improv exercises aim to help people fall into sync and collaborate fluidly together. For example, in the mirroring exercise, two people take turns producing a mirror image of the other person's movement as closely as possible. In the beginning, the 'follower' lags considerably behind the 'leader'; but with practice they end up moving almost in unison: the follower and leader are 'reading' one another's minds and therefore are able to anticipate each other's next movements. They may even end up jointly planning their next movements in synchrony. Such improv exercises can not only help actors become better attuned to each other but also make it easier for them to pick up on clues that theatre-goers might provide as to their state of mind. Perhaps improv exercises might similarly be used to improve the communication skills of non-actors by drawing attention to the needs of the audience? Actor, director, screenwriter and author Alan Alda certainly thinks so.[24]

Alda is perhaps best known for playing Hawkeye Pierce, the wisecracking army doctor, in the long-running TV series *M*A*S*H* about a field hospital during the Korean War. But he also has a keen interest in disseminating science to a broader audience, having hosted the *Scientific American Frontiers* TV programme for twelve years. In the course of his interactions with scientists, he noticed that many of them struggled to connect with the audience, despite their evident enthusiasm for their work. Alda suspected the problem was that the scientists were not 'aligned' with their audience – they were not seeing the world from the audience's point of view. The scientists were talking *at* their audience rather than communicatively collaborating *with* them. Alda reasoned that perhaps the same type of exercises that actors use to hone their abilities to connect with a theatre audience might also help scientists. And indeed, when he asked scientists to do improv exercises, such as mirroring, they became better at reading other people. The scientists became more sensitive to the needs of their audience, not by talking down to them but by empathizing with them, and thereby ensuring successful communication. Alda's method, now embodied by the Alan Alda Center for Communicating Science at Stony Brook University, has become a hugely influential and widely adopted approach, especially at universities and research institutes in the United States.

Whether we're talking about science, telling a story or just giving directions, we need to pay attention to where our audience is coming from and what they need from us. We can all improve our ability to interact with one another by remembering that communication is not a one-way street: we have a much better chance of successful communication when we pay close attention to what other people understand rather than focusing too much on what we want to say to them. This is also reflected in the golden rule of improv, 'Yes, and . . .', meaning that whatever one person is saying or doing is automatically accepted as the basis for further interaction. If we readily respect and acknowledge each other's thoughts, ideas and concerns, our conversations will move along more smoothly, to mutual benefit.

◉

Seeing language as charades helps us shake our intuitive and mistaken picture of how language works. Charades is inherently collaborative. We don't wait until somebody is finished gesticulating before jumping in with our guesses – and these guesses, along with our nods, smiles and other reactions, help the player adapt their gestures to lead in the 'right' direction. Something very similar took place during the Haush's encounters with the *Endeavour* crew – the back-and-forth of signals establishes that both sides are 'on the same wavelength', for example in having friendly intent or an interest in exchanging goods.

The language-as-charades perspective upends more than half a century's work in the social and cognitive sciences on how we communicate. Thinking of the mind as a computer has lured us into thinking that language works just like communication between computers, where information is neatly bundled in separate packages and transmitted across a wire, and that conversation can be viewed like a game of tennis, where messages are lobbed back and forth from one mind to another. Instead, language is like a game of charades, where we collaborate to build a shared understanding incrementally, improvisation by improvisation. Individual signals don't carry the sole communicative burden – they are clues to be combined with what came before, current expectations, and what we know about the world and each other. Communication depends on aligning the creative abilities of all conversational partners, using whatever shared knowledge, intuitions and memories of past playing of the game we can jointly muster.

But we cannot fully appreciate the collaborative nature of language without first abandoning another assumption thrust upon us by the computer metaphor. With lightning speed, computers can send huge 'packets' of information to each other, and it doesn't matter too much in what order the packets arrive (though it may, if we are streaming a movie). The packets of information can be downloaded, stored and reviewed in their entirety using millions of calculations carried out faster than the eye can blink. Some of the most influential theories of how humans produce and understand language adopt this viewpoint, at least implicitly – they apply the full power of modern computing to thinking about how the human brain deals with language. This perspective, however, misses an important detail: human memory, unlike that of a computer, is astonishingly limited. Unless we make sense of what we are hearing right away, our memory for what was said is quickly obliterated by the deluge of further speech. If we don't make use of language in the moment, the message is lost for ever. And this observation turns out to be unexpectedly crucial to understanding how language works.

2

THE FLEETING NATURE
OF LANGUAGE

A man just beginning to learn radio-telegraphic code
hears each *dit* and *dah* as a separate chunk. Soon he is able
to organize these sounds into letters and then he can deal
with the letters as chunks. Then the letters organize
themselves as words, which are still larger chunks, and he
begins to hear whole phrases.

GEORGE A. MILLER,
'The magical number seven, plus or minus two' (1956)

It's August 1942. War is raging across the world. In the Pacific theatre, Japanese intelligence officers listening in on Allied military
communication are suddenly dumbfounded when, instead of the
familiar English codes, they hear a baffling cacophony of strange
speech sounds: *toh-bah-ha-zsid ah-ha-tinh ah-di tehi bilh-has-ahn
dzeel be-al-doh-cid-da-hi al-tah-je-jay jo-kayed-goh nal-dzil tsin-tliti
dzeh a-chin d-ah klesh shil-loh.*[1] They were listening to the 'Windtalkers', the code name for the Allies' new secret weapon.

The war in the Pacific appeared to be turning in favour of the Allies, but they were still experiencing many major setbacks. For a while, the Japanese had been eavesdropping on the electronic communications between Allied forces. Many of the Japanese intelligence officers had been educated in the United States, enabling them to break English-based codes and giving them early warnings of Allied battle plans. But when the US Marines landed on Guadalcanal, they brought with them an ingenious countermeasure: Navajo code talkers who used their native tongue as an unbreakable code.[2]

The Allies were taking advantage of something that most of us have experienced at one time or another. When we listen to an unknown language, the auditory deluge of fluent speech seems bewildering to our inexperienced ears, as indecipherable as any secret code. Using their native Navajo language, the code talkers transmitted messages about troop movements, tactics and other battle-related details 'in the clear' over radio and telephone lines. It didn't matter if the enemy listened in on the transmissions – they would only hear an utterly unintelligible stream of hundreds of speech sounds per minute. For the Japanese, trying to make sense of the Navajo code must have felt a bit like trying to play charades with an octopus, with its eight arms flailing about in rapid sequences of completely unfamiliar gestures – an impossible task! Yet this is exactly what language would seem like according to the transmission model of communication. The sender encodes a message using their secret code and transmits it to the receiver who decodes it using the exact same cipher. The Japanese were unable to crack this secret code because none of them (or their allies) had any knowledge of the Navajo language.

Because of its complex grammar and phonology and lack of

a written form, the Navajo language provided a fast and very secure means of battlefield communication. To further stymie enemy cryptographers and linguists, there was even a code within a code: Navajo didn't have words for many military terms, so the code talkers used words familiar to them instead. For example, the Navajo code for 'battleship' became **lo-tso**, which literally translates to 'whale'; **besh-lo** (iron fish) was used for 'submarine' and **ca-lo** (shark) for 'destroyer'. More than six hundred such code words were compiled into the *Navajo Code Talker's Dictionary*, which the Windtalkers memorized by heart.

Whereas often-used words got their own code in the dictionary, other more infrequently used words were spelled out using a particular set of Navajo words corresponding to each letter in the English word. These words referred to things familiar to the code talkers, such as **tse-nill** (meaning 'axe') for the letter **A**, **shush** (bear) for the letter **B** and **moasi** (cat) for the letter **C**. To prevent the enemy from using letter frequency to break the code, multiple Navajo words were used for each English letter – so that, for example, **A** could also be coded as **wol-la-chee** (ant) or **be-la-sana** (apple). So, 'language game' (L-A-N-G-U-A-G-E G-A-M-E) might be encoded as

nash-doie-tso tse-nill tsah klizzie shi-da wol-la-chee jeha ah-nah ah-tad be-la-sana be-tas-tni dzeh

using the following letter-to-word code:

nash-doie-tso	tse-nill	tsah	klizzie	shi-da	wol-la-chee	jeha	ah-nah
L (lion)	**A** (axe)	**N** (needle)	**G** (goat)	**U** (uncle)	**A** (ant)	**G** (gum)	**E** (eye)

	ah-tad	be-la-sana	be-tas-tni	dzeh
	G (girl)	**A** (apple)	**M** (mirror)	**E** (elk)

Today, we are used to computers being cryptographical wizards, but the Navajo code talkers thoroughly beat the code machines of their time. Whereas the code talkers could encode, transmit and decode three lines of English in just twenty seconds, it took a conventional encryption machine of the 1940s thirty minutes to crank mechanically through the same message. Although the Japanese were able to crack other more conventional US ciphers, they never broke the Navajo code. Even when they forced a captured Navajo soldier, who was not a Windtalker, to translate intercepted messages, he could not make head or tail of the stream of words because of the code within a code. In fact, the Navajo code was never deciphered, and its very existence was kept secret until it was declassified in 1968.

The Japanese puzzlement when listening to the Windtalkers reveals the challenges that we all face when trying to understand language. Although we're blissfully unaware of it – except perhaps when listening to a foreign language – the limitations of our brains ought to make it all but impossible for us to understand each other in conversation. Indeed, it's something of a miracle that we're not constantly as baffled as the Japanese intelligence officers.

To start with, our sensory memory for sounds or visual inputs is incredibly short-lived, usually lasting less than a tenth of a second. On top of that, we are continually bombarded by new sounds and sights that threaten to overrun our incredibly short-lived memory for sensory input. We have enough trouble holding on to a phone number – how can we possibly grasp an entire sentence? And to make matters worse, we also have a terribly hard time with order. Hearing the clatter of clangs and crashes as a pile of dirty dishes topples over in the sink, we have no idea which bang or which crash came first – it is a confused din of noises, with few identifiable elements and no discernible order. So, although we sometimes imagine that our memory for sounds is like a mental recording device, nothing could be further from the truth. Indeed, decades of memory research have revealed that our short-term memory for sequences, whether auditory or visual, is not only very short-lived but also limited to just three to five items.[3] Yet, strangely enough, when we speak, we don't worry about this at all. Whether we use our voice or our hands (as in sign language), we talk at breakneck speed, often producing more than a hundred words per minute. Surprisingly, though, rather than being hopelessly overloaded, our audience, from toddlers to their great-grandparents, can take in and make sense of the torrent of speech with apparent ease.

The secret to this amazing feat is hidden in plain sight: it's the inordinate amount of time that we spend throughout our lives using and honing our language skills. Just as we get better and better the more we rehearse a piece on the violin, work on our backhand in tennis or go over an upcoming business presentation, so our language skills improve as we practise them over and over every day. Most of us spend the vast bulk of our waking lives immersed in language, whether chatting with others, listening to the radio or podcasts and audiobooks, watching films, reading, writing or just talking to ourselves. Not surprisingly, our language skills get pretty good. Without this repeated practice, linguistic communication would be slow, laboured and ineffective.

AN INCONVENIENT TRUTH

Whether we speak Navajo, English or any of the world's other seven thousand current languages, we do so with ease and without ever giving it a second thought.[4] Yet when visiting a foreign country, where we don't know the language well, we suddenly get the feeling that everybody is speaking at a ridiculously rapid pace. In fact, the perception that speakers of unfamiliar languages talk so much faster than we do is an illusion.[5] Talking at an average speed, a typical speaker produces around ten to fifteen speech sounds, or phonemes, per second. Speech at this rate is easy for us to follow. But if we're confronted with a sequence of non-speech sounds at the same rate – like the clatter of dishes falling over in the sink – the sounds all seem to fuse together into a blurry, indistinct clamour. We are completely unable to distinguish the individual sounds, let alone work out in what order they arrived.[6] It would seem that even at a normal pace, speech ought to be way beyond the limits of the human brain.

The tight limitations on memory are not unique to language; they also straitjacket our cognitive system in general. Our perception of the world is much more constricted than we think, as the late Dick Neisser, a former colleague of Morten's at Cornell, was one of the first to reveal.[7] One of Neisser's many contributions to the study of the mind was his pioneering demonstration of what would later become known as 'inattentional blindness'.[8] He asked people to watch a video showing two separate groups of players, each group passing a ball between them. Participants were instructed to focus on one of the groups and press a button whenever the players in that group passed a ball to another player. The task was not hard but required a lot of attention – so much so that when a woman unexpectedly and incongruously walked across the screen carrying an open umbrella, few people noticed her. Intuitively, we have the feeling that we continuously 'take in' all the details of our visual world – but clearly we don't! If we did, how could we miss such a blatant and bizarre event? Indeed, ramping up the incongruity levels further, psychologists Dan Simons and Christopher Chabris repeated Neisser's study, this time with the unexpected intruder being someone dressed in a gorilla suit, walking on to centre stage and pausing to beat its chest before sidling away.[9] Again, most people monitoring the team's ball-catching were oblivious to the gorilla – and could not believe that they had missed such an unusual event when shown the video again.

Further inspired by Neisser's work, another study by Simons, this time with Dan Levin, revealed an equally counterintuitive result.[10] On the Cornell campus, an experimenter would approach a pedestrian and ask them for directions. Two additional experimenters carrying a door would walk, rather impolitely, between the first experimenter and the pedestrian mid-conversation. In the confusion, the original experimenter was surreptitiously switched with one of the door-carriers, who then continued the conversation with the pedestrian. When the pedestrian had finished giving directions, they were asked if they noticed anything unusual. Remarkably, half of the people did not notice that the person they were talking to had been swapped with a completely different person, even though they had been looking straight at them. When Simons and Levin redid the experiment dressed up as construction workers and approached college-aged pedestrians, only a third of them noticed the change (hinting at the possible role of social categories in how we perceive other people). Most of us would like to think that we have rich representations of the world around us, and that we'd have no problems remembering a person's appearance fairly accurately over just a few seconds, but we are sorely mistaken. The apparent richness of our perceptions is nothing but a mirage – a tale spun by our brains to make sense of the world.[11]

Although most of the time we are oblivious to the remarkable limitations of our attention and memory, we have all experienced their impact on how we use language, as when a brief moment of inattention leads us to completely lose the thread of a conversation. In the light of the severe limitations of our senses and our memories, this is hardly surprising: these limitations conspire to create an incredibly narrow bottleneck through which language must be channelled. So if our attention is drawn away from the ongoing conversation to some other distracting and perhaps momentarily more interesting thought or event, that brief lapse will block our brain from making sense of the on-rushing stream of language – our memory of 'what we were just talking about' turns out to be surprisingly fragile.

The real puzzle is not that our understanding of language can become derailed, but rather that we are ever able to keep up with the onslaught of language at all. For the brain to cope successfully, it has to make sense of sounds or signs right away, just as they arrive and before they are obliterated for ever. We call this narrow funnel the 'Now-or-Never bottleneck'.[12] Language, whether spoken or signed, must be squeezed swiftly through this tight mental bottleneck if we're to understand anything at all.

When the two of us first started thinking about the bottleneck, its potential implications for how the brain deals with language, and the nature of language itself, we assumed that existing theories would have some sort of explanation for how language could squeeze through it. But the more we looked, the more we were amazed to discover that the bottleneck had not been cleverly addressed or even neatly sidestepped. Instead, it had been almost completely ignored: an inconvenient truth largely blocked out by researchers in the language sciences through something close to collective amnesia.

LANGUAGE THROUGH THE BOTTLENECK

How can we ever hope to get more than a few words funnelled through the incredibly narrow Now-or-Never bottleneck, let alone complex philosophical ideas, the oral tales that coalesced into *Beowulf*, the *Odyssey* or the *Mahabharata*, or even just directions to the nearest supermarket? Led astray by the computer metaphor of the mind, many theories in linguistics and the psychology of language have historically assumed that the brain can pick up and hang on to lengthy streams of linguistic material before getting to work on figuring out how the pieces all fit together. After all, a conventional computer has no problem storing vast quantities of information indefinitely and with perfect accuracy; then, if loaded with the right software, it can survey the patterns lurking in that data at its leisure. Yet, brains don't work this way at all – they have no handy hard drives to which sound files can be downloaded and stored for later retrieval and review. How, then, are we able to get more than just a trickle of language through this tight bottleneck?

As the two of us were mulling over the idea of language as charades that pivotal June evening at the Max Planck Institute for Psycholinguistics, we came to an important realization: with its focus on cooperation and in-the-moment improvisation, the 'charades' perspective also provides a crucial insight into how the brain solves the bottleneck challenge. When guessing what someone is trying to mime, we need to be able to carve up the different movements of their head, hands and limbs into separate units that we can interpret. For example, consider again the steepling of fingers used in Nick's family to represent the bow of a ship. The hands could either bob up and down to indicate a ship moving across an ocean (or even Columbus's voyages) or swoop downward to suggest the sinking of the ship (perhaps the *Titanic*). In both cases, the gesture for the ship needs to be considered separately from the two types of motion. We need to split the gesture into distinct and reusable elements. Typically, the meaning of these different types of hand motion will, as with communication in general, be highly ambiguous when considered in isolation. If instead of steepling our fingers we hold the hands slightly apart, pretending to grip a steering wheel, the bobbing up and down could then stand for going over a series of speed bumps, and the downward motion could depict going down a very steep hill (or even over a cliff, when combined with a suitably terrified facial expression). By partitioning a continuous movement into separate chunks, the hand gesture and the movement, these chunks can be repurposed and reinterpreted flexibly and creatively in different contexts.

What works in charades turns out also to work for language games in general. The secret to overcoming the Now-or-Never bottleneck is moment-by-moment 'chunking': a fundamental memory process by which we can combine two or more elements into a single unit (as when we remember an eleven-digit UK phone number by dividing it into two chunks corresponding to area code and line number). By chunking the incoming linguistic material together into larger units, we can make sense of it as soon as it is encountered. These chunks can then be passed on for additional, more complex analysis and possibly combined further into even larger units. To get an intuitive feel for how chunking works in language, read the following string of random letters aloud to yourself, then close your eyes and try to recall as many of the letters as you can in the right order:

muegaglegana

If you're like most people, you were able to recall only about four or five letters. In fact, we know from many decades of work that short-term memory is restricted to just a handful of items, so it is close to an impossible task to recall all twelve letters. Now, try the same task again, but this time with the reorganized version of the letter string shown below:

languagegame

This twelve-letter string suddenly is much easier to recall because you can chunk it into just two familiar words, 'language' and 'game'. Whereas you had to remember twelve random letters in the first string, which is nearly impossible, you had to recall only two words and then spell them out to recreate the second string. Indeed, the restriction on our short-term memory applies not to a particular type of element, be it letters or words, but to chunks. In this way, chunking can help us lump together smaller elements into larger ones, thereby reducing the strain on our memory and attention.

But chunking takes practice – and lots of it. You would not be able to recall much of the second twelve-letter string above without having practised reading extensively over many thousands of hours and if you didn't have a large vocabulary of English words ready at hand. If you hadn't learned to read, you wouldn't even see the twelve letters *as letters*, but only as unfamiliar uninterpretable squiggles – in which case holding on to and reproducing even one letter might be something of a challenge. As Periander, one of the Seven Sages of Greece, famously remarked, 'Practice does everything.'[13]

If this is right, then perhaps we should be able to hold on to lengthy streams of meaningless digits by combining them into meaningful and more memorable chunks and practising this trick again and again. Indeed, imposing patterns on meaningless material has been the core of mnemonic methods since the times of the orators of ancient Greece. In the late 1970s, a young undergraduate named Steve Faloon, now better known in the memory literature as SF, demonstrated how this can work in a spectacular way. He learned to recall not merely the five or so digits that most of us can manage but up to seventy-nine random digits! When he agreed to participate in the experiment run by the memory researcher and later expertise guru Anders Ericsson at Carnegie Mellon University, SF was just an ordinary undergraduate student, without exceptional memory or any expertise in mnemonic techniques.[14] His amazing memory skill didn't come easily: he spent hundreds of hours in the lab, tediously recalling strings of random digits, each read to him at a pace of one digit per second. Over time, he learned to group the sequences of digits into larger and larger chunks by recoding numbers as running times (he was an avid cross-country runner) or famous dates, such as 1944: 'near the end of World War II'. Later he developed ways of grouping these chunks into larger and larger 'superchunks', each consisting of multiple running times or dates. By practising digit recall over and over again, and learning to build chunks and superchunks, he was eventually able to accomplish the seemingly superhuman feat of recalling nearly eighty random digits. When it comes to language, our brains adopt a similar multilayer chunking strategy to deal with the relentless torrent of linguistic input.

So how does this work? For spoken language, this chunking process starts off with the complex, continuously changing spectrum of the acoustic signal that arrives at our ears. This input contains not just the speech of interest to us but also any amount of background conversation, music and noises of all kinds that are mixed in. The brain has to split off the speaker's voice from what is often a background cacophony. Pinning down the direction of the voice is particularly useful. The brain can work out roughly where a sound originates using a range of clues, the most important of which is the difference in time between when it arrives at the left and the right ears. This clue is also used when playing back recorded sounds in stereo – so that, for example, the different sections of an orchestra sound as if they are in different locations when we listen to a symphony with stereo headphones. This is why understanding a mono recording of a person talking against background noise is often surprisingly difficult – the crucial three-dimensional clues about where sounds are coming from have been lost.

Once the acoustic signal from the speaker's voice has been separated from the background, it is converted from a complex sound wave into a simple initial chunk-based format, such as phonemes (individual speech sounds) or syllables. As we've seen, these sound-based units arrive at an astonishing rate in fluent speech and therefore quickly begin to interfere with one another (just as you experienced with the first twelve-letter string). The solution is to chunk these sounds into words ('language' and 'game'). This trick provides the brain with a little more time to work on that input, but soon the words in the oncoming rush of speech begin to get mixed up with each other and are lost entirely (think of how poorly we can hang on to a random list of words). So the brain needs to repeat the chunking process, rapidly combining words into multiword chunks or phrases. Again, this buys us some extra time until interference sets in once more and the chunking process must be repeated again, now making up entire sentences, and eventually even larger units of meaningful discourse, whether conversational exchanges, stories or sets of instructions.

To illustrate this chunking of chunks, consider the following example, in which spaces have been removed between words to simulate the continuous nature of the speech stream and non-alphabetic symbols are used to indicate stray non-speech sounds in the acoustic input (we ignore here the further complication that phonemes don't really map straightforwardly onto letters):

W@ec%hunks#peechr&epeate%lyintoe@#verbigg$erch unk&sofinc#reasi%ngabstr@action

As a first step, the speech signal is separated from noise and other environmental sounds:

Wechunkspeechrepeatedlyintoeverbiggerchunksof increasingabstraction

Because we cannot hold on to the speech signal for long, as soon as we hear it, we quickly chunk it into syllables:

**We chunk speech re peat ed ly in to ev er big ger chunks
of in creas ing ab strac tion**

But once we have even just a few syllables, interference occurs
between them, so as soon as we can we chunk them into words:

**We chunk speech repeatedly into ever bigger chunks of
increasing abstraction**

—which are then subsequently chunked further into phrases to
buy more time:

**[We chunk speech repeatedly] [into ever bigger chunks]
[of increasing abstraction]**

Chunking across these different levels happens in parallel, while
we also gradually incorporate the meaning of the words, what
they convey in the current context and what else we know about
the world. Eventually, our interpretation of the whole sentence
is absorbed into our memory of the current conversation. What
we have, then, is a continual parallel cascade of mental activity.
To stem the swift tide of language input, we chunk new material
as rapidly as possible into ever-larger units and immediately
pass these chunks up to the next 'level' of abstraction for further
analysis and chunking, from syllables to words to phrases to
large chunks of discourse.

When it comes to chunking, it is imperative to get things right
the first time: the ever-present Now-or-Never bottleneck makes
it very hard to undo a previously created chunk, breaking it
down into its sub-units (say, turning a chunked word back into
its constituent sounds), and then rechunk them differently.

Once we've created a chunk, its original sub-components quickly fade and we retain only a gist of the original input, whether signed or spoken.[15] But in the light of the notoriously ambiguous nature of human language, we cannot depend on the input alone to build the correct chunks reliably. Consider hearing someone uttering the following phrase (transcribed in English phonetic spelling – try to read it aloud): /tOOrEkuhnIEspEEch/. This stream of sounds can be chunked in at least two different ways, resulting in radically different interpretations. In the current context, it seems natural to chunk the utterance into **to recognize speech**. But if we heard the same stream of sounds while walking by the seashore where a giant oil terminal was under construction, we might chunk it into **to wreck a nice beach**.[16] So, to make sure that chunking is right-first-time, we have to use all the clues available to us. Arriving at the right interpretation hinges on the submerged part of the communication iceberg, just as when we play charades. In the **to wreck a nice beach** interpretation, these clues may come from current conversation (we were talking about the construction work), past conversations (about our environmental concerns), our immediate surroundings (the construction site has just come into view) or simply background knowledge about the world (about oil tankers, construction projects, aesthetics, swimming safety and more). Chunking only works when the brain is able to draw on context: lots of it, and very fast.

The need for the brain to continually chunk the input, and make chunks of chunks, explains why human languages, despite their enormous variation, are all organized into hierarchies of units, such as phonemes, syllables, words and phrases.[17] By contrast, the transmission of information between computers doesn't follow this way of doing things at all. For example, when streaming a recording of a human voice over the internet there are no elements that correspond to any of our familiar linguistic units – instead, a stream of zeros and ones is used to transmit a digitally compressed version of the acoustic signal. The hierarchical, chunked structure of human language doesn't arise from the mere need to communicate – it arises from the profound limitations of human memory and the processes of chunking and rechunking that the brain must carry out tirelessly to deal with the ceaseless flood of input.

JUST-IN-TIME LANGUAGE PRODUCTION

So far, we've been considering how the bottleneck shapes the way we understand language. But equally puzzling is how we produce language. How are we able to generate streams of hundreds of words per minute while only occasionally pausing for breath? When we talk, we often feel we are 'speaking into the void', not exactly knowing where a sentence will take us as we begin uttering its first words. Research on how people produce speech finds that this intuition has a lot of truth in it. Although we may begin a sentence with a rough idea of what we want to say, our brain does not plan out from the outset exactly how we are going to say it, phrase by phrase, word by word, or syllable by syllable. Rather, the exact series of steps that eventually expresses our thoughts – from the specific choices of words, tense markings and prosodic patterning down to the fine-tuned movements of our mouth and tongue while we exhale and vibrate our vocal cords – is improvised on the fly. If we were to try to plan everything in advance, we would end up producing word salad: initial phrases would interfere with later phrases, early words with later ones, and phonemes would get in the way of each other. This is because the ever-present Now-or-Never bottleneck applies just as much when we produce speech as when we listen to it. Indeed, the processes of understanding and generating speech turn out to be mirror images of one another.[18] When we listen, we start with small chunks (speech sounds) and build them up into ever-larger units; when we speak, by contrast, we begin with large chunks (roughly the gist of what we want to say), and break them down into ever-smaller units until we get to the specific motor movements we use to produce language (whether spoken or signed).

To get around the bottleneck when we speak, our language system uses a strategy that in surprising ways mirrors the efficient elegance of just-in-time car manufacturing.[19] In the 1960s, the Japanese car company Toyota pioneered a revolutionary production strategy to save money by minimizing the quantity of parts and other materials kept in stock: the factory would receive parts from its suppliers *only when these were about to be put into a car*. In other words, parts should arrive just in time and, ideally, not a moment before. This strategy was so successful that General Motors later sent some of their managers to Japan to learn from Toyota how to implement just-in-time production in their US manufacturing plants. It turns out that when we're talking, we adopt a similar just-in-time strategy, keeping only a few chunks in memory at any time to avoid them interfering with one another. Just as in manufacturing, where keeping a large stock of components is costly in both money and space, so too the bottleneck means that our memory cannot hold on to a 'stock' of phonemes, words or phrases.

We can see chunking at work when we're trying to pronounce

unfamiliar words or very long words. A great example comes from the 1964 Disney movie *Mary Poppins*: **supercalifragilistic-expialidocious**.[20] This invented word, supposedly meaning something like 'extraordinarily good' or 'wonderful', is an awful mouthful and almost impossible to pronounce without mistakes the first time we encounter it. We need to chunk this tongue-twister into more manageable parts to make it easier to say. Initially, we might divide it as follows (with the brackets [ ] indicating a chunk):

[Super] [cali] [fragi] [listic] [expi] [ali] [docious]

But with more practice, we can combine these chunks into larger ones:

[Supercali] [fragilistic] [expiali] [docious]

And repeating the process, we might end up with two large chunks, like these:

[Supercalifragilistic] [expialidocious]

When Morten's daughter was little, she was a big fan of the old Mary Poppins film, watching it over and over again, so he can attest to the fact that eventually, with sufficient practice, we can all learn to pronounce **supercalifragilisticexpialidocious** with remarkable speed and accuracy (while possibly retaining traces of our chunking in the pattern of intonation).

Learning and practice are crucial to becoming a fluent speaker. Children spend most of their first year of life learning how to get their lips and tongues to work together well enough to produce their first words. Before too long, though, they approach an average speaking rate of about 300 to 350 syllables, or roughly 150 words, per minute. And some people can speak faster still.[21] Clocking in at over 667 words per minute, the American Fran Capo is the fastest speaker of English on record, uttering more than four times as many words per minute as the average person. In second place, we have Seán Shannon of Canada, who is able to produce 655 words of English per minute. This allowed him to recite the 260 words of Hamlet's 'To be or not to be' soliloquy in just 23.8 seconds! Fortunately, most of us do not have voluntary tachylalia, as extremely rapid speech is called. At this speed, it's not easy to catch much of what these motor-mouths are saying, except perhaps for a word or two.

Getting up to the speed of superfast talkers like Fran Capo and Seán Shannon requires a substantial investment of time. They seem to be particularly good at chunking together multiword combinations (paralleling what SF did for digits). But it turns out that we all routinely rely on a huge store of common word combinations. Indeed, using computers to comb through millions of words in both spoken and written language, computational linguists have found that multiword chunks make up as much as half of everything we say.[22] They come in many shapes and forms, including idioms such as 'everything but the kitchen sink' and 'kick the bucket', often-used 'frozen' word sequences like 'I think' and 'come in many shapes and forms', compound expressions such as 'car sick' and 'fire engine red', and social platitudes like 'nice weather we're having' and 'how are you?'. Because we have memorized most of the multiword combinations that we come across frequently, we can readily deploy them as convenient linguistic 'prefabs' when we speak.

This is true for native and non-native speakers alike.

Referring to an article by Morten and his colleague Inbal Arnon from Hebrew University, Michael Skapinker wrote a piece in the *Financial Times* on the use of multiword chunks by foreign managers of soccer teams in the English Premier League.[23] He noted that these managers would make all sorts of mistakes when they tried to cobble words together quickly, but that when they used multiword sequences often heard in soccer contexts, they made no errors. For example, while the former manager of the London football club Tottenham Hotspur, the Argentine Mauricio Pochettino, in one interview uttered the non-standard sentence 'We miss a little bit to be more aggressive', he then continued with a perfect multiword chunk often used in sports lingo: 'I think we need more consistency.' The upshot of all of this is that whether we're native or non-native speakers, we take advantage of the fluency that multiword chunks afford us when we talk under the ever-present pressure of the Now-or-Never bottleneck.

Although our speech is generally fluent, it is by no means faultless. As with any other skill, all of us continually make mistakes, no matter whether we're native speakers or not. But because as listeners we are normally focused on understanding what others are trying to get across, rather than how they say it, most of these little slips of the tongue go unnoticed. An adult speaker will mispronounce a word or use the wrong term about every one thousand words, and not surprisingly children make about four to eight times as many of these errors.[24] Given that we utter about 150 words per minute when speaking at a normal rate, this means that we slip up on average about every seven minutes of talking. And this estimate doesn't include other mistakes we often make when talking, like stopping mid-sentence, repairing something we just said by rephrasing it, or the ubiquitous hesitations and pauses that we desperately try to fill with **uh**, **er** and **um**. As you would expect, all of these speech errors occur even more often if we're tired, nervous or under the influence of drugs or alcohol.

For psychologists, however, these speech errors are a treasure trove of information: how we mis-speak lays bare some of the inner workings of our just-in-time language production. Indeed, the errors align perfectly with the different levels of chunking, showing evidence of interference between chunks waiting to be produced. We make errors involving individual speech sounds (as in saying **a *m*eal mystery** instead of the intended **a real mystery**, pronouncing the m-sound too early), we reorder words (like uttering **a *wife* for his *job*** when meaning to say **a job for his wife**) and we even swap whole phrases around (as when saying **if you'll meet him, you'll stick around** rather than the planned **if you'll stick around, you'll meet him**).[25]

CONVERSATIONAL DANCING

As if the Now-or-Never bottleneck didn't pose enough difficulties for our language system, there is a further challenge: conversations switch back and forth between speakers at a blistering pace, each of us taking turns talking and listening in quick succession. Just as charades is not a one-person game, so too language is not about monologue.[26] A conversation is not merely a succession of soliloquies. Far from it. Rather, language is similar to an improvised partner dance, where rapid, coordinated interchange is key. But, just as with the Now-or-Never bottleneck, the language sciences have until fairly recently also tended to ignore our conversational dancing, treating language as if we were all soliloquizing, like Shakespeare's Hamlet, speaking into the night uncertain of any response.[27]

In fact, the reality of everyday language is very different. Just how different is beautifully demonstrated by the work of the linguistic anthropologist (and gifted sculptor) Stephen Levinson. With his colleagues, he has shown that across a diverse set of languages and cultures, from Danish and Dutch to Lao and Yélî Dnye, people are astonishingly fast at conversational turn-taking:[28] on average, the gap between one person finishing their turn and the other beginning their response is just one-fifth of a second (200 milliseconds). For comparison, it takes about the same amount of time for our brains to recognize a familiar face; half a second to begin speaking a written word aloud; and a whole second to 'name' a picture of a familiar object, say, a dog. So, to be able to begin their turn 'on time', the listener needs to start getting ready well before the speaker has even finished.

To achieve such fast-paced turn-taking, we first have to figure out what the speaker is saying well enough that we can formulate the right kind of response: is it a request, a question or a statement of some sort? And what specific request, question or statement? Next, we need to find 'turn-ending' cues of all kinds (content, pitch, even facial expression) to predict when the speaker will stop so that we're ready to start talking when they're done (figure 2.1). At the same time, we must continually integrate what the person is currently saying with what was said before, what we know about the speaker and what we know about the world. And we need to respond quickly. If we don't, any delay may be interpreted as significant. For example, a longer-than-average pause after a request might be construed as reluctance, even if we are actually willing to help. Fast conversational switching is no

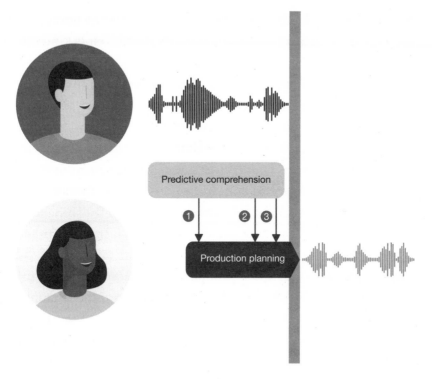

Figure 2.1. Illustration of the overlapping time course of turns in conversation. Soon after a speaker begins their turn, the listener starts (1) planning their turn in response, (2) predicting the turn's end and (3) using turn-ending cues to launch their own turn. The vertical grey bar indicates the short pause of around a fifth of a second between turns. (Illustration by Sunita Christiansen, adapted from Levinson 2016.)

rarity. Casual conversations are typically rapid-fire – dominated by short turns of about two seconds or so. Yet, despite this astounding time pressure, our turn-taking abilities generally become so automatic and function so well that we can even (often somewhat annoyingly) finish each other's sentences.

Despite all these challenges, humans are such practised conversational dancers that we are oblivious to all this complexity.

53

But there is a catch: the whirlwind pace of turn-taking, along with the ever-present pressure from the Now-or-Never bottleneck, means that we often do not actually take in the details of what we are hearing – but only a rough general impression. In fact, our understanding is often remarkably shallow.[29] For example, when asked 'How many animals of each kind did Moses take on the Ark?' most people answer 'Two!' without noticing anything peculiar. Of course, it was Noah on the Ark, not Moses, but our brain makes enough sense of what is being said to latch onto the right biblical story, and that's usually 'good enough'.

Charades is about getting our message across. Similarly, when dealing with language, we don't care about every single word and every single meaning we hear, but focus instead on the overall gist of what is being said. Rather than trying to work out a complete understanding of each and every utterance we hear, we try to arrive at an interpretation that is good enough for the task at hand. This strategy works well in most cases, and when it fails we can always ask for clarification, make a puzzled face, or deploy a special easy-to-say short word – like 'huh?' in English, 'eh?' in Spanish, or '응?' (eung?) in Korean – used across many different languages and cultures to signal that we missed something in the previous turn.[30]

Of course, this means that normal everyday conversations are nothing like the orderly, and sometimes witty, dialogue we read in books or hear in television shows and films. Real-life exchanges are messy, full of half-finished sentences, interruptions and people talking over each other. This is illustrated by the following excerpt from a face-to-face conversation taking place in Albuquerque, New Mexico, between siblings Lisa and Kevin and Lisa's friend Marie.[31] The discussion centres on a recent visit Marie made to Accident and Emergency with her sick baby (speech overlaps are indicated using brackets [ ] and indentation).

MARIE:	Well, his temperature was a hundred and four point five.
LISA:	. . . That is so high.
KEVIN:	He's lucky [that he didn't]—
LISA:	[How long] was he there?
LISA:	That [high].
KEVIN:	[How l]ong,
KEVIN:	. . . do you know?
MARIE:	Uh his fever?
KEVIN:	[Yeah].
MARIE:	[I don't] know.
KEVIN:	. . . That's dangerou—
KEVIN:	I mean [it's . . .]—
MARIE:	[The doctor s]aid,
LISA:	['Cause he could have],
LISA:	brain damage.

The whole exchange took less than twelve seconds, with rapid turn-taking and speakers cutting each other off, which forced them to continue what they wanted to say across multiple separate turns. To keep conversations on track, participants use various tricks, including 'back-channelling' to signal that they're keeping up (such as saying 'mhm', 'uh-huh' and 'yeah', as Kevin says above); making 'repairs' to fix potential misunderstandings (ranging from the above-mentioned 'huh' to requests for clarification, as when Marie asks, 'Uh his fever?'); and 'interactive alignment', where speakers recycle each other's linguistic forms using the exact same words, other words with the same meaning or similar kinds of multiword chunks (as when Kevin and Marie both use 'know' and Lisa and Kevin both say 'how long'). These conversational tactics are not just verbal but also routinely incorporate gestures and facial expressions, such as nodding to signal agreement or frowning to show puzzlement. Together, these collaborative devices help us understand each other and quickly correct misunderstandings as we squeeze our conversational turns through the Now-or-Never bottleneck.

◉

It is easy to imagine that the apparent chaos of casual conversation is a degenerate form of elegantly formulated prose – yet the natural state of language is interactive conversation, not monologue. But how can such chaotic interactions ever be meaningful? Mere complex interaction surely can't be enough in itself. Otherwise, we would have to attribute meaning to the planets in our solar system, carrying out their intricately coordinated dance in elliptical circles around the sun. Again, we shall seek the answer in the game of charades.

We don't first bottle up what we want to say in the depths of our minds and only then decide how to translate our thoughts into English, Hindi, Swahili or whatever language we speak. Instead, we improvise meaning collaboratively in the moment, funnelling it through the Now-or-Never bottleneck to address the communicative challenges at hand. Although we only ever notice the words, phrases and sentences that make up the tip of the communication iceberg, the hidden part – our knowledge of culture, social structures, the world and each other – is crucial if we are to understand one another. Indeed, we can only hope to understand what meaning is when we see language as conversation first, and monologue second. Language at its core is fundamentally interactive, fluent and cooperative: linguistic charades is beautifully coordinated conversational dancing, creating meaning on the fly, step by step, in time with one another.

3

THE UNBEARABLE
LIGHTNESS OF MEANING

Consider, for example, the proceedings that we call 'games'.
I mean board-games, card-games, ball-games, Olympic
games and so on. What is common to them all? . . . don't
think, but look! . . . And the result of this examination is:
we see a complicated network of similarities overlapping
and criss-crossing: sometimes overall similarities, sometimes similarities of detail . . . I can think of no better
expression to characterize these similarities than 'family
resemblances'.

LUDWIG WITTGENSTEIN,
Philosophical Investigations (1953)

The Czech novelist Milan Kundera famously explores the vertigo
induced by confronting the momentary, ephemeral, open-
ended capriciousness of our existence. This is the 'unbearable
lightness of being' of each human life, the first and only rehearsal
for a play with no author and no final performance – a play

whose meaning, if any, we perceive only dimly.[1] But the lightness of the meaning of life is no more striking than the astonishing flexibility, creativity and metaphorical lightness of meaning in language. And such lightness is not merely the stuff of poetry or abstract thought; it is so ubiquitous in day-to-day conversation that we scarcely notice its very existence.[2]

Let's take, as an example, the word **light** itself. Things we describe as light include a morning, a room, a play, a piece of music, a package, an aircraft, a machine gun, an infantry battalion, a meal, a shade of red, a beer . . . the list seems endless. And yet what do all these 'light' things have in common? Philosophers and linguists have tended to assume that there must be a common 'essence' that each word picks out. This common essence might perhaps be a single concept, somehow represented in our minds; perhaps, too, it is a property of reality. So, from this point of view, the meaning of each word is assumed to connect in some way with something beyond language itself: whether a component of our thoughts and/or a property of the external world.[3] Indeed, working out what these common essences are for words that appear particularly important for understanding the human condition has been a major philosophical preoccupation since Plato's time. If we could only be clear about the meanings of **truth**, **value**, **justice**, the **good** and, for that matter, **meaning** itself, then we would seem to be well on the way to solving many of the great conceptual problems that puzzle us, and generally straightening out our confused thinking. But, as we'll see shortly, the very idea of common essences, even for everyday words like **light**, is a mirage.

Until the twentieth century, most philosophers followed the commonsense line that words straightforwardly 'point' to corresponding aspects of the world. After all, the book of Genesis tells a reassuringly simple story of names and things going all the way back to Adam: 'And out of the ground the Lord God formed every beast of the field, and every fowl of the air; and brought them unto Adam to see what he would call them: and whatsoever Adam called every living creature, that was the name thereof.'[4] St Augustine takes a similar perspective when explaining how the meanings of words are passed on to each new generation: 'When they (my elders) named some object, and accordingly moved towards something, I saw this and I grasped that the thing was called by the sound they uttered when they meant to point it out.'[5]

Just attaching labels to specific objects does little to explain what words mean. For example, putting a linguistic 'label' on a specific dog, Fido, is not terribly informative. Does **dog** refer to dogs in general, name this particular animal or call out Fido's specific breed? Does it refer to the entire class of domesticated animals or to mammals or even to all living things? For that matter, why does the phrase **the dog** refer to a whole Fido rather than his fur, coat, flank, body (rather than legs and head), size or tendency to bark?[6]

There is, though, a further problem with the simple idea that words merely label visible objects or observable actions: so many words in our vocabularies have highly abstract meanings that can't possibly be pointed to. Consider the previous sentence, for example; note the challenge of explaining the meaning of **there**, **is**, **though**, **a**, **problem**, or any of the words in that sentence by providing labelled examples. These words are meaningful in relation to other words – they don't just call out 'chunks' of reality that we can touch, see or hear.

It is nonetheless tempting to think that there must be some kind of 'thing', even if it is shadowy and mysterious, that is associated with each word – at least for nouns and verbs. After all, we learned at school that nouns are supposed to refer to things, and verbs to actions. And mustn't each word have a well-defined meaning that corresponds to some aspect or other of the external world?[7] Ludwig Wittgenstein, originator of the idea of 'language games' that we discussed in the preface, warns against such thoughts. Very few, if any, words have a single common thread or a unifying definition that links together all the ways it can be used. Where is the single thread of meaning for the word **light**, for example? At best, there is, perhaps, some loose metaphorical link between light beer and light cream; between light winds and light remarks; and between light trading on the stock market and light traffic.

But with the parallel of charades in mind, this is all we need: loose metaphorical links are quite enough for us to be able to communicate effectively. In Wittgenstein's famous metaphor from the start of this chapter, words encompass a complex pattern of family resemblance. Some family members share a distinctive chin, some have a common build or gait, others have a particular shape of nose, and so on, in various combinations. There is no common essence from which family members are all slight variations. There are only criss-crossing patterns of similarities.

A light breakfast, lunch, supper and snack are clearly closely connected by being of modest calorific value. Similarly, light tanks, light frigates and light infantry are connected regarding manoeuvrability, speed of movement and lack of armour. The flexibility with which we redeploy language also shines through in the Navajo code talkers' names for military terms. For example, **da-he-tih-hi** (the word for 'hummingbird') is used to denote a fighter plane, while **jay-sho** (the word for 'buzzard') refers to a bomber. Similarly, **ca-lo** (shark) refers to a destroyer, while **lo-tso** (whale) means a battleship. The Navajo language doesn't have vocabulary for military terms, but such terms can easily be co-opted from existing vocabulary, given the human capacity for playing charades. For that matter, the English words for military hardware have been through the same process. The very idea of planes 'fighting' is a metaphorical extension of people fighting, and a **fighter plane** is a further jump still. A **battleship** is, of course, a ship for battle (originally between land armies, and extended to naval conflicts), and this rather general description has been recruited to refer to a particular class of large military vessels. It is the lightness of meaning, its shape-shifting, metaphorical quality, that allows the meanings of our existing stock of words to keep up with a continually changing world. Our charades-playing ability allows us to concoct new words (often from old components) when new vocabulary is needed.

We don't normally talk of the lightness of being, as Kundera does – or indeed the lightness of meaning – but we can make some approximate sense of these more novel uses, too. And, as with charades, communication only has to be 'good enough' to do the job of the moment. We may be able to, say, guess that the film is *King Kong* even if we don't quite understand a charades player's attempts to mime swatting planes from the top of the Empire State Building or efforts to re-enact the characteristic screaming of Fay Wray.[8]

The complexity and unruliness of the meaning of even the simplest words are both familiar and perplexing. After all, don't words have definitions listed in the dictionary, and fairly pithily at that? And can't we learn the meaning of a new word just by looking it up? But on closer inspection the story looks very different. The *Oxford English Dictionary* entry for the adjective **light** lists more than twenty senses of the word, and most of these entries are further divided into additional and more specific senses. These include, among many others:

- 'Applied to elements whose specific gravity (or atomic number) is relatively low; light metal, a metal of low specific gravity, esp. aluminium or magnesium.'
- 'Bearing a small or comparatively small load. Of a vessel: Having a small burthen, or (the usual sense) unladen, without cargo.'
- 'Having little momentum or force; gentle, not violent; acting gently; moving, impelling, or manipulating something without heavy pressure or violence. Said esp. of the hand, a step, the wind, a medicine.'

Remember, too, that **light** is not only an adjective. It works as a noun (**turn on the light**, **have you got a light?**, **seeing the light**, **the light of reason**) and a verb (**light the fire**, **light a film set**, **light the Christmas tree**) and can be transformed into an adverb (**treading lightly**, **snowing lightly**). The variety of meanings and the criss-crossing metaphorical links between them are remarkable.

The dictionary entry for a word is not a distillation of a single, essential, literal meaning but a compendium of a great variety of uses, largely explained by illustrative examples. So when we are interpreting **light** on any particular occasion, we need to draw on the hidden part of the communication iceberg: our shared experience of the details of the specific occasion, our knowledge of each other, and our background knowledge about the world and the endless contexts in which we have encountered **light** before. But not only that. Without accessing the hidden parts of the communication iceberg, we'd also be unable to make sense of the dictionary itself. After all, the dictionary merely gives us helpful clues and examples, counting on *us* to 'get the general idea'. While aiming to be as explicit as possible, lexicographers are inevitably forced to convey the meanings of words using linguistic charades, too. It's just the way language works. The richness and complexity of language are by no means arbitrary. Quite the reverse. Meaning is the product of a network of creative analogies linking **light** colours, **light** liquids and **light** suppers. The meanings of even the most prosaic of words have been built up through the continual action of generations of language users, each of us endowed with remarkably poetic imaginations.

We've considered adjectives, such as **light**. Yet the same points apply to words of all kinds. The quote from Wittgenstein at the start of this chapter points out the complexity of the network linking together **games** of all kinds. Games can be competitive (tennis), but need not be. They may or may not involve teams (football vs pool), a single player (solitaire), or tens, hundreds or thousands of people (massive multiplayer online games). Games may have sharply defined rules (chess and Go) or may be collaborative and open-ended (role-playing games like Dungeons and Dragons). They may involve physical strength or verbal dexterity, moving pieces around a board, building an imaginary city, running a football team or commanding a military force in a virtual world. Indeed, the meaning of **game** continually, and unpredictably, extends in new directions as new types of game-like activity are invented.

The way word meanings creatively mutate is driven by the immediate communicative challenges of daily life rather than the careful planning of a lexicographer. But some forces do pull meanings into some degree of order. Words with similar meanings tend to pull apart and find their own communicative niches.

Think of the subtle distinctions between **smells**, **scents**, **perfumes** and **stinks**, or between **smiles**, **grins**, **smirks** and **simpers** – indeed, true synonyms are remarkably rare in English or any other language. Just as with biological species, no two words can occupy exactly the same niche for long – if both are to survive, they must develop distinctive roles. So, for example, scents are pleasanter and more subtle than smells, whereas stinks are quite the opposite. Perfumes are mostly deliberately designed, whereas scents need not be. Similarly, grins are broad, amused smiles; smirks are smug, whereas simpers are ingratiating and perhaps not entirely sincere. To maintain its place in the communicative toolbox, each word needs to do a distinct communicative job.

And words work together in loose alliances. Consider how the significance of an everyday phrase such as **the front of** changes depending on what we are talking about. **The front of** a house, an envelope, a head, a body, a queue, a coin, a watch, a class of students or a pack of runners – all these uses are only loosely and metaphorically linked; but once we know **the front of**, we also can guess what must be the **back**. Similarly, things as varied as bulbs, diamonds, people, pieces of dialogue and film scores can be sparkling, brilliant or just plain dull; and a comedy, a mood or a winter's day can be not only light but also dark. Such patterns are local and irregular. We can talk about the front of a shop and the back of a shop – but though we can talk about shop fronts, there is for some reason no such thing as shop backs. We can touch the front, back or side of our heads; a thought can be in the front of our mind or at the back of our mind, but not in the side of our mind. Thus, these forces of competition between words are continually pulling meanings of related words into partial alignment as they shift from one context to another. Language thus becomes a partially coherent *system* for conveying what we want to say rather than just a haphazard collection of words. And these partially coherent networks of meaning develop in different ways for different languages: in Spanish, *light* **blue** is **azul** *clara*; a *light* **jacket** is **chaqueta** *ligera*; and so on. These different networks of meanings make each language wonderfully unique. This means that translation can never be quite perfect, and makes anything beyond an approximate understanding of human language incredibly difficult for computers (as we'll see later in the book).

The local patterns in language are nicely exemplified by the jumble of different metaphors that we use to describe the world – often using the language about the physical world to help describe more abstract realms.[9] This occurs, for example, when we talk of an idea being 'in the front' or 'at the back' of our mind, clearly a non-spatial entity. Similarly, we talk of thoughts or memories being 'buried' in our mental depths and occasionally coming to the 'surface', where they become consciously accessible; the more deeply thoughts are buried, the more difficult they will be to uncover.[10] We can imagine that ideas, once brought to the mental surface, can be packaged up in language and 'sent' to another person (or 'broadcast' to many), where they are unwrapped and placed in the mind of the recipient – perhaps later to be buried or merely forgotten in that person's mental 'depths' (as we saw in chapter 1, this way of thinking about how communication works is dangerously misleading).

The ubiquity with which we use the language of physical, observable things to talk about abstract ideas is rather startling once we start to notice it. Think for a minute about how we talk about arguments. We 'find holes' in each other's logic, just as we might search for holes in a sweater. Our reasoning can have 'gaps' that need to be 'filled in'. An argument can be tenuous or solid, weak or strong. We have 'chains' of reasoning (that can get 'tangled'), or 'steps' in an argument, some of which might be a 'stretch'. Sometimes conflicting arguments seem to be engaged in a medieval siege: one line of reasoning may try to chip away at, undercut or undermine another. Arguments may have solid foundations or be entirely unsupported; our case may need to be shored up or be in danger of collapsing entirely.

Within this tangle of ways in which we all talk about minds, meanings, arguments or anything else, it is still tempting to feel that there must be a single 'right' way: that for each word, there must be a true underlying meaning, an ultimate source from which an ever-dividing river delta of metaphors must emanate. Perhaps, one may suppose, this essence is the *literal* meaning of each word. But we argue that there is no underlying essence, just an endless stream of moment-by-moment communicative improvisations – an almost endlessly varied sequence of loosely and partially connected charades. As in charades, communication in the here and now is the goal, using whatever past experience and creative tricks we can. Our confused and criss-crossing ways of talking and thinking are all there is. The idea that words have essential meanings that somehow reveal the truth about how we see the world (or how we ought to see the world) is an illusion. Rather than encapsulating a single, coherent picture or model of reality, language continually invokes a plethora of different and often irreconcilable models.[11] If we prune away all the tangles and thickets of language in our search for the essence of what words really mean, then we will be left with nothing.

THE SHALLOWS OF MEANING

Pre-school children learn the meanings of more than ten new words each day, and they understand the meanings of those words well enough to use them in fluent communication. They use these words to express a welter of opinions on what they think is good or bad, right or wrong, and all too readily wail 'It's not fair!'. But how can a young child – and the rest of us – really know what these words mean? After all, the most brilliant thinkers across millennia have found that these everyday notions – goodness, the difference between right and wrong, the nature of fairness – are sunk in conceptual quicksand. How can young children master concepts that philosophers struggle to analyse?

The answer is that philosophers wrestle with the challenge of providing a general theory of 'deep' concepts – concepts that are supposed to work in every possible case and context – to explain the fundamental meaning of such notions as **good**, **fair**, **cause**, **mind** and so on. But children and adults only have to get meaning sufficiently clear to deal with the specific communicative challenge of the moment. To communicate successfully, a cry of 'It's not fair!' must express the outrage a child feels when given a smaller slice of cake or made to wait in a queue. But this communication does not require the child (or the unfortunate parent) to have a general theory of fairness in mind. Indeed, the 'meaning' that allows us to get by successfully is often unexpectedly shallow.

Consider, for example, how children use **alive** and **dead**.[12] Susan Carey, a developmental psychologist at Harvard, had the following instructive and rather delightful interchanges with her daughter Eliza on the subject. When someone is shot on a TV programme, Eliza (three years and six months) explains: 'He's dead – I can tell because he's not moving.' This seems promisingly similar to how we adults define **dead**. But then, Carey asks about Eliza's toy bear:

> **E:** . . . She'll always be alive.
> **S:** Is she alive?
> **E:** No – she's dead. HOW CAN THAT BE?
> **S:** Is she alive or dead?
> **E:** Dead.
> **S:** Did she use to be alive?
> **E:** No, she's middle-sized in between alive and dead.
>   She moves sometimes.

And then comes the astonishing question:

> **E:** How do dead people go to the bathroom?
> **S:** What?
> **E:** Maybe they have bathrooms under the ground.
> **S:** Dead people don't have to go to the bathroom. They
>   don't do anything; they just lie there. They don't eat or
>   drink, so they don't have to go to the bathroom.
> **E:** But they ate or drank before they died – they have to go
>   to the bathroom from just before they died.

Eliza doesn't, surely, have a clear and distinct concept of **alive** and **dead**. Her toy bear is not alive; but then again, her bear moves sometimes, so it must be alive, or perhaps it's in some intermediate state. And dead people are, it seems, still carrying on with normal bodily functions. On a separate occasion (aged three years and eight months) she exclaims: 'Isn't it funny – statues aren't alive, but you can still see them?' Her grandfather is not alive, and you can't see him, she notes.

Eliza is clearly a very observant reasoner. And she is also an astute player of verbal charades. People throw around the words **alive** and **dead**, but what are they getting at? Well, dead things don't seem to move; and you can't go to see dead people. But the idea that **alive** and **dead** only apply to biological organisms – which seems so central from an adult perspective – seems to be absent or perhaps only secondary for Eliza. What is really astonishing is that, in most of our interactions with pre-school children, we don't have the faintest inkling that their understanding of words is so radically different from ours. Just as with the interpretation of actions and gestures in charades, children learn to understand words well enough to make sense of the current, specific context in which they hear a word used. The motionless person who has been shot is called **dead**. Relatives and pets – who are no longer seen – are also described as dead. Young children can create their own charades for the adults around them, using those same words remarkably well – in fact, well enough that huge conceptual contradictions (such as toy bears being both alive and dead) almost never show up in daily conversation.

But the same issues arise when adults communicate. What is it, precisely, to be **alive**? Typical biology textbooks can do no better than a descriptive list: living things grow, reproduce, eat and excrete, regulate their internal chemistry and temperature, are composed of one or more cells, pass on their traits through their genes and so on. But this leaves tricky cases such as viruses (not composed of cells, not able to reproduce independently), viroids (circular RNA strands that replicate autonomously inside a host plant), prions (infectious proteins) and even the androids of the future (could a machine be conscious without being alive?). The definition of **life**, like the definitions of **good**,

justice, **right** and **wrong**, has been the subject of endless and unresolved debates for millennia. And our conception of **life** is full of contradictions. Wouldn't an afterlife be a type of life? And if so, should the biological criteria be mostly thrown out? The people in an imagined afterlife aren't actually dead, are they? And what about cryogenic freezing – is suspended animation a form of life, or death, or does it fall somewhere in between?

These types of questions are mostly irrelevant in the vast majority of linguistic charades we play in everyday communication – the tricky cases just don't arise much in ordinary conversation. What matters is that we can get along well enough when dealing with the situations that actually occur in daily life. We no more need a mental definition of **life** to talk about living relatives or dead pets than we need a biological definition of **gorillas** to mime King Kong.

Both pre-school children and adults use words as players use gestures in charades – in creative, contradictory ways that are good enough to get through the language games of the moment. In learning a language, we are learning to play creative conversational games with words. And playing those conversational games requires paying attention to likely communicative objectives, the contents of the environment and past linguistic usage – the hidden parts of communication iceberg are just as important as the words themselves.

Wittgenstein asks us to imagine a simple language game between a builder and an assistant in which commands such as **Slab!** are sufficient to allow construction to proceed successfully. Perhaps there is just one vaguely slab-like object in view – so **Slab!** must refer to that. Neither player in the game has to worry about pinning down the precise boundaries of the category represented by the word **slab** (does it include tiles, chunks of concrete, flat pieces of stone?). Or, for that matter, what precisely is being said about the slab. There are so many possible variants and shades of meaning, even for this single word: **Bring it to me!**, **Bring it right away!**, **Hand it to me gently!** – or, in a slightly different context, the utterance of **Slab!** might mean **Cement it into place!**, **Break it into pieces!** or just **Take it away!**. All that matters is that the assistant can work out what to do, given the specific objects lying around and the task at hand.

For Wittgenstein, communication in specific situations is the starting point for language – the objective is to play the communicative game well enough for the purposes of the moment. Learning a language does *not* involve swallowing a dictionary. As we have seen, dictionary entries, even for scientific terms like **life**, turn out to be surprisingly threadbare. They give us hints, clues and examples, yet leave it to our creative imaginations, experience and the communicative challenge of the moment to do the rest.

We mentioned that pre-school children learn about ten words per day – that is, their vocabulary expands at this astonishing rate. But they are not gobbling up the meanings of words one after the other – instead, they are gradually learning to make use of an increasing number of 'tools' to help them get along with the people around them. So, although ten words per day is roughly the rate at which a child's vocabulary grows, the process of learning how to use each word in conversation is slow and incremental rather than all-or-nothing. And there is no point when fully fledged meaning finally lodges in the child's mind.

The charades viewpoint helps us make sense of some apparently puzzling experimental data. Consider the following situation: a two-year-old and an adult experimenter are playing with various objects, some familiar to the child and some not. The experimenter refers to one of the unfamiliar objects with a made-up name that the child has not heard before (e.g. **cheem**). The child cleverly infers that this name most likely refers to the new object (because the child knows the names of the other objects). In the momentary interaction, the child is able to pass the cheem to the experimenter on command by a process of elimination. But what has the child learned, exactly? At one end of the spectrum is the possibility that the child, like an attentive audience in charades, has made sense of a signal in the moment of this concrete interaction – but that the child's memory for this inference is fleeting. At the other end of the spectrum, Susan Carey has suggested that perhaps the child has come up with a hypothesis concerning the essential meaning of **cheem** (i.e. a meaning that is supposed to apply across all contexts), which will be cross-checked and updated when **cheem** is mentioned in the future. Which of these possibilities is right? Well, it turns out the data are pretty unequivocal: words that the child has cleverly interpreted in the moment are largely forgotten, even when tested only five minutes later. Charades are the starting point for language – but the significance of the charade of the moment is often rapidly forgotten (particularly by two-year-olds).[13]

Meaning is fleeting, emerging in the moment of communication (**you must mean that strange object**). But it can accumulate over time. Over endless communicative episodes, our minds gradually order the unruly meanings formed in the moment, refining, modifying and reorganizing the way words are used. And metaphor allows word meanings to leap chasms (**front/back of the house**, **queue**, **mind**), not just in poetry but in everyday speech. Across generations of speakers, words take on new meanings (now people 'tweet' when once only birds did), and generate and break free of countless patterns. The result is a tapestry of collective insights – a collection of shallow, contradictory but nonetheless tremendously useful sets of conventions – shaped not around deep scientific or philosophical theories but around the kinds of things we actually want to convey in the daily round of conversation.

THE EDGE OF ARBITRARINESS

In charades, to use linguists' jargon, gestures are often 'iconic': they look like what they represent. We hope a chest-beating action will bring to mind a gorilla; we try to stagger like a zombie, imitate Superman's take-off or recreate the distinctively tiny arms of *Tyrannosaurus rex*. If we use sounds rather than gestures, we can try whooshing noises, bird whistles and roars to conjure up the right object in the audience's mind. And, as we saw in chapter 1, we're surprisingly good at such vocal charades.

If human languages originated from something like charades (whether using gestures or sounds), then we should expect some traces of these iconic links between symbols and the world to remain. In many sign languages, we can see direct links between gesture and meaning. For example, the American Sign Language sign for **book** is the opening of outstretched palms that resembles opening the pages of a book; the symbol for **tree** positions one arm vertically (the trunk) with fingers outstretched (branches) and the other arm horizontal (the ground). Similarly, in spoken languages we have onomatopoeia – the very sounds of words like **buzz**, **squeak**, **splosh** and **click** remind us of the things they refer to. Yet if language is so similar to charades, shouldn't such 'sound symbolism' be everywhere? But it seems that sound symbolism is the exception rather than the rule. Consider words for **dog** in a variety of languages: **chien** (French), **perro** (Spanish), **hund** (Danish), **anjing** (Indonesian), **собака** (Russian). None of these sounds remotely like the others, or like a bark or a growl. In short, our puzzle is: Why doesn't each language refer to dogs with some variant of the sound-symbolic **woof**?

The **arbitrariness** of the link between sound and meaning has been a core assumption in linguistics for more than a century.[14] From the language-as-charades viewpoint, where links between sound and meaning seem only to make communication easier, how can such arbitrariness arise? One obvious answer is what we might call 'drift' (analogous to genetic drift in biology). Because both sounds and meanings are continually shifting over time, any iconicity is likely to be increasingly obscured. Sounds (or gestures) erode as they are simplified and stereotyped over time, a point to which we will return in the next chapter. Recall the steepling of hands in Nick's family's charades. This gesture iconically represents the prow of a ship, butting through the water; but when it is repurposed to represent 'Columbus', 'the Americas' or 'expeditions' in general, iconicity is lost.

Drift aside, there is also an active force pushing towards arbitrariness, as pointed out by our friend and long-time collaborator Padraic Monaghan at the universities of Lancaster and Amsterdam.[15] Padraic's insight is that having too close a link between sound and meaning can actually make communication more difficult (even if it makes learning the language easier). To see why, suppose that each breed of dog was named by imitating its bark. But the barks of akitas, beagles, collies and dachshunds sound awfully similar – and are therefore very difficult to tell apart. Contextual clues (such as that we are at the dog show or in the park) can tell us that the speaker is talking about dogs, but they are unlikely to help define which breed. Padraic's argument pushes this thought further. Context gives us clues about what people are likely to mean (**akitas, beagles, collies**), while sounds/signs give us clues about the specific word they are using (**beetles, beagles, beadles**). So given a context *and* some specific speech sounds/signs, we can pin down the precise word pretty accurately (here: **beagle**). It turns out that this type of argument can be generalized using the mathematics of Shannon's information theory that we met in chapter 1. For communication to work optimally, any two sources of communicative clues (here, sound and context) need to be as independent as possible so that each can help the other – and that, in turn, means weakening the connection between sound and meaning. From this point of view, the (fairly) arbitrary relationship between sound and meaning is driven by the continual pressure to communicate effectively.

This insight about what makes an effective communication system was very much *not* in the mind of John Wilkins, a seventeenth-century clergyman and scholar who proposed a language in which the letters should precisely and systematically map onto meanings (see figure 3.1).[16] Plants, for example, should all begin with a **g**; animals with a **z**. The second letter subdivides further: leafy plants start with 'gα', flowers with 'ga', seed vessels with 'ge', shrubs with 'gi' and trees with 'go'. Subsequent letters in a word narrow down the categories even further. According to Padraic's argument, however, this approach is likely to lead to terrible confusion in practice, because contextual cues (that we are talking about plants when we are in the garden) are no help in distinguishing subtly different plant words. As noted by Umberto Eco, Wilkins inadvertently exemplifies this pitfall when illustrating his own system, mistakenly writing **gαde** (barley) in place of the intended **gape** (tulip).[17] By

Tranfcend.			Animals			Action		
General	Bα	Exanguious	Zα	Spiritual	Cα
Rel. mixed	Ba	Fiſh	Za	Corporeal	Ca
Rel. of Action	Be	Bird	Ze	Motion	Ce
Difcourfe	Bi	Beaſt	Zi	Operation	Ci
God	Dα	Parts — Peculiar	Pα		
World ·	Da	General	Pa	Oecon.	Co
Element	De	Quantity — Magnitude ·	Pe	Poſſeſ.	Cy
Stone	Di	Space	Pi	Relation — Proviſ.	Sα
Metal	Do	Meafure	Po	Civil	Sa
Herb confid. accord. to the — Leaf	Gα	Power Nat.	Tα	Judicial	Se
Flower	Ga	Quality — Habit	Ta	Military	Si
Seed-veffel	Ge	Manners	Te	Naval	So
Shrub	Gi	Quality fenfible	Ti	Ecclef.	SY
Tree	Go	Difeafe	To		

Figure 3.1. A fragment of Wilkins's strange 'philosophical' language. Wilkins's classification has forty more general categories into which all things are divided, including **habit**, **peculiar parts**, **ecclesiastical**, **manners**, **shrubs** and **motion**.

aligning letters or sounds with meaning so precisely, Wilkins had created an artificial language that is utterly unusable.[18]

It turns out, then, that a good deal of the arbitrariness that we find in the links between sign and meaning is not an imperfection of natural languages but a crucial strength. Still, if language arises from charades, where the resemblance of symbols to their meanings is the norm, one might still wonder whether traces of iconicity might show through if we look closely.

There are individual cases where the sounds and meanings of words seem to be related – some families of words with similar meanings (**slither**, **slip**, **slide**, **slick**, **slimy**...) occasionally do have similar sounds. But to see whether there is a more systematic connection across the vocabularies of the world's languages, we need to adopt a 'big data' approach. In an international collaboration, Morten and colleagues looked at a list of forty to a hundred words from each of nearly two-thirds of the world's seven thousand or so languages.[19] Their analysis applied the latest statistical methods to determine whether certain word meanings tend to be associated with certain speech sounds – even across different parts of the world, where any sound–meaning links cannot be explained by a common history.

The results showed that sound–meaning links remain, but that these links are subtle. It turns out that even among unrelated languages from different continents, some sounds are used more often than would be expected by chance to refer to certain concepts and ideas. For example, if you pick a language at random that includes the concept of redness, then the word for it is more likely to have an **r** sound in it than would be expected by chance. The analysis found many such relationships – seventy-four in total. To mention a few, words for **tongue** tend to have **l** or **u**, **round** often appears with **r**, and **small** with **i**. In some cases, the relationship was negative, meaning that particular sounds are often avoided when conveying certain meanings – for instance, the pronouns **I** and **you** tend to avoid **p**, **t**, **s** sounds.[20]

Where do these links between sound and meaning come from? Because the relationships span unrelated language groups, historical links between languages can't be the answer. Instead, there must be some inherent link between certain kinds of sounds and certain kinds of meanings. If this is right, then nonwords may not be quite as meaningless as we think – and not just because of their similarity to real words in whatever language we speak. A line of research going back nearly a century to the great German psychologist Wolfgang Köhler shows that this is indeed the case.[21]

Suppose, in a game of 'verbal charades', we are presented with a spiky, star-looking shape and a rounded, blob-like thing (see

Figure 3.2. Kiki or **bouba**? You decide!

figure 3.2). Which shape is called **kiki** and which is **bouba**? If the relationship between sounds and meanings were arbitrary, then either option would be as good or as bad as the other: the sounds would tell us nothing about which figure goes with which word. But almost everyone has the sense that **kiki** should denote the spiky shape and **bouba** the rounded shape. In the study that introduced these figures, by Edward Hubbard and the celebrated vision scientist V. S. Ramachandran, fully 95 per cent of US English-speakers felt the same. Not only that, the **bouba–kiki** effect is not specific to English-speakers or industrial society. It works the same way with the semi-nomadic Himba in northern Namibia, who speak Otjihimba, a Bantu language completely unconnected to the Indo-European language group.[22] Similar, though weaker, sound–shape mappings have even been shown in four-month-old babies, who have yet to learn any language.[23]

Where do these sound-to-shape links come from? Morten and his collaborators Arash Aryani and Erin Isbilen wondered if our emotional states might play a role here.[24] After all, **bouba** and rounded shapes seem somehow calming – they have what psychologists call low 'emotional arousal'. By contrast, **kiki** and spiky shapes seem to convey activity and tension, or high emotional arousal. Indeed, people rated **kiki** (and similar words) and spiky shapes as higher in arousal than **bouba** and rounded shapes. The team then created a set of new non-words associated with different levels of arousal. Sure enough, high-arousal non-words were associated with spiky shapes and low-arousal non-words with rounded shapes. So at least some sound–meaning links seem to be routed through our emotional responses. From the language-as-charades perspective, this is just the kind of link we should expect. The creative charades player can deploy any common ground with the audience, whether using resemblance, referring back to past charades or exploiting our common emotional responses. And the languages that emerge from generations of charades-playing will therefore show the imprint of these and other forces overlaid to produce elaborate interlocked patterns with a mixture of both regularity and disorder.

THE LANGUAGE OF PERFECT REASON

The unpredictable inventiveness of charades is what makes it worth playing. The best charades players are the most creative: a rigid, plodding and predictable approach (e.g. always mime syllable by syllable, always use rhyme) is painfully slow and ineffective. Clever charades players shape their strategy around the specifics of the message, the audience and the moment – flexibility is vital. And the same is true of the world's languages, which have been shaped by countless generations of diverse and diverging communicative demands. The fact that we can talk of **light beers**, **light music**, **light infantry**, **the unbearable lightness of**

being and, now, **the lightness of meaning** is the product of generations of human communicative ingenuity.

Yet the unruly nature of human languages has often been viewed as an imperfection rather than a strength. Scholars have long dreamed that there must be (or perhaps once was) a perfect language that can transparently represent both thought and reality. The vocabulary of the perfect language would correspond to clear and distinct concepts and would map neatly on to the world, carving nature at its joints. A perfect language might, moreover, provide a transparent medium for expressing our thoughts, eliminating ambiguity and misunderstandings entirely. If there were a single true way to conceive of and reason about the universe, perhaps the world's languages might be pulled slowly but relentlessly towards a single perfect reflection of thought and reality. From this standpoint, the languages of the world are no more than stumbling steps towards this ideal. This idea offers scholars an entrancing goal: to help construct the perfect language of reason, mathematics and science. This ideal language promises to hold the key to resolving many (and perhaps even all) philosophical problems, to creating artificial intelligence and to understanding the nature of the human mind.

Such was the dream of the great seventeenth-century German mathematician and philosopher Gottfried Wilhelm von Leibniz – creator of the calculus (independently of Sir Isaac Newton, with whom he feuded over priority). Leibniz imagined a *characteristica universalis*: a universal system for expressing thoughts and evaluating arguments, with the hope that differences of view could be settled by calculation, just as different opinions about how to divide a restaurant bill might be settled by following the laws of arithmetic. How might this work? Leibniz, like Wilkins, envisaged that human knowledge could be broken down into simple ideas, each with its own number or symbol.[25] He proposed that it might be possible to create a precise grammar for combining simple ideas into complex wholes, and that there could be a set of mathematical rules for sound reasoning in this perfect language. Leibniz's ambition for this project was vast. He hoped to show how to represent all knowledge and reasoning in a way that could definitively settle any argument. Scientific, moral, legal and theological disputes would supposedly yield to unambiguous analysis once translated into the *characteristica universalis*. Agreed principles of calculation – a sort of arithmetic of thought – would be applied and would yield only a single answer to each question addressed. The parties to any dispute would then be in the position of people with differing guesses about the answer to $1,982 \times 76$. To resolve the dispute, they would declare, in Leibniz's famous phrase, 'Let us calculate!'[26]

The reality was less spectacular. At the time of his death, Leibniz's dream was unrealized and perhaps unrealizable. Yet his vision foreshadowed the creation of the artificial languages of modern logic that, in twentieth-century philosophy, became a key tool in attempts to regiment and clarify the apparent jumble of everyday language. The German mathematician Gottlob Frege, the British polymath Bertrand Russell and the great American philosopher Willard Van Orman Quine all had different versions of the dream that the conceptual tangles of everyday language could be unknotted by using a language of perfect precision. In English, for example, we can get into a terrible muddle trying to work out what kind of entity the nouns **nobody** and **everything** might be, or wondering about the meaning of **it** in 'it's raining' and whether this is the same as or different from the **it** in 'it's possible', or what exactly 'a round square' refers to in the apparently true statement 'a round square is a contradiction in terms'. The hope was that by translating English into logic, such confusion and paradox would disappear.

To put this programme into practice, twentieth-century mathematicians and philosophers created and applied artificial logical languages and then attempted to translate our thoughts from the jumble of natural language into a regimented, organized and mathematically orderly form. Words in logical languages can be given precise meanings using the mathematics of set theory: names refer to individuals (**Fido**), concepts (**is a dog**) to sets of individuals, relations (**father of**) to sets of pairs of individuals. And most impressively, in logical languages, the meaning of any statement can be mechanically constructed from the meanings of its parts and how they are arranged. So an infinite number of possible meanings can be constructed from a finite number of words and rules.

Another great attraction of artificial logical languages when compared with natural languages was that they offered the possibility of sharply delineating sense from nonsense. Mystics might speak of 'the unity of all things'. Catholic priests can talk of transubstantiation (the supposedly literal identity of the body and blood of Christ with the wafer and wine of the Eucharist). German philosophers could postulate a 'will to power',[27] an unknowable 'noumenal' world lying beyond the reach of the senses,[28] or the ethereal 'phenomenology of spirit'.[29]

But could such statements be converted into a precise and testable form? Could they, in particular, be translated into the exacting framework of a logical language? Many philosophers suspected not. And they further suspected that any statements that could not be translated into logic should be discarded as meaningless. In his early period, even Wittgenstein famously claimed: 'What can be said at all, can be said clearly; and whereof one cannot speak, thereof one must be silent.'[30] This austere viewpoint places a regimented logical language at the very centre of the intellectual universe, specifying the contours and boundaries of what can be said and thought. From this point of view, if human language is improvised charades, then so much the worse for human language.

After the Second World War and the invention of the digital computer, scholars began to view the link between natural and artificial languages in a new way. In addition to trying to simplify, sharpen and generally tidy up the jumble of real natural languages, they began to use ideas from mathematical logic as a set of tools for analysing (rather than merely eliminating) the complexity of real human languages. Indeed, the development of the new discipline of artificial intelligence, which had the goal of building computer models of intelligence, took a further bold step: asserting that logic itself must surely be the basis of the language of thought on which our reason operates.[31] Understanding or speaking language must involve mapping the apparent disorder of each of the thousands of human languages into a single, logical language somehow embedded in the human mind. Thus, as the psycholinguist Steven Pinker writes: 'People do not think in English or Chinese or Apache; they think in a language of thought.'[32] And this language of thought was imagined not to have the quirks and peculiarities of actual spoken languages, but to be a precise, logical language designed to make reasoning as easy as possible.

Logical methods for understanding meaning in everyday human languages were developed in a range of ways and became widely used in many areas of philosophy, linguistics and cognitive science. Among the most important was the work of the brilliant mathematician and philosopher Richard Montague. In the 1960s, Montague tried to create mathematically precise rules for mapping sentences of natural language (specifically, English) piece by piece into logical sentences that captured their meaning. The ultimate aim was to find a method for mapping everyday sentences into their logical forms in a completely automatic way, which could in principle be done by a computer. Then, once we have the logical forms, we can apply logic to work out what can and cannot be inferred from each sentence, using rules that can also be programmed into a computer. If such a project was feasible across the full range of natural-language sentences, we would be pretty close to writing a computer program that understood human language – one of the holy grails of artificial intelligence. Montague's work became hugely influential, founding an entire sub-field of linguistics known as 'formal semantics', which provides a powerful set of tools to help philosophers and linguists analyse and describe fragments of real languages.[33]

Though a remarkable intellectual achievement, the programme of formal semantics is at best a narrow framework for analysing restricted aspects of the meaning of human languages. The goal of creating a single logical framework (perhaps corresponding to Pinker's language of thought, quoted above) into which the whole of language (and indeed, all languages) might be translated is no more viable than John Wilkins's philosophical language or Leibniz's *characteristica universalis*. Like our miming actions in charades, words do not have stable meanings; they are tools used in the moment. For both children and adults, the instability of language, as reflected by the ubiquity of analogies and metaphors, turns out to be its essence, not a curious anomaly. Not only that, as in charades, meaning in language is fundamentally public and social in nature – like the ideas of monetary value, ownership or being married. This, in turn, implies that the very idea that tantalized early researchers in artificial intelligence – that a perfect logical language might capture meanings residing in an individual mind – is hopelessly incoherent.

Indeed, as the twentieth century progressed and even before Montague's programme began, the very idea of a logical language that might lie behind the meaning of natural language gradually began to fall into disrepute.[34] In philosophy, it was Wittgenstein, formerly the arch-exponent of this viewpoint, who became its destroyer: his concepts of language games and the sprawling family resemblances (rather than common essences) underlying word meanings undercut the idea that meaning could be distilled, purified and bottled using the tools of mathematical logic. He noted: 'Let the use of words teach you their meaning' – and the uses of words, as we've seen (recall the many meanings of **light**), turn out to be almost unlimited.[35] And as the philosophical foundations of the logic-based approach to meaning were dissolving, so too the ideal of a logic-based universal language of thought, so central to much thinking in linguistics, cognitive science and early artificial intelligence, dissolved with them.[36]

◉

It is true, of course, that artificial languages, from logic to programming languages, are hugely important innovations. Indeed, they have been fundamental to computer science and to the economic and social revolutions that computers helped to create. But to equate these 'languages' with human languages is to be tricked by the power of our own metaphors. To imagine that the meaning of human linguistic charades can be translated into a precise mathematical system is a fundamental mistake. The flexibility, playfulness and capriciousness of language are not weaknesses to be ironed out by applying the austere tools of formal logic. These are the very essence of how language works. It is the very lightness of meaning that allows us to wield language so deftly – to deal with ever-shifting communicative challenges in an ever-changing world. Human language is poetry first, and prose second.

Yet, poetry or not, language is orderly in a wide variety of ways, from the patterns of sound that comprise words to the patterns of stress or intonation that shape our speech and the grammatical regularities that govern how words fit together. If each linguistic charade is focused purely on getting a message across in the moment, where do these rich and complex patterns across words, phrases and whole sentences come from? The answer is that order emerges bit by bit as new patterns emerge, become entrenched, and are pulled into (partial) alignment through continual use and reuse across many speakers and successive generations. As we'll see in the next chapter, only gradually does linguistic order emerge from communicative chaos.

4

LINGUISTIC ORDER
AT THE EDGE OF CHAOS

Words strain,
Crack and sometimes break, under the burden,
Under the tension, slip, slide, perish,
Decay with imprecision, will not stay in place,
Will not stay still.

T. S. ELIOT,
'Burnt Norton' (1935)

The celebrated British broadcaster John Humphrys is concerned. He rails against what he calls 'language obesity', which he sees as 'the consequence of feeding on junk words. Tautology is the equivalent of having chips with rice. We talk of future plans and past history; of live survivors and safe havens.' Humphrys sees the decline of English as inexorable: 'Ultimately, no doubt, we shall communicate with a series of grunts.'[1] There has also been a measure of panic concerning the especially deleterious effects of texts, emojis and tweets. Could excessive compression be mangling our language, potentially undermining the expressive powers of new generations of language users? Humphrys writes, perhaps slightly tongue-in-cheek but with genuine passion, of 'the relentless onward march of the texters, the SMS (Short Message Service) vandals who are doing to our language what Genghis Khan did to his neighbours eight hundred years ago.'[2] Occasionally, there is the darker fear, famously expressed in a speech by former government minister Norman Tebbit, that 'if you allow standards to slip to the stage where good English is no better than bad English', this will 'cause people to have no standards at all, and once you lose standards then there's no imperative to stay out of crime'.[3] A slippery slope indeed! Thankfully, we have the Queen's English Society, which declares itself to be 'a guardian of proper English . . . striv[ing] to prevent any decline in standards in its use'.[4] Nevertheless, fear is in the air.

Curiously, though, the fear of language breaking down seems to be a perennial worry. The preface of Dr Samuel Johnson's celebrated 1755 *Dictionary of the English Language* warns: 'Tongues, like governments, have a natural tendency to degeneration.' The seventeenth-century Irish writer Jonathan Swift lamented that 'our [English] Language is extremely imperfect; that its daily Improvements are by no means in proportion to its daily Corruptions, that the Pretenders to polish and refine it, have chiefly multiplied Abuses and Absurdities, and that in many instances, it offends against every part of Grammar'. And we can go back further in history still. Linguist Jean Aitchison notes that a fourteenth-century monk complained that the English practised strange 'wlaffyng, chytering, harryng, and garryng grisbittyng' (stammering, chattering, snarling and grating tooth-gnashing).[5]

And fear of linguistic decline is not confined to English. Since 1635, the Académie Française has battled to maintain the purity of the French language by keeping 'loan' words from creeping in from English (**le weekend, le sandwich, le hashtag**) and other languages, and by maintaining exacting grammatical standards. In much the same way, the Icelandic Language Institute has attempted since 1985 to preserve and extend Icelandic to deal with the modern world (so that a computer, **tölva**, is a 'witch of numbers' from **tala** [number] and **völva** [witch]). Moreover, grammar books and dictionaries in all languages seem to lay down the linguistic law to schoolchildren, writers and casual speakers alike. This bleak picture of inescapable decline sees linguistic perfection lying deep in the past, a perfection that is continually eroded and undercut by the ravages of time and loose speech.

Some of these worries are about the blunting and blurring of meaning, such as when words are vaguely or 'incorrectly' used. But the most profound worry, and our main focus in this chapter, is that the very *grammar* of the language is changing. This is not merely a worry about so-called prescriptive grammar – the rather picky rules that we are taught at school, for example, that we should never split an infinitive or end a sentence with a preposition. For linguists, grammar is much more fundamental. It is the collection of patterns that govern how we put words together – so we can say, in English, **Ella sings jazz**, but not **sings Ella jazz**. Similarly, it's fine to say **I like jazz, I dislike jazz** and **I like to play jazz**, but it would be distinctly odd to say **I dislike to play jazz**. Or consider how in **Ella saw her in the mirror**, **her** cannot refer to Ella, but in **Ella saw herself in the mirror**, **herself** can *only* mean Ella; we can say **she saw her** but not **her saw she**, and so on. Worriers about linguistic decline aren't just concerned about niceties of style (though they often see style as the thin end of the wedge); they are worried that sloppiness in language is leading us towards linguistic anarchy.

But how is the complexity of human language, with its layered patterns of sounds, words and meanings, supposed to have arisen in the first place? Learning a new language makes the sheer scale of this complexity all too evident – second-language learners struggle to master pronunciation, stress, verbs and their many tenses, rules of word order, and so on. It is hard to avoid wondering: Where do all these endless patterns come from? And why do they have to be so bafflingly complicated?

SPONTANEOUS ORDER

No one planned language. The complexity and order of language emerge from the chaos of countless games of linguistic charades. In each game, speakers have no concern other than to make themselves understood to a particular person on a specific occasion. Yet, over generations of language use, patterns of amazing richness and subtlety have gradually appeared. Languages exhibit baffling intricacies in their syntactic categories of tense, aspect, case and word order. They have strange and varied repertoires of speech sounds from which words are composed. And each language contains vast inventories of words describing the entire gamut of the physical, biological, moral and spiritual worlds. All this complexity, and much more, arises from the cumulative power of spontaneous, undesigned order. In a very real sense, the most important human invention is an accumulation of accidents.

How is this possible? In linguistic charades, time is of the essence: each new message is followed urgently by the next. The rush to improvise in the here and now forces us to reuse and recombine past messages. New linguistic forms are shaped from the old; specific interactions of linguistic forms generate partial patterns that over time become ever richer and more subtle. But this continual change of language is not a downward path of inevitable linguistic decline; on the contrary, it is a sign of a 'living' language that constantly adapts itself to make it easier for its users to say whatever is on their minds.

Insights into the emergence of linguistic order out of everyday disordered interactions came to us from an unexpected source: a private physics-minded think tank nestled in the Sangre de Cristo foothills of New Mexico. The Santa Fe Institute (SFI) is the world's centre for complexity science: a heady intellectual environment where you might find Nobel laureate Murray Gell-Mann conversing with Pulitzer Prize winner Cormac McCarthy. At SFI and elsewhere, complexity theorists have shown how 'local' interactions between elements of a system can lead to unexpected 'global' patterns across the entire system. Examples occur throughout the natural world. Simple rules governing the contraction of neighbouring patches of cooling molten lava created the more than forty thousand hexagonal basalt columns of the Giant's Causeway. Simple molecules continually self-assemble into complex proteins inside each living cell. Individual termites lay down and follow trails of pheromones, leading eventually to the self-organization of huge colonies.

Morten spent nine months at SFI from August 2006 to May 2007, when Nick dropped in for a week-long research visit in the spring. It was an inspiring environment, where anything felt possible and no question was off the table. The SFI is devoted to understanding how simple processes generate complex patterns and how complexity can build upon itself to create yet greater complexity. Researchers from physics, anthropology, economics and psychology consider questions ranging from the preconditions for the origin of life to why some religions flourish and others disappear. Language – especially its origins, diversity and patterns of change – is a topic that crops up frequently.

Just as natural scientists have become fascinated with the emergence of complexity in the physical, chemical and biological worlds, so social scientists have uncovered similar principles of spontaneous order that lead to the emergence of rules, norms, legal systems and entire societies. After all, just as no one designed language, neither did any clever central planner design the myriad rules and structures that govern our collective lives. Of course, we can and do actively debate the rules and institutions by which we live. We gradually remould attitudes and behaviours concerning gender, race, class, deference and much more. We change laws and endlessly re-engineer the institutions through which laws are made and upheld. And while the economy is full of individuals and businesses who relentlessly engage in planning, their plans are limited and mostly concerned with immediate advantage (making more of what sells, raising or reducing prices depending on demand).[6] Yet from the chaos of these individual actions emerges a hugely complex economic order, with a vast web of manufacturers, bankers, lawyers, traders, shopkeepers, online retailers and ultimately consumers, whose activities and interactions vastly exceed the understanding of any one of us. We are more like termites than we'd like to think, largely oblivious to the intricacy of our society. Indeed, like the actions of termites, our individual and momentary thoughts, reactions and choices are each but a tiny part of a vast dance that is our collective, if largely inadvertent, creation.

Although this perspective is quite natural at the SFI and within the wider network of complexity sciences across the globe, it seems strangely at odds with so much thinking about the nature of language. According to one influential approach (to which we'll return later), the complexity of language is *not* explained in terms of something simpler. Instead, the complexity of a particular language, such as Finnish, is explained in terms of something equally complicated, a so-called universal grammar, which is assumed to capture all the linguistically interesting patterns in human languages. In this 'central planning' view of linguistic order, the genetic code directs the construction of a 'language organ', which somehow embodies the supposedly universal grammatical patterns of language.

The focus on spontaneous self-organization suggests a very different viewpoint, one that builds naturally on seeing language as charades. First, spontaneous order arises from the interplay of momentary interactions and the mutual constraints on those interactions. Second, some mechanism allows spontaneous order to propagate and, crucially, to accumulate. Languages, like termite mounds, social norms and economic networks, do not appear fully formed in an instant. Complexity is the product of history.

IN SEARCH OF THE FIRST LANGUAGE

Since the dawn of time, people have been wondering how we humans, apparently uniquely in the animal kingdom, have language.[7] Often, the gift of the gab is viewed quite literally as a gift, bestowed by mysterious spiritual or divine powers. In Norse mythology, the ability to speak and listen, alongside life and intelligence, was granted to the first two humans, Ask (a man) and Embla (a woman). According to the indigenous inhabitants of the Andaman Islands in the Bay of Bengal between India and Myanmar, language was gifted to their forefather and foremother by the god Pūluga. The Okanagan people, whose territory straddles the US–Canadian border between Washington State and British Columbia, tell of an ancestor, Coyote, who settled people in different places and gave each group a different language. Aboriginal Australians talk of 'Dreamings', spirit ancestors who travelled across the land creating life, such as when Emu, Corella (a white cockatoo) and Jurntakal (a giant snake) entrusted the languages Ngarinman, Bilinara and Malngin to three different groups living in the Victoria River district of the Northern Territory. And in the Middle East, the Abrahamic tradition has language originating with Adam, who patiently named all living things, as mentioned in the last chapter. Because language is so integral to our nature, to how we interact with one another and to the intricate workings of society, variations of these origin stories crop up again and again throughout the world, underscoring just how fundamental our linguistic abilities are to how we think of ourselves: *to talk is to be human.*

Not surprisingly, scholars and religious thinkers have also been fascinated by where language comes from. The sixteenth century saw the emergence of the first European glottogonists, scholars who study the origin of language.[8] Their aim was to reveal the original language of Adam, spoken by all before the *confusio linguarum*, the confusion of tongues that, according to the Bible, humanity brought upon itself by building the Tower of Babel in an attempt to reach the heavens. By finding the original language, the scholars would discover where the order in language comes from – why language is governed by complex grammatical patterns rather than being a chaotic jumble of sounds and words. And what could be a more natural source of this first, perfect language than divine intervention?

In this light, it is not surprising that the early money was on Hebrew as the original Adamic language. Hebrew was, after all, the language of the Old Testament and thus presumed to be the 'one language and one speech' of Genesis. In 1493, James IV of Scotland reputedly commanded a deaf and mute woman to raise two babies in complete linguistic isolation on the Isle of Inchkeith, a few miles due north of Edinburgh. Reportedly, the children spontaneously began to speak good Hebrew. Further backing for this implausible conclusion came from European scholars who studied the sources of the increasing variety of languages they encountered. For example, while working as an interpreter for the French diplomatic service, the sixteenth-century French scholar Guillaume Postel travelled throughout the Ottoman empire and central Europe, where he accumulated arcane texts in a variety of scripts and languages, and broadened his wide knowledge of contemporary European, classical and Semitic languages. In 1538, he published *De originibus seu de hebraicae linguae et gentis antiquitate* (*On the origins or antiquity of the Hebrew language and people*), in which he claimed to have uncovered hidden patterns underlying languages as various as Chaldean, Hindi, Arabic and Greek, suggesting that they had indeed descended from Hebrew. In the same year, his *Linguarum duodecim characteribus differentium alphabetum* (*Alphabet of twelve languages differing by their characters*) made a case for the primacy of the Hebrew alphabet on the basis of a comparison of twelve different scripts.

But as knowledge of other ancient civilizations and their

languages grew in the seventeenth and eighteenth centuries, new ideas proliferated. One suggestion, made in 1669 by the British architect John Webb, was that Noah's Ark had landed in China after the Flood. This, Webb thought, made Chinese the likely original language, because the people of China had no part in the Tower of Babel debacle and therefore would not have had the *confusio* inflicted upon them. A century later, the French philologist Antoine Court de Gébelin proposed that Celtic was the true Adamic language by virtue of its being the original tongue of all Europe. And as nation-states, old and new, jostled for power and position on the European stage, the growing nationalism spilled over into glottogonist thinking. Soon many a European language was elevated as the true heir to Adam's original language, among them Dutch, German, Castilian (modern-day Spanish), Tuscan and Swedish. This pandering to national pride in scholarly research attracted a measure of ridicule. Responding to the claim that Swedish was the original language, made by the Swede Olof Rudbeck the Elder in a 1675 treatise, his compatriot Andreas Kempe wrote a tongue-in-cheek parody that took place in Eden, with God speaking in Swedish to Adam who responded in Danish, only to have the serpent tempt Eve in French.

By the nineteenth century, the biblical focus began to wane. Post-Enlightenment thinkers started to see language as a human, rather than a divine, creation. Yet the search for the Adamic language, while doomed, did pave the way for what we today call 'comparative linguistics', the study of the similarities and differences among languages and their historical origins. The attempt to reconstruct historical connections between languages became a central focus of research, reaching its height in nineteenth-century Germany. During the early part of that century, Friedrich Schlegel and Franz Bopp began to notice links between Sanskrit, Greek, Latin, Persian and German, thereby uncovering the foundations of what is now known as the Indo-European language family. But it was the Danish philologist Rasmus Rask who put these observations on a solid scientific footing.[9] Rask was an unusual character who already stood out from other students during his teenage years in Latin school. A fellow student later reflected that 'his short stature, his lively eyes, the ease with which he moved and jumped over tables and benches, his unusual knowledge, and even his quaint peasant dress, attracted the attention of his fellow students'. Rask had a voracious appetite for language, eventually learning twenty-five different languages and dialects and building up a working knowledge of perhaps twenty-five more.

Rask used his formidable linguistic knowledge to reveal how the sounds of consonants change across languages and time, establishing not only the relationship between Old Norse and the Germanic languages but also how Baltic and Slavic languages are related to classical Latin and Greek. For example, in Germanic languages, the 'p' sound shifted to 'f'. Thus the word for **foot** was in ancient Greek πούς, ποδός (**poús, podós**); in Latin, **pēs, pedis**; in Sanskrit, **pāda**; in Lithuanian, **pėda**; in Latvian, **pēda**; but in West Frisian, **foet**; in German, **Fuß**; in Gothic, **fōtus**; in Icelandic, **fótur**; in Danish, **fod**; in Norwegian and Swedish, **fot**; and, of course, in English, **foot**. These and other patterns were codified a few years later in what became known as Grimm's law, proposed by Jacob Grimm, the elder of the fairytale collectors the Brothers Grimm. Unfortunately for Rask, because he only ever published in Danish (with the exception of *A grammar of the Danish language for the use of Englishmen*), much of the credit for his pioneering work on sound change fell not to him but to Grimm.

The careful study of the history of language reveals that languages have always been in flux – and that the result of the compounding of gradual changes is by no means a story of continual decline. For example, Old Norse has mutated into modern Danish, Swedish, Norwegian, Icelandic and Faroese through innumerable tiny steps. It would seem very strange to view these languages merely as decadent versions of Old Norse, on the way to complete degeneration. Recalling the constant sense of ongoing decline throughout the history of English, one can easily imagine vociferous objections at every step of the linguistic transition and a foreboding sense that the language was 'going to the dogs'. But modern Scandinavians are able to communicate perfectly well! For reasons of this sort, academic linguists (rather than self-appointed linguistic guardians) tend to view modern fears of alarming linguistic decline with considerable scepticism. The key insight that the history of language reveals is that alongside the breaking down of existing patterns there is the simultaneous creation of new patterns. Language undergoes a continual process not of decay but of metamorphosis.

But these insights into how languages change over the centuries don't seem to answer the more fundamental question of how language got started in the first place.[10] The mid-1800s saw many imaginative proposals come to light, including the **onomatopoeic theory**, suggesting that language began with humans imitating natural sounds in their environment, from the barking of a dog to mean 'dog' to the splashing of a river to signal 'water'. By contrast, the **interjectional theory** proposed that the instinctive sounds humans make when expressing intense emotions such as pain, fear, surprise, pleasure and joy were the original source of our linguistic abilities. Another notion, embodied in the **universal resonance theory**, was that an omnipresent harmony (or resonance) exists between the properties of things in the world and the sounds humans use to name them, as exemplified by the tendency to use vowels produced in the front of the mouth to describe small things, like **teeny-weeny**, and vowels articulated in the back of the mouth for large objects, such as **humongous**. Yet another perspective, the **communal rhythm theory**, saw words as originating from the grunts, groans and chants that people utter when working together doing heavy physical labour, such as the **heave-ho** hollered by sailors pulling a rope to raise a sail. Each of these theories, thought to be mutually incompatible, was fiercely championed by its proponents and derided by its detractors. Derision lives on in the less-than-flattering epithets that have stuck with the theories to this day. The onomatopoeic theory was labelled the **bow-wow theory**, the interjectional theory became known as the **pooh-pooh theory**, the universal resonance theory was called the **ding-dong theory** and the communal rhythm theory was named the **yo-he-yo theory**.

Although all these theories are now for the most part roundly dismissed as baseless speculations from a bygone era, each may contain at least a grain of truth. In chapter 1, we saw that vocal charades using only non-speech sounds can actually work surprisingly well, as one might expect from the onomatopoeic (bow-wow) theory. Similarly, emotional states do link with how words sound, as reflected by the **bouba–kiki** experiments mentioned in chapter 3, which is consistent with the interjectional (pooh-pooh) theory. The universal patterns of sound–meaning associations (also discussed in chapter 3), such as names for the concept of **red** tending to include an **r** sound, are in line with the universal resonance (ding-dong) theory. And the emphasis in the communal rhythm (yo-he-yo) theory on the sounds people produce to coordinate their efforts when toiling together seems compatible with the collaborative nature of our language-as-charades perspective. What ultimately doomed these early glottogonist speculations was that they all took on the impossible task of arguing for a single origin for all aspects of language. The nineteenth-century philologist and Oxford don Max Müller noted after an early flirtation with the universal resonance theory: 'My only doubt is whether we should restrict ourselves to this one explanation, and whether a river so large, so broad, so deep as language may not have had more than one source.'[11]

The glottogonist debates grew more and more heated and increasingly speculative over time. With no empirical evidence in sight to support any of the rival theories, the premier academic body for the study of language, the Société de Linguistique de Paris, decided to ban any discussion of the origin and evolution of language from 1866 onward, which also put a stop to the search for the universal Adamic language.[12] This ban didn't completely squelch the glottogonists, but it did reduce the previous flood of books, pamphlets and papers to a trickle, sidelining the topic of language evolution from mainstream scientific discourse for over a hundred years.

LANGUAGE AS BIOLOGY

Although often fanciful, the nineteenth-century speculations on the origin of language all agreed on one point: language is a human creation somehow built up from elementary communicative efforts. Language was viewed, in short, as part of human culture, along with music, art, dance, religion and technology. And, like these other cultural forms, the world's languages were viewed as having arisen from accumulated innovations through long historical processes. The cultural view of language was taken for granted, too, for the first half of the twentieth century, when linguistics (the study of the sounds, patterns and meanings expressed in human language) was often carried out in university departments of anthropology, classics, English and modern languages. Seeing the world's languages as part of the tapestry of human culture seems natural, unavoidable and, we believe, entirely right. But something extraordinary happened in the middle of the twentieth century – a seismic shift that created an entirely different perspective on language: one that viewed linguistics as a branch of **biology**.

Noam Chomsky's entry into the study of language in the mid-1950s sparked a revolution, both in terms of ideas and more literally as an academic *coup d'état*. The young Chomsky was an iconoclastic and brilliant scholar, deeply immersed in philosophy, logic and what would now be called theoretical computer science. He had a radically new agenda aiming to wrench linguistics from the study of culture and reconstruct it on abstract mathematical and scientific foundations.[13]

Chomsky saw that logicians were building rigorous artificial languages for logical reasoning, as we mentioned in chapter 3. Logicians were primarily interested in using logic to capture *meaning* in human languages. Chomsky's interest, by contrast, was in the *grammar* of logical languages – the rules determining how complex logical formulas could be built up from simple components. With logical languages and computer programming languages, the grammar is a carefully designed set of mathematical rules that spell out how symbols can be combined in a proper order. The attraction of this approach is its precision: the mathematical rules of the grammar leave no room for ambiguity and judgement. The rules specify precisely whether each possible string of logical symbols is or is not allowed by the grammar, separating those sequences that count as logical 'sentences' from those that are just jumbles of symbols. But human languages are a lot more complicated than logical languages or programming languages. Chomsky wondered whether the mathematical principles for setting out the grammars of artificial languages could be applied to natural languages.

This was a truly radical move – to describe the apparent chaos of human language using precise mathematical methods. The result was what became known as 'generative grammar', an idea that went on to dominate the field of linguistics for several decades. For Chomsky, mathematical rigour could turn linguistics into a scientific enterprise.

To get a flavour of what generative grammar looks like, consider the following simple set of rules, which captures a tiny fragment of English.

S→ NP VP
NP → D N
VP → V NP
D → the, a, some, every, . . .
N → dog, bird, cat, . . .
V → saw, liked, ate, . . .

These rules can be used to generate simple sentences, such as **the dog saw a bird.** The first rule means that a sentence (S) consists of a noun phrase (NP) and a verb phrase (VP). Applying the NP rule, we can then unpack the initial noun phrase as a determiner (D) – words like **the, a, some, every** – and a noun (N). This allows us to create the noun phrase **the dog**. Next, we employ the VP rule to generate a verb phrase consisting of a verb (V) and a noun phrase (NP). Inserting **saw** as the verb and reusing the NP rule, we have the verb phrase **saw a bird**, which can be combined with the initial noun phrase **the dog** to produce the sentence **the dog saw a bird** (see figure 4.1).

Now the same rules can, if applied in different ways, create other sentences, such as **a bird liked every dog** or **some dog ate a bird**. The idea behind generative grammar is that we have a precise set of mathematical rules that create a large (indeed, potentially infinite) set of possible sentences. Clearly, the rules in our example are absurdly oversimplified in innumerable ways – but they are at least mathematically precise. The task of

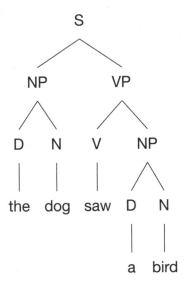

Figure 4.1. The syntactic 'tree' structure for the sentence **the dog saw a bird**, generated using our tiny grammar fragment. In linguistics, grammar rules are often used to create such visual depictions of the syntactic relationships between different components of a sentence, such as noun phrases (NP) and verb phrases (VP).

the linguist is to try to work out the far more complex set of equally precise rules that generate all and only the sentences of English, Arabic, Yoruba or whatever language is the focus of interest. The key is that the rules should define a precise and entirely automatic procedure for generating all and only the sentences of a language. No need to worry about what the sentences mean. The mathematical rules of grammar should be able to do their work without any human insight or intervention.[14]

Chomsky made a second, equally radical move in his attempt to pull the study of language out of the grasp of the humanities. Rather than seeing language merely as the raw material for crafting the specific things we actually say and write (and hence as part of the external, cultural world), he reconceptualized language itself as an abstract mathematical system that is somehow lodged in the head of each speaker. From Chomsky's point of view, what linguistics is really about is trying to systematize the *intuitions* that we – the native speakers of a language – have about which sentences are allowed and which are not. Linguists don't have to worry too much about what people actually say or write, which is riddled with false starts, quirks and errors of all kinds. Instead, linguistic theory needs to smooth over the rough edges of everyday language to have any hope of revealing the hidden mathematical system.

The task of the linguist, then, becomes the scientific challenge of figuring out a mathematical system – the generative grammar – that captures the linguistic intuitions of the speakers of a language. And, in Chomsky's view, when learning a language, each individual child must similarly be trying to figure out this abstract grammar, and must do so from scratch, without explicit instruction or assistance, just from hearing what people say. That is, each child is seen as a mini-linguist, trying to piece together the abstract mathematical patterns of the particular language that surrounds them. For Chomsky, mastering these patterns is the essence of learning a language.

But how can this possibly work? Scholars have been puzzling over the abstract grammatical patterns of English and other languages for centuries. How could children ever hope to figure this out in just a few years? Enter Chomsky's third radical idea: because the child cannot learn all these abstract mathematical patterns from experience, we are forced to conclude that these patterns must be built into the child's brain, and ultimately our genes, from the very outset. For Chomsky, it logically follows that children must be born with an innate 'universal grammar' – a genetic blueprint comprising the abstract mathematical principles that govern language. Learning the patterns that govern a specific language, such as Mandarin, Hopi or Basque, is just a matter of fine-tuning the universal grammar to capture the fine details of that language.

This viewpoint has its own answer to the doom-mongers of continual linguistic decline. There is no danger of linguistic degeneration because the essence of language is safely locked up in our genes. Indeed, Chomsky has compared language to an organ of the body, and to the developing wing of a bird that unfolds through the operation of a biological program. The question of what people actually say, and whether speech is becoming ever sloppier, is simply beside the point. It is just a superficial matter of cultural variation. This variation seemed important when we thought of languages arising through history. But for Chomsky, this continual linguistic turbulence is merely superficial: the linguistic changes that so fascinated Rasmus Rask and his fellow philologists are inconsequential details – the underlying architecture of language remains entirely unchanged. And this architecture arises from biology, not culture. It is an unchanging core of human language somehow wired into our genes.

Chomsky's thesis has further striking consequences. According to his view, it follows logically that all languages that children can learn must fit the patterns of universal grammar. So, Chomsky can triumphantly conclude, all languages must be essentially the same. Musing about a hypothetical extraterrestrial looking down upon Earth, Chomsky suggested that 'the Martian scientist might reasonably conclude that there is a single human language, with differences only at the margins'. A single human language, not seven thousand languages – the variations would be too trivial to mention. Not only that, despite strong appearances to the contrary, languages don't *really* change, either; rather, they change only in uninteresting, superficial ways. The essence of human language, its genetically coded universal grammar, remains constant.[15]

It seems extraordinary, even incredible, to derive such conclusions from mere logic alone. But in the high-octane intellectual environment of MIT's famously ramshackle Building 20, radical theoretical claims were commonplace, and often spectacularly successful. Building 20 was a temporary wooden structure, put up in 1943, that had housed nine Nobel Prize winning scientists in its fifty-five years of service. From this vantage point, where abstract thought had proved so triumphant, it was all too easy to imagine that the bright light of pure theory could reveal universal patterns to which the world's languages must necessarily conform. Using English as a guide, Chomsky and his colleagues attempted to spell out the nature of the universal patterns that must apply across all languages.[16] The work of fitting the specific details of the world's languages into this universal framework would be left as an extended exercise for linguists of the future.

This was not at all how things turned out. For more than a century, field linguists and anthropologists have fanned out across the world to document the languages of remote groups, from the Ona people (the surviving neighbours of the Haush) and other indigenous peoples of South America to the indigenous peoples of the Australian interior and the rainforests of Papua New Guinea. But rather than finding endless variations on a single universal theme, they found a seemingly limitless supply of strange and wonderful new ways by which people can convey information, as we'll see in more detail in chapter 7. The supposedly universal features of sounds, grammar and meaning turned out to be no more than an unsubstantiated myth: within and between languages, variety, disorder and exceptions reign. Indeed, if the Martian scientist were to strip away the particular quirks of English, Haush, Danish or Ona to discover their common essence, nothing would remain.

This is, of course, a story we have encountered already, in the last chapter. We had the naive intuition that for each word there must be a common core that binds all its uses together – so that, to recall our example, **light tanks**, **light wines**, **light music** and **light moods** must share some essence of 'lightness'. But we found instead that the interconnections between different uses of a word are linked only by a criss-crossing pattern of metaphorical leaps. The word **language** (or indeed, **grammar**) is no different. The world's languages have many and complex patterns of resemblance, but no underlying core.

But if the patterns in language don't come from a universal grammar, where do they come from? To see how the elaborate patterns in each of the world's seven thousand languages might arise in the absence of a built-in grammar, we need a fresh start – or rather, we need to return to thinking of language not as a part of biology but as a part of culture. We must view the intricacies of language as parallel with the complexity of music, art, technology and social norms – created not by a blueprint in the genes or the brain but by millennia of accumulated human ingenuity.

THE BUILDING BLOCKS OF LANGUAGE

In the past few decades, the field of linguistics – or at least parts of it – have undergone a quiet revolution. Rather than attempting to formulate 'grand systems' to capture the hidden and supposedly universal patterns across the world's languages, many linguists have decided instead to start small. The new approach is captured by the umbrella term **construction grammar**.

The idea, in short, is that to understand the complexity of language we need to start with elementary units known as **constructions**. Focusing on these building blocks, we can then uncover how the rich patterns of language derive from the interactions – and frequent conflicts and inconsistencies – between such constructions. The patterns in language arise through the continual jostle of constructions attempting to align coherently rather than to clash. So the patterns in language are the outcome, not the starting point. And we, as individual learners and speakers of a language, only know the constructions and how they interact. We don't know, and don't need to know, the complex patterns that the interplay of the elements of language create – any more than a termite needs to consult a blueprint to help construct and run its colony.

What, then, are constructions? They are usually viewed as

learned pairings of form and meaning that range from meaningful parts of words (such as word endings, e.g. **-s**, **-ing**) and words themselves (e.g. **penguin**) to multiword sequences (e.g. **cup of tea**) and more abstract patterns (such as **the X-er, the Y-er**, e.g. **the bigger, the better**). These constructions correspond neatly to the chunks that our brain uses to decode the continual stream of linguistic input. From this point of view, we can think of constructions as corresponding to mental operations: procedures our brains use to make sense of (and generate) language. If you don't make sense of a construction right away (work out the meanings of words, word endings, idioms and so on), then it will be too late – the message will never make it through the Now-or-Never bottleneck and will therefore be obliterated by the on-rushing torrent of language.

Note that, like charades, constructions are not just self-contained 'packages' linking together a form (a sound, a gesture) and the meaning this form can be used to convey. Constructing the meaning of a sequence of gestures to infer the underlying message requires shared background knowledge, creativity and imagination – drawing from the crucial, hidden parts of the communication iceberg. It is not merely the 'snapping together' of standardized Lego-brick components using a set of equally standardized rules. The very idea of perfectly abstract patterns of linguistic categories is a mirage. Language is a patchwork of competing constructions, a mix of order and chaos, patterns and exceptions. Look closely, the construction grammarians say, and we can see that language doesn't really *look* well planned at all: linguistic order is always at the edge of chaos.

Language is built out of recycled constructions. If this is right, then we should expect children to learn language construction by construction – and indeed, this seems to be what they do, as revealed by the intriguing and sometimes amusing patterns in the errors children make. So, for example, errors like **me do it!** (which the child has probably never heard directly) make sense when we realize that this is a sub-chunk of **Let me do it!**[17] In the same way, the apparently peculiar **pick you up me** (rather than **Pick me up!** or **Will you pick me up?**) makes sense when we see that **pick you up** can easily be mistaken for a sub-chunk in phrases such as **Shall I pick you up?** Or consider the delightfully bizarre **I am being have**, as a response to **Behave!**. The child may reason that **I am being quiet** is a perfectly good response to **Be quiet!** so why shouldn't **Behave!** follow a similar pattern? The child is continually trying to find and generalize from the chunks – or constructions – in the language. But occasionally this process goes awry, triggering strange and telling errors.

One particularly significant aspect of these examples, and of young children's speech in general, is the focus on specific chunks and patterns of variation around those chunks. According to standard textbook grammar, and the generative grammar approach made popular by Chomsky, words can be divided up into distinct syntactic categories: nouns, verbs, adjectives, adverbs, prepositions and so on. The rules of languages spell out how these syntactic categories can be strung together (as we saw in our grammar fragment above). Using the old-fashioned grammar-book terminology, suppose the child has learned that **John** is a proper noun (perhaps an animate proper noun) and that **sings** is an intransitive verb, and that a proper noun and intransitive verb can form a sentence: **John sings**. But suppose that child knows lots of other animate proper nouns (**Fido, Billy, Pops**) and lots of other intransitive verbs (**runs, eats, hides**). Accordingly, we might expect that a full variety of combinations will immediately be at the child's disposal: **Fido eats, Pops runs,**

Billy hides and more. And, the story would go, as the child learns more words, and their syntactic categories, and more patterns, they should be able to fluently generate an ever-wider set of combinations, deploying different tenses (**doggy is hiding/hid/will hide**), passives (**the cake was eaten**), questions (**Who ate the cake?**, **What got eaten?**, **What did Billy eat?**) and many more.

But this isn't how children learn language at all! Very early child language seems to consist of a repertoire of whole chunks – **All gone**, **Dadda**, **What's that**, **juice**, **down**, **up** – each consisting of one or more words. These patterns, considered as a whole, often convey a message that is only discernible (if by anyone) by the child's caregiver. So, in different circumstances, a cry of **Up!** might be used to mean **Pick me up**, **I want to go up the stairs** or **Put me in the high chair** (just as the same gesture can mean different things in different games of charades). Toddlers soon start to use language more flexibly – but they introduce combinations of words in a very particular way: locking on to patterns containing specific words or combinations of words.

Michael Tomasello, the leading language researcher whom we first met in chapter 1, conducted an extensive analysis of the language of his two-year-old daughter, Travis. Among the common phrases she used, he discovered many intriguingly standardized patterns (see table 4.1). For example, **Find it __** is a construction with a 'slot' that can be filled in mostly with nouns (**bird**, **ball**, **bricks**) but also the occasional adjective (**funny**). And, of course, **to find something funny** is an idiom in English – one that Travis will almost certainly have heard and is presumably reflecting back. Another construction is **__ get it**, this time with an initial slot filled in by nouns. Sometimes the noun refers to the object which is to be 'got', as in **block get it**; but in other cases, a more likely interpretation is that the noun is the subject of the

Table 4.1. The strange, rule-like patterns in verb use in a two-year-old child

Find it __	__ get it	__ gone
Find-it funny	Block get-it	Peter Pan gone
Find-it bird	Bottle get-it	Raisins gone
Find-it chess	Phone get-it	Doo-doo gone
Find-it bricks	Towel get-it	Cherry gone
Find-it Weezer	Bedus get-it	Fox gone
Find-it ball	Coffee get-it	Hammer gone
Find-it stick	Mama get-it	French fries gone

verb – the potential finder, such as **Mama get it**. Not only that, the __ **gone** construction is applied to all manner of nouns – **raisins gone** or **doo-doo gone** – though, as with the other cases, there is no variation in word order or tense. Finally, note that this construction seems to be learned independently of other uses of the verb **to go**, from which, linguistically, **gone** is of course derived.

The message conveyed by these multiword utterances depends very much on what is going on in the conversation with the child.[18] For example, the construction **no __** is used by children in at least three ways: objection (**no bed** = 'I don't want to go to bed'), denial (**no wet** = 'I'm not wet'), and expression of non-existence (**no pocket** = 'there is no pocket [in mother's skirt]'). All of this flexibility is just what we'd expect from a language-as-charades viewpoint. The communicative signal just has to be 'good enough' for the parent to figure out the intended message, and the child should use whatever linguistic resources are at hand.

What is interesting about all of these patterns is how inflexible they are, in striking contrast to the flexibility with which they can be used to convey meanings. A fixed and known phrase such as **find it!** or **get it!** is co-opted to new purposes – to talk about finding or getting specific things. Of course, to an adult, the **it** in **find-it ball** or **towel get-it** is redundant. The adult would say: **find the ball** or **get the towel**. But for the child, **find-it** is simply a single, trusted communicative unit, blithely to be reused and adapted to the present circumstances.

In each conversational exchange, the child (wanting to be moved, fed, handed a toy and so on) typically faces a specific and immediate problem of directing the actions of a potentially uncomprehending adult. So the child latches on to simple communicative patterns that seem to work, and explores minor variations of these patterns (e.g. putting different words in a fixed slot) to achieve the right communicative result. The child's trick is finding and exploiting reusable constructions. As the child's language grows, this repertoire of constructions and their variations becomes increasingly rich.[19] But as different momentary conventions become established and generalized, they begin to conflict and jostle for precedence.

The pressure to resolve such conflicts grows as the communicative range of the child expands. The child initially begins to talk by using constructions as independent communicative units, but over time uses these units together as building blocks to convey ever more complex messages. And, like any good building blocks, they need to be knocked into increasingly standardized 'shapes', with edges squared off and bumps smoothed, to interlock successfully. These continual processes of mutual adjustment of the elements of language by both child and adult speakers provide a powerful mechanism for driving language change.[20]

THE PATCHWORK OF LANGUAGE

The sheer vastness of any human language is striking. For example, every English-speaking adult knows the meanings, syntactic uses and pronunciations of tens of thousands of words – enough to fill many hundreds of dictionary pages. And to this we must add all the grammatical regularities that govern how we combine these words: the monumental *Cambridge Grammar of the English Language* extends to more than a thousand pages, and yet remains incomplete.

Somehow each child learns all this complexity from scratch, in just a few years, while simultaneously learning to walk, count, manipulate a pencil and, in general, grapple with a complex physical and social world. But not only that: the child has to learn the intricate patterns of language from the garbled, incomplete and generally scrappy things that people actually say. And, as scholars have started to uncover, everyday language turns out to be very shambolic indeed. To highlight one prominent source of evidence, the CHILDES project, coordinated by Brian MacWhinney at Carnegie Mellon University, draws together over forty-four million words of conversational interaction between small children and adults across thirty languages. The goal of the CHILDES project is to find out what children actually hear and how this connects with what they say. Huge databases of adult-to-adult conversation have also been amassed, containing hundreds of millions of words. And the internet provides easy access to vast quantities of written language, from informal chat to blogs, newspaper articles and literary fiction.

These transcripts of language 'in the wild' reveal that our everyday speech tends to be mangled, fragmented and stumbling (as we glimpsed in chapter 2). We continually backtrack, correct ourselves, stop mid-sentence, complete each other's sentences and talk over each other. Indeed, a recent cross-linguistic study has shown that during normal conversation we need to repair our utterances on average about every eighty seconds.[21] Moreover, everyday talk is highly formulaic – the same old greetings, idioms, interjections and complaints take up a good proportion of what we say. According to one estimate, about half of our conversational language is built out of recombinations and slight variations on well-worn linguistic fragments and patterns.[22] So far, so good, for the construction-based approach.

But what about the rest of what we say? Isn't this all elegantly governed by the rules of grammar rather than comprising a melee of specific constructions? In fact, if we zoom in on just about any specific linguistic pattern, we find that general rules break down and that chaos and complexity abound. For example, in English, we can say the first three of the following sentences, but the fourth is distinctly peculiar (here marked with the linguist's asterisk, indicating unacceptability):

I like skiing
I enjoy skiing
I like to go skiing
*I enjoy to go skiing

Or consider the baffling patterns we somehow learn, even for arcane phrases like 'no matter':

No matter how clever he is, I'm not hiring him
No matter how clever he is or isn't, I'm not hiring him
*No matter how clever he isn't, I'm not hiring him

Or the mystifying pattern:

What you said was unclear
It was unclear what you said
Your answer was unclear
***It was unclear your answer**

Viewed from an abstract, mathematical point of view, these cases are all rather puzzling. The 'odd' things that we can't say seem to follow closely the patterns of things that we can say. The problem isn't that we can't make out the meaning. We have no difficulty in understanding a person who remarks **I enjoy to go skiing** or **It was unclear your answer**. But these sentences are quite unnatural and are not 'allowed' for native English-speakers. The answer doesn't lie in the mathematical structure of the patterns – certainly, there is nothing in Chomsky's theory of universal grammar that is any help in explaining these and innumerable other quirks.

In fact, the more linguists pore over the minutiae of language, the more they uncover partial patterns, sub-patterns and exceptions. The mathematical rules of language are a mirage. Up close, language turns out to be ramshackle and riddled with holes and idiosyncrasies. Peter Culicover, a past student of Chomsky whose ideas diverge radically from his former mentor's, calls these patterns 'syntactic nuts' – ubiquitous linguistic puzzles that each requires its own analysis and explanation.[23] And every language has its own idiosyncratic repertoire of syntactic nuts that defy any supposed universal principles and instead rely on specific words and grammatical constructions.

If only we could strip away these imperfections and idiosyncrasies, perhaps a skeleton of elegant, mathematically abstract rules might then be revealed? Culicover's research, and the wider movement of construction grammar, suggests quite the opposite: language is quirky to its very core. From Chomsky's generative perspective, all this disorder is a puzzle. The perfect, universal system that is supposed to be embedded in the genes and brain of each child turns out to be horribly scrambled with endless exceptions, which would seem only to make learning and using language far more challenging. But if we see language, whether in the mind of each child or across many generations of a linguistic community, as arising through spontaneous order from disparate charades-like communicative episodes, then residual imperfections, clashes and mismatches are precisely what we should expect. Expecting language spontaneously to slot perfectly into a completely regular grammatical system is like hoping for the frozen surface of a pond miraculously to form a single gigantic ice crystal. It's just not going to happen.

With all this idiosyncratic complexity to learn, it is rather astonishing that human children can pick up the languages they are immersed in over the course of a few short years. Chomsky attempted to answer this puzzle by postulating that the universal aspects of language are built in, giving each child a huge head start. But the idea of a universal blueprint underpinning the languages of the world turned out to be a myth. So there must be another explanation for how language learning is possible without a built-in universal grammar. And indeed there is, as we'll see in chapter 6.

THE FORCES OF ORDER AND DISORDER

Languages change continually and in a wide variety of ways. New words and phrases appear, while others fall into disuse. Words subtly, or less subtly, shift their meanings or develop new meanings, while speech sounds and intonation are constantly changing. Yet perhaps the most fundamental shift in language change is gradual conventionalization: patterns of communication are initially flexible, but over time they slowly become increasingly stable, conventionalized and, in many cases, obligatory. This is spontaneous order in action: from an initial jumble, increasingly specific patterns emerge over time. The tendency towards increasing conventionalization occurs in all aspects of language, and it is largely a one-way street. Conventions become more rigid, not less. As in charades, when we face the *same* communicative challenge multiple times, our behaviour becomes increasingly standardized. Once we've established a gesture for 'Columbus' in one charade, we'll stick with it in the unlikely event he comes up again, and the gesture will rapidly become simplified. Yet when we face *new* communicative challenges, we retain the ability to be tremendously inventive – including the ability to rework and repurpose the conventions we've already established. So our 'Columbus' gesture, with adornments, might later be reused for 'sea voyages', 'the Americas', 'sailors', and abstract concepts from 'invasion' to 'navigation' or 'discovery', and many more.

How do these twin forces, of conventionalization for conveying familiar messages and of creative blending and rebuilding conventions to deal with unfamiliar messages, play out in language? To start with, consider one of the most basic aspects of any language: word order. In English, the word order **Mary likes**

dogs tells us that Mary is the subject of the verb (she is the 'liker') and that dogs are the object (they are the 'liked'). By contrast, **dogs like Mary** has **dogs** as the subject and **Mary** as the object of their affection. In English, then, the standard word order is subject–verb–object (SVO).

For speakers of English, the SVO order is so familiar that it may seem inevitable. But not at all. There are six ways of ordering three items (S, V, O), and the world's languages display them all (table 4.2). Interestingly, the most frequent order is not the SVO of English and most European languages but the SOV (with the verb at the end of the sentence) of Japanese, Korean and Turkish. Both orders put the subject at the beginning of the sentence; indeed, more than 80 per cent of the world's languages follow this pattern. But there are nonetheless many languages that put the verb at the beginning of the sentence: VSO (e.g. Celtic languages, including Welsh and Breton) and VOS (e.g. the Mayan language family, including Tseltal and Quiché). Finally, a

Table 4.2. Frequencies of word orders across the world's languages

Word order	Illustration with English	Number (proportion) of languages
SOV	**Mary dogs likes**	2,275 (43.3%)
SVO	**Mary likes dogs**	2,117 (40.3%)
VSO	**Likes Mary dogs**	503 (9.5%)
VOS	**Likes dogs Mary**	174 (3.3%)
OVS	**Dogs likes Mary**	40 (0.7%)
OSV	**Dogs Mary likes**	19 (0.3%)
No dominant order	Many or all options	124 (2.3%)

relatively small number of languages put the object at the beginning of the sentence: OVS (e.g. Huarijio, an Uto-Aztecan language spoken in north-west Mexico) and OSV (e.g. Xavante, a language spoken in the Brazilian Amazon).

How does word order get established in the first place? In charades, sequences of gestures can come in any order. But if we use charades to convey who did what to whom, some orders may, perhaps by chance, come to be more prominent. Eventually, one order might even become entirely standard. Once a particular order (such as SVO) becomes established, it will tend to stick – after all, if we violate the expected order, then, other things being equal, we are likely to be misunderstood. And historically, languages do indeed seem to shift inexorably from so-called free word order patterns to increasingly rigid word orders.

Consider the Romance languages, the family of European languages descended from Latin, which includes Spanish, Portuguese, Italian, French and Romanian. Classical Latin has a free word order:[24] **Audentes fortuna iuvat** (fortune favours the brave) works just as well in any of the other five possible orders: **Audentes iuvat fortuna**, **Fortuna audentes iuvat**, **Fortuna iuvat audentes**, **Iuvat audentes fortuna**, **Iuvat fortuna audentes**. Still, even in classical Latin, some orders tend to be preferred. The standard version of the phrase is in the OSV order: **Audentes** (object) **fortuna** (subject) **iuvat** (verb); yet the more common pattern in Latin is SOV. So, assuming that this SOV word pattern over time would have become increasingly standardized and entrenched, one might expect that the Romance languages of today would have an SOV word order. But that is not how things turned out. Why?

Although the most common pattern in classical Latin was SOV, what really matters is not the literary Latin of Cicero and

Julius Caesar but the Latin 'of the street'. This Vulgar Latin, which was spoken colloquially throughout the Roman empire from the second century BC onward, happened to fix upon a different word order: SVO. And it is this everyday Latin from which modern Romance languages have descended, hence inheriting its SVO word order.

Languages, like Latin, in which subject, verb and object can arrive in any order must include some other way of signalling the difference between subjects and objects (to distinguish between **John likes Fido** and **Fido likes John**) because the order of words is so unreliable. A common solution, and one used by Latin, is to mark case. Modern English retains case only in a vestigial form, for example, in the difference between *she* likes dogs and **dogs like** *her*. But Latin's system of cases is much more complex: it uses nominative case for subjects; accusative case for (direct) objects; and many more cases besides (dative, genitive, ablative, vocative and the rarely used locative). Cases are signalled in Latin with distinct noun endings, but these endings are always vulnerable to conventionalization and simplification (just as a commonly used charade gesture becomes ever simpler). So noun endings erode, and word order becomes increasingly conventionalized.[25] Thus, historically, languages tend to shift from relying on case endings to relying on word order, but not the other way around. Modern English is the endpoint of this trend: the complex case system of Old English has almost entirely disappeared apart from vestiges retained in the pronouns (e.g. *she* vs *her*; *he* vs *him*).

But where do case markings on nouns and markings for tense on verbs come from in the first place? How can a process of charades – focused almost entirely on immediate, visible, concrete objects and actions – possibly end up conveying abstract ideas like subject, direct object or indirect object (in **Sunita gave the book to Maya**, these would be **Sunita**, **the book** and **Maya**, respectively)? And how can successive verbal charades create the plethora of verb endings for different subjects (**I**, **you**, **he/she**, **we**, etc.) and tenses? For that matter, where do all the short 'grammatical' words (**of**, **to**, **and**, **on**, **by**) that glue language together come from? Charades may seem a credible metaphor for thinking about the origins of nouns and verbs, which pick out objects and actions – but what about grammar?

The answer comes from the fascinating phenomenon of grammaticalization: the strange process by which words with concrete, specific meanings transmute into the grammatical machinery of language.[26] The idea of grammaticalization (and research on language change more broadly) was a complete revelation to both of us, having been trained in the generative approach to language (Chomsky's 'principles and parameters' and its many rivals), which sees language as a vastly complex but immutable mathematical object. Grammaticalization explained how grammatical complexity could emerge, and how grammar was continually in flux.[27]

So what is grammaticalization? Roughly speaking, it is the series of steps by which collections of individual words that refer to objects and actions gradually mutate into complex systems of grammar, with pronouns, prepositions, conjunctions, verb endings, agreement and so on. The steps operate on words (or, more broadly, multiword constructions) one at a time, and they follow a (roughly) predictable sequence with a fixed direction. It is from the sum of these changes, and their interactions, that the complexity of language spontaneously arises.

With charades in mind, consider how we might expect this to

work. First, and most obviously, if we communicate the same message repeatedly, the signal will become ever more simplified and standardized. Simplification over time leads to what is known as 'erosion'. So, in English, **going to** becomes **gonna**; **did not** becomes **didn't**. Over longer periods of time, erosion can be far more dramatic. Starting with the Latin **mea domina** (my mistress), we progress through French (**ma dame** or **madame** for Mrs), to English **madam**, **ma'am**, **mum**, and sometimes even just -**m** (as in **Yes'm**).[28] Relatedly, erosion collapses forms with communicatively inessential differences. Contrast Early Modern English (the language of Shakespeare and the King James Bible) and Modern English:

I have	**I have**
thou hast	**you have**
he/she/it hath	**he/she/it has**
we have	**we have**
ye have	**you have**
they have	**they have**

Here, **thou** and **ye** have fused into **you** (the singular/plural distinction has gone); **hast** has disappeared and **hath** has mutated into **has**.

But the sheer scale of erosion in English becomes clearer when we look further back in time. The path from Old English (the language of *Beowulf* and the Arthurian legends) through Middle English (the language of Chaucer) to the English of today is a story of collapsed distinctions and lost endings.[29] Old English, like Latin, had a relatively free word order, and nouns had a complex system of case markings (nominative, accusative, genitive, dative and instrumental) to signal who was doing what to whom. It had three grammatical genders that applied not just to nouns but to demonstratives and adjectives. So the Old English equivalent of **that good woman** would have the neuter gender (not feminine, as it happens, because **wif** [woman] is neuter) signalled for each word. Table 4.3 gives a sense of how drastically things have changed in a thousand years.

But now we have a puzzle. If complex case markings and verb endings relentlessly albeit gradually disappear, where did they come from? Here, again, the analogy of charades provides a crucial clue. If we repeat a standard pattern involving two elements, pretty soon the abbreviated forms of those gestures start to fuse together. For example, **Wimbledon** might initially be conveyed by a mimed tennis shot followed by vertical fingers waving to imply **grass**. But after a while the vertical fingers might smoothly follow an abbreviated swooshing, and these may turn into a single gesture. Indeed, before too long, we might even forget why this bizarre gesture ever came to have its current meaning. The same phenomenon of fusing common patterns together occurs historically in many aspects of language. We already mentioned how in French the two words **ma dame** drifted into the single word **madame**. In English, **into**, **onto**, **wanna**, **gonna** and many more illustrate fusion in action. But this process also explains where the patterns for cases and verb endings come from. What is now a single word is the fossilized remains of a fusion of pairs of once separate neighbouring words.

And this is the key to the mystery of where verb endings come from – they were once independent words that gradually fused into the 'stem' to become a mere suffix. The Romance languages, descended from Latin, provide a nice illustration. We begin with

Table 4.3. The astonishing erosion of Old English verbs. Compare the exuberant variety of Old English forms of the two common verbs, *to have* and *to live* (**bold italics**), with their few and abbreviated counterparts in modern English (*plain italics*)

Tense/mood		Old English	Modern English	Old English	Modern English
Infinitive		tō **hæbbenne**	to *have*	tō **libbenne**	to *live*
Present	1st person	iċ **hæbbe**	I *have*	iċ **libbe**	I *live*
	2nd person	þū **hæfst**	you *have*	þū **leofast**	You *live*
	3rd person singular	hē/hēo/hit **hæfþ**	he/she/it *has*	hē/hēo/hit **leofaþ**	he/she/it *lives*
	Plural	**habbaþ**	*have*	**leofaþ**	*live*
Past indicative	1st person	iċ **hæfde**	I *had*	iċ **lifde**	I *lived*
	2nd person	þū **hæfdest**	you *had*	þū **lifdest**	you *lived*
	3rd person singular	hē/hēo/hit **hæfde**	he/she/it *had*	hē/hēo/hit **lifde**	he/she/it *lived*
	Plural	**hæfdon**	*had*	**lifdon**	*lived*
Present subjunctive	Singular	**hæbbe**	*have*	**libbe**	*live*
	Plural	**hæbben**	*have*	**libben**	*live*
Imperative	Singular	**hafa**	*have*	**leofa**	*live*
	Plural	**habbaþ**	*have*	**libbaþ**	*live*
Present participle		**hæbbende**	*having*	**libbende**	*living*
Past participle		(ġe)**hæfd**	*had*	(ġe)**lifd**	*lived*

Latin constructions, such as **cantare habeo** (I have [something] to sing).[30] Of course, if you have something to sing, then inevitably the singing will occur in the future, if it occurs at all. Over time, the meaning broadens to apply to any future event; but the independent verb **habere** remains. What this creates is a new way of talking about things that will happen in the future: that is, it creates a new future tense. Now consider the modern descendants of Latin: French, Italian and Spanish (table 4.4). Notice how in French, Italian and Spanish the forms of **have** are tacked on to the infinitive form of the verb (and in some cases have eroded) to give the future tense.

Table 4.4. Clues to the origin of the future tense in Romance languages. Infinitives (to have, to sing) are shown in *italics*; forms shared between the present tense and future tense endings are shown in ***bold italics***

French		Italian		Spanish	
have	**will sing**	**have**	**will sing**	**have**	**will sing**
avoir	*chanter*	*avere*	*cantare*	*haber*	*cantar*
j'***ai***	je chanter***ai***	io h***o***	cantar***ò***	he	cantaré
tu ***as***	tu chanter***as***	tu h***ai***	cantar***ai***	has	cantar*ás*
il/elle/on ***a***	il/elle/on chanter***a***	lui/lei h***a***	cantar***à***	ha	cantar*á*
nous av***ons***	nous chanter***ons***	noi abbia***mo***	cantare***mo***	he***mos***	cantare***mos***
vous av***ez***	vous chanter***ez***	voi av***ete***	cantar***ete***	hab***éis***	cantar***éis***
ils/elles/on ***ont***	ils/elles/on chanter***ont***	loro h***anno***	cantar***anno***	h***an***	cantar*án*

There is a final puzzle: where do grammatical words such as the auxiliary verb **have** (the Latin **habere**) come from? Charades deals with concrete objects and actions – how could there be gestures for abstractions (e.g. of **having** to sing), let alone apparently purely grammatical words – **of**, **in**, **the**, **a**, **and**, **because** and so on?

Here again, charades provides an interesting clue. Once we have used a gesture for some specific, concrete meaning, we can co-opt it later in the game to depict all sorts of related meanings. Our swooshing and finger-wiggling gesture might originally denote 'Wimbledon', the tennis tournament. But once established, it can be reused in a variety of possible ways, for example, to denote the district of south-west London or Wimbledon Common or Wimbledon underground station, or to refer to specific tennis stars such as Serena Williams or Roger Federer. Concrete meanings can be co-opted to convey much more abstract messages. Suppose that we have a charade for a mode of travel (such as a stepping action with downward-pointing fingers to indicate walking). This action might generalize to travelling of all kinds, whether on foot or not. It is then natural to follow that gesture with another symbolizing action, like an eating gesture, to convey going to the café to get lunch. And because actions that occur after travelling occur in the future, the walking gesture might eventually even come to mark the future tense. This would parallel the development of the English construction **I am going to swim**, where **to go** has mutated into a marker of the future, with movement no longer implied (the same pattern arises in French: **je vais nager**, and Spanish: **voy a nadar**).

Of course, the details of this charades example are pure speculation. But the historical analysis of languages indicates a powerful tendency for some words with concrete semantics to gradually become, in the wonderfully evocative phrase, 'bleached' of meaning, ultimately to play a standardized, purely grammatical role. So, whereas the sounds of language are continually subject to simplification and erosion, meanings are continually broadened; and in some cases words are almost entirely emptied of meaning.

Consider how in English the word **that** has shifted from indicating a nearby item (in Modern English: **Look at that!**), through 'pointing' to something a person said (roughly, **Mary shouted that the house is on fire!**), to the purely grammatical uses (**John doubted that the proof had a fatal flaw**, or **it is possible that the film will have a sequel**). Similarly, the word for 'a pace' or 'a step' (**pas**) came to be a grammatical marker for negation in French.[31] Starting with the Latin **non dico** for 'I do not say', we move to **je ne dis** (notice the erosion of **non** to **ne**). Additional words, **pas** (step), **point** (dot), **mie** (crumb) are added for emphasis, such as **je ne marche (une) pas** (I won't walk a step), **je ne mange (une) mie** (I won't eat a crumb). These constructions **ne ... pas**, **ne ... point**, **ne ... mie** become bleached of any meaning about steps, dots or crumbs and simply signal negation; **ne ... pas** gradually dominates, giving the standard form **je ne dis pas**. In some varieties of colloquial French, the **ne** is eroded into oblivion to leave **je dis pas**. A noun for a concrete observable action, a step or a pace, now fully takes on the most abstract of grammatical roles – flipping a statement (**je dis**) into its denial (**je dis pas**). In this way, words that were once about things and actions gradually evolve into the small but crucial grammatical words that are the building blocks of grammar.

BANISHING THE SPECTRE OF
LINGUISTIC DECLINE

Is language declining? Are the grammars of English, French, Icelandic and Mandarin falling into ever greater decay? As we saw at the beginning of this chapter, this is a common and perennial worry, like the continual concern about the 'youth of today'. Unless we appreciate the self-organizing forces that have shaped language, it is natural to see language change as a relentless process of corrosion. From this point of view, lexicographers and grammarians are essential bulwarks against the continual decay of common speech: language change is the outcome of sloppiness and downright error, and the forces of linguistic corruption should be resisted as vigorously as possible.

But once we realize that the complex patterns of language arise through processes of spontaneous order, we see that these worries are ill-founded. Language is constantly in flux: it is the product of the continual overlaying of sound shifts, word changes, grammaticalization and more at work over decades, centuries and millennia. The result of such recurrent tinkering is orderly while remaining delightfully capricious and capable of capturing poetry, law, science and the full gamut of human experience. Yet each generation of speakers tends to see any hints of shifting language not as indications of vigour and creativity but as the harbinger of linguistic degeneration, even mental and social decay. Indeed, the processes of grammaticalization can result in something close to cross-generational language wars.[32] For most people born before 1970, the increasing use of **like** to indicate a quotation makes them wince: 'I was like, OMG' is deemed poor language use. But the quotative use of **like** is here to stay, and has now even been extended to involve non-linguistic elements, such as 'I was like, [**speaker rolls eyes**]' and emojis: 'He was like, 😒.' The specific patterns of grammar are subject to continual change; but the balance of regularities, sub-regularities and exceptions that comprise the complexity of each human language remains the same.

◉

Order is not collapsing into chaos (as the sticklers for grammar, like Humphrys and Swift, earnestly worry). Instead, the order of language arises out of chaos: partially, incompletely, but to wonderful effect. The languages we collectively create, from one improvised episode to the next, are remarkably effective for conveying the things people care about in ways they can easily learn, produce and understand. The expressive resources we have available to us have been shaped to fit our immediate needs over millions of prior interactive moments.

When we leave language to its own devices, without interference from schoolteachers, august scholarly bodies and self-proclaimed experts in grammar, it doesn't collapse into a series of grunts. Those worried about linguistic anarchy see language as a garden that will grow unruly unless continually tended, or perhaps a piece of machinery requiring continual repair and adjustment. But is this right? Perhaps language should be compared instead to the orderly patterns that arise in the natural world – most obviously, the astonishingly complex designs of living creatures, from bacteria to beech trees, from beetles to bats, birds and basking sharks. The intricate patterns of biology don't require continual interference to guard against degeneration. Similarly, as we'll argue in the next chapter, the variety and complexity of the world's languages have emerged through similar processes of growth and evolution.

5

LANGUAGE EVOLUTION WITHOUT BIOLOGICAL EVOLUTION

> The speech of Man in his mother-tongue is not, like the song of birds, an instinct implanted by nature in the constitution of every individual of the species, and either exercised from the moment of birth or spontaneously called into play at a certain period of growth . . . Language in its actual condition is an art, like baking or weaving, handed down from generation to generation.
>
> HENSLEIGH WEDGWOOD,
> *On the Origin of Language* (1866)

Upon his return to England on 2 October 1836, after having spent nearly five years on board HMS *Beagle*, circumnavigating the globe while collecting fossils along with flora and fauna specimens, Charles Darwin had much to think about. The observations he made during this voyage seeded what would eventually grow into his revolutionary theory about the origin of species. Two years later, when the idea of evolution through natural selection finally began to crystallize in his mind, he was very much aware that his thesis would be controversial. As he would later note in his autobiography, 'I was so anxious to avoid prejudice, that I determined not for some time to write even the briefest sketch of it.'[1] Darwin knew that he would have to make the strongest case possible for his theory – otherwise, his ideas would be rapidly dismissed, ridiculed or worse. Help would come, however, from an unexpected direction: the study of linguistic change.

Darwin was probably introduced to comparative philology by his cousin and brother-in-law, the English magistrate, philologist and later spiritualist Hensleigh Wedgwood, one of the founding members of the Philological Society, the oldest learned society in the United Kingdom dedicated to the study of language. Wedgwood helped spread the word within British scientific circles about the groundbreaking work by German linguists on reconstructing the Indo-European language family (which we discussed in the previous chapter).[2] Languages as varied as Sanskrit, Greek, Latin, Persian, English and Danish had all been traced back through their genealogical relationships to a common root in an ancestral Indo-European proto-language. The idea that continual change over time could result in such a diverse linguistic family tree provided a model for Darwin's proposal that the taxonomy of all living things arose from a historical tree of variation (see figure 5.1).[3] The struggle for existence of linguistic forms (sounds, words, phrases) over generations of language use could be viewed as a model for the struggle for life among biological forms – in both domains, the key ingredients of evolution are variation and selection.

When it came to making the case for Darwin's evolutionary theory, the language–species analogy had an additional rhetorical advantage. Comparative philology in the mid-1800s was

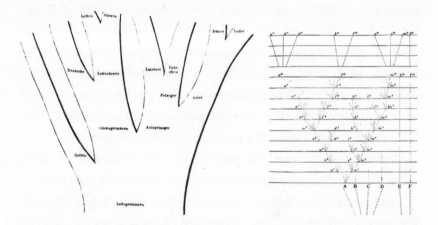

Figure 5.1. On the left, August Schleicher's visualization from 1853 of the genealogical relationships among the Indo-European languages, one of the first depictions of a linguistic family tree; and, on the right, Charles Darwin's tree of life diagram in *On the Origin of Species* from 1859. In both cases, diversity arises through a process of tree-like branching from a common root.

considered a model science, on a par with comparative anatomy and geology, because of its successful application of methods from natural science. The high academic status of the study of language seems likely to have been on his mind when Darwin penned his notebook entry from March 1839: 'I may put the argument, that many learned men seem to consider there is good evidence in the structure of language, that it was progressively formed ... seeing how simple an explanation it offers of radical diversity of tongues.'[4] Twenty years later, in *On the Origin of Species*, he would use the language–species analogy several times to back up his theory, including to show how biological classifications of species into genera, sub-families,

families and so on can follow from a tree-like genealogical
pedigree:

> It may be worth while to illustrate this view of
> classification, by taking the case of languages . . . The
> various degrees of difference between the languages of
> the same stock would have to be expressed by groups
> subordinate to groups; but the proper or even the only
> possible arrangement would still be genealogical; and this
> would be strictly natural, as it would connect together all
> languages, extinct and recent, by the closest affinities, and
> would give the filiation and origin of each tongue.[5]

The parallel between the origin of linguistic and biological
diversity was no whimsical analogy: it played a crucial role in
arguing for, and perhaps inspiring, Darwin's theory of natural
selection.

Darwin returned to the language–species analogy again in
1871 when discussing the evolution of language in *The Descent of
Man*: 'The formation of different languages and of distinct species, and the proofs that both have been developed through a
gradual process, are curiously the same . . . The survival and pre-
servation of certain favoured words in the struggle for existence
is natural selection.'[6] He approvingly quoted the Oxford philologist Max Müller as saying that a 'struggle for life among words
and grammatical forms . . . is constantly going on in each language . . . The better, the shorter, the easier forms are constantly
gaining the upper hand.'[7] In line with the thinking of many
others of his time (including his cousin Wedgwood, quoted at
the beginning of this chapter), Darwin's perspective on language
evolution was not about how humans might have evolved a

biological capacity specifically for language. His insight was about the *cultural* evolution of language – what we described in chapter 4 as the gradual emergence of partially overlapping linguistic patterns that emanate from our momentary attempts at making ourselves understood. In short, language evolution is language change writ large.

THE LANGUAGE ORGANISM

It may be tempting to object, at this point, that language change is not the same as language evolution. Surely, humans must have evolved some sort of specialized neural machinery to make language possible in the first place. After all, only humans have language – not even our evolutionary cousins, the other great apes, have anything resembling human language. So it would seem reasonable to assume that evolution endowed us with a biological adaptation just for language, and only once that was in place could processes of language change come into play. Indeed, this perspective has been quite influential in much of the language sciences and beyond.[8]

Even as PhD students, we were never convinced by the idea of an evolved genetic capacity for language. The separation between language evolution and language change is a fiction. It's largely based on the hypothesis – incorrect, as we have seen – that some sort of innate machinery specific for language is needed to explain how we learn and use language. If language works as we have proposed in this book, then there is no separation between the two. It's language change all the way down – no language-specific biological adaptations are needed.

But how did complex language emerge if there was no linguistic Rubicon, the evolutionary crossing of which transformed us from mere grunting brutes to loquacious modern humans? Fortunately, our view of the fleeting, flexible and cooperative nature of language offers a new and compelling answer to this question. Building on Darwin's insight, we view language as an evolving system in its own right. Instead of asking, 'How did the human brain become so well adapted to language?' we ask, 'How did language become so well adapted to the human brain?'

Our perspective on language evolution shifts the focus from the biological adaptation of language users to the cultural evolution of languages themselves. This is not to say that humans are simply born as 'blank slates' upon which language can be chalked during development, without any biological constraints.[9] Far from it! Only humans have complex language, and this undoubtedly has a great deal to do with our biology. As the late world-renowned language scientist Liz Bates put it, the question 'is not about Nature vs. Nurture, but about the "nature of Nature"'.[10] We don't have to debate whether there are biological constraints on language – there clearly are. Instead, the key issue is whether such constraints are specifically linguistic in nature, which would require adaptations for language, or whether they derive from other non-linguistic abilities that predated the evolutionary emergence of language and thus do not require any (or only very minimal) biological changes. Our money is on the latter: language evolved by piggybacking on pre-existing mechanisms for learning, memory and socio-communicative interaction.

But what shapes the cultural evolution of different tongues? What gives rise to the fit between linguistic structure and human language learners and users – a fit that makes human languages particularly easy for our brains to learn and use? Once more, the idea of language as charades can provide some helpful insights.

First, to play charades at all, we need to be attuned to each other. We have to be sensitive to what others might know and, perhaps even more importantly, what they don't know, as well as the kind of inferences they are likely to make. Without this, we will be unable to evoke the right ideas and concepts in the minds of our team-mates. Clearly, we won't get very far if we run around, bouncing up and down, to mime the speedy and jumpy Mario as a clue to the word **plumber**, if the rest of the team has never heard of Mario (the Italian American character from the Super Mario video game franchise), let alone played the game. Constraints on the various thought processes that go into reading each other's minds make up much of the hidden part of the communication iceberg, and therefore play a key role in shaping how languages evolve. To be useful, languages need to provide us with the resources to convey a wide variety of messages, speedily and with just enough precision to keep the conversation running smoothly. For example, languages have been shaped by cultural evolution to help conversation partners split apart information they both know from the key message to be conveyed. In the sentence **the man next door has bought a new dog**, we can take it as given that we both know a man lives next door and that the speaker is conveying the *new* information that he has just bought another dog.[11] More broadly, languages help us convey the types of things we want to communicate, such as who did what to whom, when and why. The types of linguistic charades that we create depend on the kinds of things we want to tell each other. But the specific ways by which the world's spoken and signed languages achieve these objectives show prolific variation.

Second, our physical bodies restrict what we can do when playing charades. There's no point in acting out something that others can't see, or trying to denote 'yoga' by struggling to contort ourselves into a pretzel pose that we aren't supple enough to manage. Similarly, languages, whether signed or spoken, are also shaped by such perceptuomotor factors, ensuring that they involve perceptual units that can easily be recognized and produced given the way that our body works. The speech sounds we produce, for example, have to be among those we can create by vibrating our vocal cords and using our tongue and lips to shape the sound waves as they resonate within our vocal tract – although the variety of sound patterns people can create and understand is remarkably broad.

Third, limitations on what we can learn, attend to and remember shape both charades and the evolution of language. For example, a long and rapid improvised sequence of intricate movements, which we might imagine to be an accurate mime of car repair, will probably be too complex and baffling to elicit successful guesses of the word **mechanic**. Not only that, but it will also be too complex to 'catch on' and be reused by others in future games of charades – although some radically simplified version might. Similarly, the evolution of linguistic structure is shaped by a bias towards short, simple and easy-to-remember patterns that can more easily pass through the Now-or-Never bottleneck.

Fourth, the process of conveying abstract meanings by conventionalizing initially iconic labels arises in both charades and language. For example, the previously mentioned steepling hands gesture, originally used for 'boat', became conventionalized in Nick's family at first to signal Columbus's voyage to the New World and then to simply denote America. Languages, too, are

moulded by similar processes of conventionalization to facilitate communicative efficiency, as we detailed in chapter 3. As we
saw, powerful communicative pressures push in the direction of
an arbitrary link between sounds and meanings (so that not all
words for breeds of dog sound alike; instead, we have **akitas**,
beagles, **collies** and so on). This drives the speech signal and
contextual cues to become as independent, and hence complementary, as possible. Ultimately, though, if a specific word is to
come to life and continue to flourish in the language, it needs to
be adaptable so that it can fit the needs of the communicative
moment yet still be sufficiently grounded in conventions to be
understood by those with whom we talk.

These constraints – deriving from how we think about others,
how our perceptuomotor system works, what we're able to
learn and remember, and how we create meaning through
conventionalization – may be weighted in various ways as they
come together to create different languages. Repeated learning
and use give rise to partially systematic patterns of linguistic
structure through the regularizing force of grammaticalization,
as discussed in the previous chapter. Over time, forms that fit
the constraints well tend to proliferate, while those that do not,
if ever generated in the first place, soon succumb in Darwin's
'struggle for existence'. Words and constructions that are hard to
learn or use soon disappear from the language, whereas those
that are easily picked up and used with little effort are passed on
to subsequent generations. In other words, language evolution
is driven by grammaticalization combined with other processes
of linguistic change and reined in by the limitations of our
brains and how we interact with one another.

Metaphorically speaking, we can think of a language as akin

to an 'organism' that must adapt to its environmental niche.[12] And that niche is the human brain – viewed broadly as including the body that carries it around and the community of other brains to which it is socially connected. This 'language organism' depends on us for its survival. Language only exists because we do. If all of humanity suddenly disappeared in a puff of smoke, language would vanish too – except in the inert texts housed in abandoned libraries. But if language disappeared, we would still be around (though we'd have a hard time keeping our societies going). So, in biological terms, language forms a dependent and symbiotic relationship with its human hosts.

Symbiosis, referring to the close interaction of two distinct organisms, is ubiquitous in nature. For example, we all carry around trillions of micro-organisms, living on and in our body, from the hair on our head to the soles of our feet, from the inside of our nose and mouth to deep in our stomach and intestines.[13] Together, these tiny hitch-hikers make up the human microbiome, weighing in at about 3 pounds (about 1.5 kilograms) in an average adult (which is also roughly the weight of a typical adult brain).[14] Many are 'commensal', meaning that they take advantage of their human environment without giving us anything back, apart from not harming us. Others are in a mutualistic, symbiotic partnership that benefits both microbe and human host. Consider *Bacteroides thetaiotaomicron*, or *B. theta* for short, which is one of the most common bacteria found in our gut. In return for providing much-needed help in breaking down complex carbohydrates, such as starch, we feed and nurture it in our innards. So, our symbiotic alliance with these microbes is a win–win relationship.[15]

Our symbiotic relationship with language is also mutually

beneficial: language gets to survive, thrive and proliferate, and humans get to communicate better, teach each other new skills, pass along knowledge, and create increasingly complex cultures, societies and civilizations. When two species are in this type of mutualistic symbiosis, they often co-evolve. But the evolutionary relationship between humans and language is lopsided, because biological adaptation is considerably slower than the cultural evolution of linguistic structure. Hominin evolution, from our *Australopithecus* ancestors to modern humans, occurred on the timescale of hundreds of thousands, even millions of years; but it took less than nine thousand years for languages as varied as Breton, Catalan, Danish, Greek, Hindi, Lithuanian and Persian to emerge from a common ancestral language, known as Proto-Indo-European.[16] Computer simulations of such asymmetrical symbiotic partnerships have shown that the faster-evolving organism ends up adapting more closely to the slower-evolving one, rather than vice versa.[17] The rapidly changing species essentially becomes yoked to its host. Indeed, many of our bacterial symbionts have become uniquely adapted to live on and within our bodies.[18] And the same goes for the rapidly changing language organism, which is compelled to adapt to its human host. Language is shaped by the brain – not the other way around.

LANGUAGE INSTINCTS AND PROMETHEUS'S GENES

Once we view language as emerging from a myriad momentary communicative interactions, then it seems clear that language must have evolved primarily by way of cultural evolution.

Indeed, it is hard to imagine how it could be otherwise. Yet, this was not how many language scientists thought about language evolution when interest in the topic revived towards the end of the twentieth century, following the long slumber induced by the 1866 ban imposed by the Société de Linguistique de Paris.[19] Most of these researchers had forgotten Darwin's original insight about language as an evolving system. Instead, they saw the core issue in the field of language evolution as uncovering an explanation for the biological evolution of a supposed genetic blueprint for language.

As a case in point, the psycholinguists Steven Pinker and Paul Bloom proposed in 1990 that the human ability for language is a species-specific biological adaptation that evolved through a standard neo-Darwinian process.[20] By analogy with established evolutionary accounts of the visual system, from the crude patches of light-sensitive cells that emerged five hundred million years ago (and still found on today's flatworm) to the intricate design of the mammalian eye, they argued that natural selection for enhanced linguistic skills would have resulted in the gradual evolution of ever more elaborate 'universal grammars' built into our genes.[21]

The basic idea is as follows. Imagine a band of hunter-gatherers who are already communicating with one another using a learned set of linguistic conventions, perhaps one comprising single words and simple multiword combinations. As a result of random genetic variation, some individuals are more adept than others at using these specific linguistic forms to persuade and engage listeners, cement friendships, outmanoeuvre competitors, instruct the young and otherwise enhance their social standing in the group. As a consequence, these individuals will have more surviving children, and the genes for producing this particular idiosyncratic but socially efficacious patterning in language would gradually spread in the population. Over time, repeated genetic modifications would appear, enabling more and more complex linguistic structures, until the modern-day universal grammar is in place. This innate endowment can be thought of as a network of syntactic principles (or rules) covering all the languages of the world, with a set of switches that can be flipped to capture the specific pattern of individual tongues.

This notion of an evolved biological specialization for language – what Pinker subsequently called 'the language instinct' – soon became the standard view of the origin of our linguistic abilities.[22] There are, however, several reasons to be sceptical about the idea that our brains adapted to language to give us a universal grammar.[23] First, as noted earlier, linguistic conventions, and languages in general, change more quickly than biological evolution occurs. The linguistic environment changes much too fast for genes to adapt to it through natural selection.

With our collaborator Florencia Reali, from Universidad de los Andes in Colombia, we have confirmed this using computer simulations of the interplay of genetic and linguistic change.[24] Although a specific genetic disposition might give an individual a temporary advantage with one particular idiosyncratic linguistic pattern, this would soon turn into a disadvantage when that very pattern inevitably changed into something else. Because language change is so much faster than biological adaptation, the genes continuously have to 'chase' the language, only to find that when they do catch up, the language has already moved on. The fast-changing language is a 'moving target' with which the slow-moving genes can't keep up, making biological adaptations for specific abstract linguistic patterns highly unlikely – and indeed almost certainly counterproductive.

The dispersion of human populations, initially throughout Africa and subsequently across the rest of the globe, provides a second reason for doubting that humans evolved a genetic blueprint for language. Because children adopted from anywhere in the world can learn the language of their new home country, any putative universal grammar must therefore have evolved before the African exodus. If not, then a Chinese girl adopted by American parents in New York would not be able to learn English, and an English boy brought up in a Chinese family in Beijing could not learn Mandarin. But let's assume, for the sake of argument, that an early group of humans in Africa somehow managed to genetically assimilate the arbitrary linguistic conventions of their community. As this population grew, sub-groups spread to new areas and soon became isolated from one another – and because they would have no way of keeping in touch over long distances, their linguistic conventions would quickly diverge.

Computer simulations show that if natural selection is fast enough to genetically encode the initial set of language patterns, then the genes cannot help but adapt to later linguistic changes as well.[25] So, if the genes could (implausibly) keep up with the frenetic pace of linguistic change in our imaginary group of humans in Africa, then they would also keep pace with the further changes in language patterns that would undoubtedly happen as the populations spread across Africa and beyond. This kind of adaptation to divergent languages by separated human sub-populations parallels what Charles Darwin observed in the Galapagos Islands, where groups of finches isolated from one another on different islands evolved into different species, each exquisitely adapted to its specific local environment. But when it comes to language, such adaptation to the local linguistic patterns would mean that a person would have to be born to ethnically Chinese parents to learn Mandarin, hail from the Mexican state of Chiapas to master Tseltal, or be native to Denmark to pick up Danish. This is clearly not the case.[26]

Even if the first two problems for Pinker and Bloom's adaptationist view of language could somehow be solved, there remains a third reason to doubt this account: why would evolution yield a universal grammar that is so abstract and so highly unspecified that it can accommodate a plethora of radically different languages? As we shall see in chapter 7, languages differ in almost every imaginable way, from the specific sounds used to form words to the way those words are put together into sentences to how context is used to make sense of what is said. But evolution has no foresight. The first human language could not have encompassed all this astonishing variation. It would have been but a single language with a particular set of sounds and specific ways of assembling the sounds into words and the words into phrases and sentences. Biological adaptation is not driven by which environments *might* exist in the future, such as the seven thousand different languages of today. Rather, natural selection adapts organisms to the *immediate* environment, and human evolution is no exception.

As hominins spread out across the world, they physically adapted to their specific local environments; an example is the Neanderthals' (*Homo neanderthalensis*) genetic adaptations for colder climates (some, apparently, shared with the woolly mammoth).[27] Another more dramatic example is Flores Man (*Homo floresiensis*), nicknamed 'Hobbit' because of its short stature. This early species of human lived on the island of Flores in Indonesia and underwent a process of insular dwarfism, becoming smaller as an adaptation to the limited resources available on the island.[28] Similarly, we would expect the same to hold for other human traits, including language. So, if language started with a gradual biological adaptation to the local linguistic conventions of a single group of linguistic savants, as Pinker and Bloom suggest, why didn't evolution genetically encode the specific sounds they used, the way they combined sounds into words and the syntactic composition of their sentences? In other words, why don't we all speak the same language?[29] The idea that natural selection would adapt our brains not to the local linguistic environment but to a universal one that encompasses all possible future human languages is analogous to suggesting that an animal living in the sands of the Sahara could somehow develop genetic adaptations that not only allow it to thrive in its arid desert home but also would enable it to flourish in the lush rainforest of the Amazon, among Manhattan's concrete skyscrapers and on the icy tundra of northern Siberia. Not a very likely scenario.

There are good reasons to question the idea of a biological adaptation for language in the form of a universal grammar. The linguist Noam Chomsky also doubts that a universal grammar could arise through natural selection. Instead, he puts forward the idea that the biological foundation for language came about not through gradual natural selection, as suggested by Pinker and Bloom, but with a sudden mutational event in a single human about a hundred thousand years ago. In a single momentous evolutionary step, this human, dubbed 'Prometheus', was for the first time able to carry out a process called 'recursion', which Chomsky sees as a fundamental, perhaps even *the core*, property of language.[30]

Recursion is an important concept in logic and computer

science that makes it possible for a process to 'call on' a copy of itself. As such, recursion is often considered foundational to language because it allows phrases to be nested within phrases of the same type, like Russian Matryoshka dolls. For example, if we take the two English sentences **The dog ran away** and **The cat scared the dog**, we can apply recursion to embed the second within the first to produce (square brackets indicate the embedded sentence):

The dog [that the cat scared] ran away.

We can repeat this embedding process, adding the sentence **The mouse surprised the cat**, to yield (with curly brackets indicating the second embedding):

The dog [that the cat {that the mouse surprised} scared] ran away.

In fact, Chomsky suggests that we can do this ad infinitum. Note, though, that even with just two embeddings, as above, the resulting sentence is exceedingly difficult to understand. With three embeddings it's all but impossible, as illustrated by the following (with parentheses indicating the third embedding):

The dog [that the cat {that the mouse (that the bug startled) surprised} scared] ran away.

According to Chomsky, Prometheus would have been the first human being able to construct these and other kinds of embedded sentences of potentially limitless depth. Yet it seems likely that Prometheus would have struggled to produce or make sense of sentences with multiple embeddings – just as we do today. Puzzling as this may seem, Chomsky's essential point is that the human ability to use language came about in one evolutionary fell swoop: before Prometheus, there was no language, but with the advent of recursive grammar, language existed (albeit initially only in the mind of a single human).

You may feel that this is a pretty marginal, rather than fundamental, aspect of language – and a strange focus for the apparently crucial evolutionary 'moment' when human language became possible. Indeed, Morten wrote his PhD dissertation on how our ability to deal with such 'centre-embedded' recursion in language is actually quite paltry – a point that, given the discussion so far in this book, is not unexpected: for centre-embedded sentences run headlong into the limitations of the Now-or-Never bottleneck, which imposes the urgent need to chunk the input as quickly as possible. Sentences with more than one embedding tax our language system beyond its normal capacity. It is therefore not surprising that centre-embedded sentences are extremely rare across languages.[31] So, whereas Chomsky's mathematical approach to grammar sees unlimited recursion as central to language – the Matryoshka doll can supposedly hold any number of smaller copies within it, in principle – language in reality is nothing like that. In fact, real spoken sentences make for rather disappointing Matryoshka dolls, as they contain at most one copy within them. Or, in many cases, none whatsoever. And some languages don't use recursion at all: Pirahã, which is spoken by a contemporary community of hunter-gatherers living deep in the Amazonian rainforest of Brazil, has become famous in academic circles for its apparent lack of recursion.[32]

Not only does recursion seem like an unlikely candidate for the 'missing ingredient' humans needed to get language off the ground, but the idea of a complex cognitive skill like recursion suddenly appearing fully formed via a single mutational incident is also exceedingly improbable. And a further puzzle is how a single individual, like Prometheus, with a supposedly newfound capacity for recursive language, would have gained any selective advantage. After all, recursion would be of little help in communicating with anyone else because others would not have the same recursive ability. Chomsky's answer is that recursion does not assist with communication but in some mysterious and unspecified way helps with thought – as if Prometheus exercised his language just for the purposes of internal monologue, with such huge resulting benefits that the 'recursion gene' spread rapidly through the population. Again, not a likely proposition, and Chomsky provides no evidence to support it.

Although we have argued that humans could not have evolved a special language faculty or universal grammar through either natural selection or a single mutation event, the creation of language through generations of charades has had huge implications for the evolution of our species. As we'll see in chapter 8, language changes everything: from the size of our brains and the complexity of our societies to the dazzling growth of human knowledge, technology and culture. Indeed, when we do uncover genes that are implicated in our language ability, we do not expect them to be specific to language but instead to play a role in the development of more general skills underlying our linguistic abilities.

LANGUAGE GENES

In early October 2001, newspapers and science journals were awash with sensational headlines like 'Whisper It Quietly, But the Power of Language May All Be in the Genes', 'First Language Gene Found' and 'First "Speech Gene" Identified'.[33] The excitement was about a landmark study that revealed that the disruption of a single gene called *FOXP2* was associated with a severe speech and language disorder suffered by half of the members of a three-generation British family from West London.[34] Prior work had suggested that affected members of this family, known as KE, had particular problems with grammatical morphology (such as noun and verb inflection).[35] For example, they failed the famous 'wug test', which assesses knowledge of the plural **-s** rule in English.[36] In this test, they were first shown a depiction of an imaginary animal and were told, 'This is a wug.' Next, they were shown a second picture with two of these fanciful creatures and asked, 'These are __?' Although children as young as four years of age will quickly shout out 'wugs!' the afflicted KE family members couldn't get this right. Often, they would simply respond 'wug', indicating that they had not picked up on the general pattern in English of adding **-s** for plurals (whether **cars**, **dogs** or **wugs**). They fared no better when tested on the default **-ed** ending used to signal the past tense of many English verbs, such as **walk** and **kiss**. When tested with prompts like, 'Every day he walks eight miles. Yesterday he __?' they would typically omit the past tense ending, simply saying 'walk', whereas even preschool children have no problems responding 'walked'.

This kind of deficit, which seems to affect only language and causes no other cognitive disabilities, is often referred to as specific language impairment, or SLI for short. Because the affected

KE individuals did not appear to have problems with intelligence or other aspects of cognition, it was suggested that their impairment was specific to complex morphology and that a single gene might be responsible for this deficit. This selective pattern of breakdown just for language is exactly what might be expected if humans had evolved biological adaptations for different aspects of language, such as morphology. Not surprisingly, the finding that damage to a single gene, *FOXP2*, resulted in SLI was welcomed like manna from heaven by scholars championing the idea of an innate blueprint for language. Steven Pinker even called it 'a smoking gun for a genetic cause of one kind of language disorder'.[37]

Ten months later, the proponents of a genetic endowment for language received a further boost, accompanied by another round of tantalizing *FOXP2* headlines in news media and scientific journals: 'Language Gene Is Traced to Emergence of Humans', 'Gene Linked to the Dawn of Speech' and '"Speech Gene" Debut Timed to Modern Humans'.[38] Whereas the first study had located the *FOXP2* gene disrupted in the KE family on the long arm of chromosome 7 in humans, the second study involved a comparison of the human version of *FOXP2* with those of the chimpanzee, gorilla, orangutan, rhesus macaque and mouse.[39] Given the apparent importance of *FOXP2* to language, it may seem surprising that other animals have this gene at all – but *FOXP2* is not unique to humans, primates or even mammals. *FOXP2* is important for the development of the brain, lungs, heart and gut and is highly conserved across species, from humans and apes to mice and bats to birds and zebrafish. It is a gene that you shouldn't mess with. When mice have their version of *Foxp2* (known by its lowercase letters to distinguish it from the human variant) 'knocked out', they die within twenty-one days. Note that we all have two copies of *FOXP2* – one from our mother and one from our father. Only one of these two copies of *FOXP2* was 'broken' in the affected members of the KE family, whereas both copies had been damaged in the dead mice. The KE family's one functioning copy of *FOXP2* was sufficient for the development of their lungs, heart and gut, but not for the brain basis of language.

The importance of not disrupting *FOXP2* is reflected in the fact that there has only been one amino-acid change in the gene in the seventy million years since the evolutionary split between mice and chimps. But what prompted the new excitement about *FOXP2* was that, since humans split from chimps about six million years ago, there have been two amino-acid changes in the human version of the gene. Comparisons of a small set of human genomes suggested that these changes became 'fixed' in our lineage at some point during the past two hundred thousand years, meaning that a particular version of *FOXP2* had spread throughout the human population – probably because it conferred a powerful selective advantage. Natural selection had incorporated the new version of *FOXP2* into every living human on Earth in what, in evolutionary terms, was a blink of an eye. Could it be that *FOXP2* spread so rapidly because it had specifically evolved to support language, as might be expected by advocates of a genetically programmed universal grammar?

The promise of *FOXP2* as an evolved language gene unique to modern humans would turn out to be short-lived. The first blow came in 2007 from a genetic study of the Neanderthals, previously believed to be grunting brutes without much language. Once the technique for extracting ancient DNA from fossil bones was developed, one of the first targets for sequencing was the Neanderthal *FOXP2* gene. It turned out to have the same two amino-acid changes as the modern human version, making the genes of the two species practically identical from an evolutionary perspective.[40] So, if *FOXP2* is a language gene, then Neanderthals must have had language, too. This also means that the version of *FOXP2* that both modern humans and Neanderthals have must go back much further than originally thought, at least to our last common ancestor some three hundred thousand to four hundred thousand years ago.

The second blow came about a decade later when a comprehensive study comparing hundreds of genomes from human populations around the globe failed to find the reduced genetic variation within *FOXP2* that had been taken as a signature of recent selection in the earlier smaller-scale study.[41] It is possible to find some genetic differences even in conserved genes, such as *FOXP2*. If we compare the genomes of two random individuals, they will be almost identical. About 99.9 per cent identical, in fact, when we compare the order of the four nucleotides – adenine (A), thymine (T), cytosine (C) and guanine (G) – that are the building blocks of DNA. But every once in a while, a difference appears – on average, once per one thousand nucleotides – where one person might have an A and the other has a G, or one has a T where the other has a C. This is to say that they have two different *alleles* for this specific location in their genome.[42] The same is true when we look at individual genes. If the new variant of *FOXP2* had spread rapidly throughout the early human population, as might be expected if it conferred the huge reproductive advantages provided by language, then there should be little allelic variation within this stretch of DNA in modern-day people anywhere on Earth. The language-gene theory flunked this crucial test: there was no sign of the telltale reduction in *FOXP2* alleles, and hence no evidence for selection favouring *FOXP2* in the human population. The new, more comprehensive study showed that because the original study had sampled only a small set of genomes primarily from individuals of Eurasian descent, it had missed much of the actual allelic variation found within *FOXP2* across the world. In other words, whatever natural selection our human ancestors may have undergone over the past two hundred thousand years, it is unlikely to have involved biological adaptations of *FOXP2* specifically for language. So much for *FOXP2* being the evolutionary linchpin for either Pinker's human language instinct or Chomsky's linguistic Prometheus.

But how closely is *FOXP2* related to language? At first this might seem like an odd question, given that the disruption of this gene leads to the language problems experienced by the affected members of the KE family. Note, however, that the logic of this inference relies on linking two negatives: it associates the breakdown of a biological component, *FOXP2*, with a deficit in behaviour, language. To see why such a double-negative inference might be problematic, consider Huntington's disease, which is caused by a mutation to a copy of the *huntingtin* gene.[43] An early sign of this disease is trouble with walking, but this does not make *huntingtin* a 'walking gene'. Rather, the mutation in this gene causes a neurodegenerative disorder that initially manifests itself most clearly in problems with movement and coordination, which have a dramatic effect on walking. With this issue in mind, Morten and colleagues from the University of Iowa set out to determine whether normal genetic variation in *FOXP2* among the general population might contribute to individual differences in their language skills.[44] Specifically, they looked at whether variation in thirteen different *FOXP2* alleles was associated with individual differences across several language tasks involving vocabulary, grammar and narration in a large sample of 812 school-aged children. Dealing yet another blow to the view that *FOXP2* is a 'language gene', they found no relationship between common allelic variation in *FOXP2* and language ability. So, even though the disruption of *FOXP2* in the KE family is linked to a rare form of language impairment, allelic variation in this gene in the general population does not contribute to normally occurring differences in our language abilities.

We're left with the question: in which aspects of behaviour might *FOXP2* be involved, if any? Perhaps *FOXP2* influences language skills through a more indirect route? A decade-old mouse study provides some initial insights into this question.[45] Geneticists from the Max Planck Institute for Evolutionary Anthropology in Leipzig used molecular tools to modify the *Foxp2* gene in a strain of mice to make it functionally equivalent to the human *FOXP2* gene – essentially, they inserted a human version of *FOXP2* into these mice. As one might expect, the resulting 'humanized' mouse was no Stuart Little, the talking mouse-boy in E. B. White's beloved children's book. But there were some intriguing changes in its corticostriatal circuits, a part of the brain important for learning. When the geneticists explored the behavioural effects of making *Foxp2* humanlike in these mice, they observed better and more efficient learning, suggestive of the kind of fast chunking of rapid sequential input we discussed in chapter 2. Intriguingly, the same corticostriatal brain circuits have also been associated with complex sequence learning in humans.

Perhaps, then, the evolution of the human version of *FOXP2* involved changes to these neural circuits to facilitate sequence learning – a type of learning long considered to be important for language.[46] If this is the case, then people with disrupted *FOXP2* genes might be expected to struggle not just with language but also with sequence learning of all kinds. This prediction has been investigated in a mother and her daughter, both of whom had a disrupted *FOXP2* gene like the affected members of the KE family. In addition to their language problems, the pair also struggled to learn non-linguistic sequences. Indeed, it turns out that, more broadly, individuals with SLI seem to have problems with sequence learning regardless of whether they have damage to *FOXP2*.[47]

The upshot is that *FOXP2* is not a language gene at all. Instead, it is likely that it plays a role in the development of general-purpose brain circuits that, among other kinds of learning, are recruited for language. Not only that: despite its name, specific language impairment turns out not to be *specific* to language at all. Rather, SLI is a broad developmental deficit that affects sequence learning and possibly other non-linguistic skills; but because we spend most of our waking hours using language, the linguistic deficit is much more noticeable. What SLI shows us is that language is not an isolated ability that can be damaged selectively, though it can be impaired when some of its many underlying skills are disrupted. But this is exactly what we would expect if language has evolved by piggybacking on pre-existing brain mechanisms, including our ability to learn sequences.

A NEW MACHINE BUILT OUT OF OLD PARTS

When children learn language, their brains are not relying on genetically programmed 'machinery' for language. Instead, the developing brain recruits and repurposes neural circuits that evolved long before the emergence of language, such as those involved in planning and enacting complex sequences of actions. Genes, of course, do play a role, but not in a language-specific way.

But there is another apparent puzzle for the viewpoint we have laid out here. For more than a century and a half, scientists have been studying areas of the brain that seem to be specialized for language. For example, Broca's area, a region in the left frontal part of the brain, has been found to be important for speech production, while Wernicke's area, located in the upper part of the left temporal lobe, is often associated with under-standing language (see figure 5.2).[48] In adults, damage to these

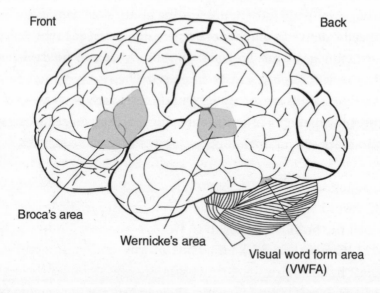

Figure 5.2. A left-hemisphere view of the human brain, showing the approximate location of two regions involved in language, Broca's and Wernicke's areas, as well as the visual word form area that is involved in reading. (Adapted from a brain drawing by H. Gray, 1918.)

158

areas caused by a stroke or head trauma has been associated with problems in producing and understanding language. And brain scans show that these areas (along with other parts of the brain) are highly active when we use language. How could such 'language areas' arise in the brain if they're not preprogrammed in our genes? A crucial clue to answering this question comes not from language itself but from another closely related product of cultural evolution: literacy.

Writing is at least 5,500 years old, yet for almost all of human history, the ability to read and write was confined to a tiny fraction of the population. Only within the past century did literacy spread widely across the globe. This is far too little time for selective pressures to affect our genes, let alone for the evolutionary emergence of biological adaptations for reading and writing. Literacy is therefore uncontroversially considered a culturally evolved ability that by necessity must piggyback on pre-existing brain mechanisms – just as we argue is the case for language.

Writing systems around the world differ in several ways, from the alphabets of languages like English and Danish, where letters stand for individual sounds, to the 'syllabaries' used by Japanese and Cherokee, where a symbol refers to a syllable, to the 'logograms' of Chinese, where a character represents a whole word.[49] Nonetheless, there is surprisingly little difference in the brain areas involved in reading across individuals and cultures.[50] Near the underside of the temporal region in the left hemisphere sits a tiny brain area known as the visual word form area (VWFA), which is consistently activated no matter the writing system.[51] The existence of the VWFA is important to our argument for two reasons. First, it shows that a cultural invention – literacy – can recruit quite similar neural substrates no matter who is doing the reading or what script is being read, suggesting that the brain deals with all written languages in the same way. Second, the VWFA becomes increasingly dedicated to recognizing words as the reader becomes more and more proficient in reading. Given that language is also a product of cultural evolution, the fact that the same seemingly specialized language areas are activated in different individuals, no matter which language they speak, does not mean that these areas have evolved as biological adaptations for language. Rather, like the VWFA, they emerge through experience with language, in some cases resulting in neural circuits that are mostly, and perhaps sometimes even completely, dedicated to language.

Just as language is shaped by the brain, so writing systems, too, have been optimized by cultural evolution to be easy for us to learn and use. For example, individual letters in alphabets from around the world on average consist of three strokes per character (as in A, F, N, K). This tendency probably reflects the basic limitations of our visual system, while also allowing for the creation of enough different letters to capture all speech sounds without too much ambiguity.[52] In a similar vein, the contours created by the intersection of different strokes in letters (such as T, Y, L, Δ) follow the same patterns of regularity observed in natural scenes, that is, similar combinations of line intersections and occlusions to those we see when looking at a wooded landscape, a mountain vista or an ocean view. It turns out that letters have been shaped to fit already existing biases in the visual system for object and scene recognition.[53] And, counterintuitive as it may seem, reading engages, at least partly, mechanisms for visual object recognition that we share with other primates. This was demonstrated by a study in which baboons learned to distinguish real English words, like **done**, **land**, **them**, **vast**, from non-words, such as **drke**, **lagn**, **tewk**, **vibt**.[54] This was, of course, not a case of monkey see, monkey read. The baboons in this study couldn't read or understand English; but, remarkably, they were able to learn enough about how letters are typically combined to form words in English to pick out, at a rate well above chance, the letter strings that were actual English words and reject those that were not. When put together, these findings suggest that writing systems have been shaped by cultural evolution to fit a neuronal niche that includes the VWFA to make them easier to learn to read, just as languages have adapted to how our brain works to facilitate their learning and use.

The existence of language areas in the brain does not, then, pose any problems for the idea that language has evolved primarily through cultural evolution. Just as the VWFA is not a genetically encoded brain module for reading, so language regions like Broca's and Wernicke's areas are not biological adaptations for language. Rather, these areas become increasingly specialized for language or literacy over our lifetimes through years of talking and reading. So it should come as no surprise that if these brain areas are damaged by a stroke, traumatic brain injury or neurodegenerative disease, the result is selective deficits in language (the various forms of aphasia) or reading (acquired dyslexia, when people with normal reading ability develop reading difficulties).

The parallel between language and reading extends to the genetic level. Damage to *FOXP2* can lead to problems with speech and language. Similarly, when specific genes associated with reading, such as *DCDC2*, are disrupted, the result is difficulty in learning to read (known as developmental dyslexia).[55] In both instances, the genes do not code directly for language or reading but indirectly influence the development of the brain mechanisms on which these two skills rely. *DCDC2* influences neural development in brain areas important for handling sound, which is an integral component of learning to read: without a good representation of speech sounds, the brain has no clear target on to which letters can be mapped. And, as we have seen, *FOXP2* affects the development of neural circuits important for handling rapid sequences of input, such as spoken language.

◉

Literacy is a cultural product, supported by specialized brain areas that gradually emerge as we learn to read. Language, too, is a culturally evolved skill. It develops as we learn to speak or sign, relying on existing neural machinery that becomes specialized for linguistic functioning. As Liz Bates so aptly puts it, 'Language is a new machine built out of old parts, reconstructed from those parts by every human child.'[56] But how do children do this? If language evolution consists of repeated games of linguistic charades writ large, how do children know how to make the right guesses? According to the universal grammar viewpoint, children make the right guesses because language is wired into their genes. But if there is no such innate knowledge of language, the fact that children learn to play linguistic charades so quickly and so easily needs a different explanation. We must ask: what happens when language learning meets language evolution?

It turns out that the explanation is surprisingly simple: learning a language is child's play because language has evolved to be learnable by us, and by children in particular. Language learning comes easily to us because we are learning *our* language, and learning it from previous generations of humans with similar brains and cognitive skills. Language learning is possible, as we shall see, because we are not learning some arbitrary set of patterns and meanings created by a computer or extraterrestrials, but because we learn by tracing the steps of previous learners, who are just like us.

6

FOLLOWING IN EACH OTHER'S FOOTSTEPS

Most situations ... provide some clue for coordinating behavior, some focal point for each person's expectation of what the other expects him to expect to be expected to do.

THOMAS SCHELLING,
The Strategy of Conflict (1960)

Suppose you're asked to meet a stranger tomorrow in New York City but have no way of contacting him or her. When and where would you meet them? This seems like an impossible task! New York City is huge, consisting of five boroughs – Brooklyn, Queens, Manhattan, the Bronx and Staten Island – encompassing 302.6 square miles (784 square kilometres), and has a population of more than eight million people.[1] How could you ever expect to meet up with someone you don't know in such a vast city?

However, if we reframe the problem as: 'Pick a time and place tomorrow in New York City that somebody else, just like you, might also choose,' suddenly it becomes doable. A popular answer is: 'Twelve noon at Grand Central Station.' Although you can choose any hour of the day or night, noon seems a particularly salient meeting time, and one that others are also likely to pick, whereas 2.39 a.m. is clearly a bad choice. Similarly, New York City is full of places to meet, but Grand Central Station, Times Square or the base of the Empire State Building are particularly popular because they are well-known meeting spots. Heading to a random point on the map of New York and hoping the other person happens to pick the same random location is obviously a hopeless strategy.

The New York City problem was originally posed by the American economist and Nobel laureate Thomas Schelling, the originator of the mutual assured destruction (MAD) doctrine of nuclear deterrence. His influential 1960 book *The Strategy of Conflict* considers not only the ways in which adversaries with opposing objectives fight for dominance but also the complementary problem of how people with the same objective successfully coordinate their behaviour to achieve a common goal. Schelling introduced the idea of a 'focal point', a shared expectation of what we and our partners will think or do in a particular situation when we're trying to coordinate our behaviour. That is, for a given decision, each of us aims to do the same thing as our partner, knowing that our partner is also trying to coordinate with us. When Schelling asked his students what they would do in the New York City problem, they mostly chose such popular times and places that any pair would have a fair chance of successfully meeting up at the same time and place. We are surprisingly well attuned to solving coordination problems intuitively, even when they might seem impossible at first glance.

Of course, new focal points can rapidly emerge. If the two of us last met at a small café on East 76th Street, we might both turn up there, each hoping the other would remember our last meeting. The reason that 'Schelling games' work is that we all can rely on having similar brains and cognitive skills, and often similar background knowledge, norms, social conventions and other aspects of the hidden part of the communication iceberg. The same, too, goes for language games of any kind.

Charades, as well as communication more generally, is all about focal points. The charade creator produces a sequence of actions that could be interpreted in any number of ways. What matters is that a shared focal interpretation comes to mind for both the creator and the audience. When it does – the audience's guess is what the creator of the charade intended – the charade will have communicated its message successfully. If a focal point cannot be found, communication fails, and further actions are needed. As we've seen, communicating with language works in the same way. Language isn't a strict code where each message has a single, distinct meaning, but is a series of clues that can be interpreted with any amount of flexibility and creativity. The interpretation of today's clues depends on the interpretation of yesterday's clues, so that linguistic conventions gradually emerge.

LANGUAGE LEARNING
MEETS LANGUAGE EVOLUTION

Language is a communicative tool shaped by our brains, just as physical tools, like forks, saws and spades, have been perfectly shaped by cultural evolution to fit our hands, legs and body. Consider how the modern pair of scissors is so exquisitely adapted to the shape of our hands and to the precise task of cutting (so that they have taken on many different specialized forms: kitchen scissors, surgical scissors, nail scissors and so on). Over hundreds of years, scissors have been shaped by cultural evolution to be easy to use given the anatomy of our hands, to the point that they are differentiated in shape for use with the right and left hand. Indeed, Morten, who is right-handed and lives with a lefty, is painfully aware that a left-handed pair of scissors does not work well when used in the right hand. And because scissors are so well adapted to our anatomy, children can handle them with little instruction (though cutting neatly or in a straight line usually takes quite a bit of practice). By contrast, scissors are of absolutely no use to a cow with its hooves, a dog with its paws or a dolphin with its flippers. If we ignore the fact that scissors have been adapted to the cutting needs of previous generations of scissors users whose hands were the very same shape as ours, the ease with which both adults and children use scissors would seem exceedingly puzzling. But scissors are easy to learn to use precisely because they are not a haphazard arrangement of bits of metal or tools from a Martian civilization. Instead, they have been shaped by generations of past human users to be like focal points for our hands.

What works for scissors also works for language – both are superbly adapted by cultural evolution to be used by us.[2] To explain how language learning is possible, we must turn to language evolution. The immediacy of language, and the Now-or-Never bottleneck that it creates, implies that children must learn the patterns and meanings in language one chunk or construction at a time. And they must learn to extrapolate from past experiences to combine known bits of language and meaningful clues in new ways to make themselves understood and to grasp what others are saying. But how are children able to improvise in just the right way to join in with linguistic charades? The solution is beautifully simple: every current speaker was a child once. Children make the right generalizations because they do it in the same way as everyone else who came before them. The patterns of language that each generation has to learn have been created by previous generations of language users who had the very same abilities, limitations and predispositions. To learn language, like learning to use any other culturally evolved tool or product, you need only follow in the footsteps of others.

Not all learning, though, is cultural learning, where our task is to follow in each other's footsteps. To survive in the world, humans need to overcome two distinct challenges: we need to understand and navigate the natural world, and we need to coordinate with others in our community. The first, learning about the natural world, we call 'N-learning', and the second, learning about the cultural world, we call 'C-learning'.[3] In N-learning, the world provides the yardstick with which learning is measured. So, when we practise throwing a ball or a spear, what other people think or do has no effect on the outcome. Whether we hit the target or not depends on how our throwing ability measures up against gravity, air resistance and other external forces that affect the trajectory of the hurled object. N-learning is clearly important for human evolution – we must figure out how the physical world works in order to negotiate it properly. For example, we need to develop an understanding that objects persist (they do not magically disappear), that they have weight and momentum (important if one is tossed in your direction), and that they can causally influence other objects in specific ways (compare dropping a heavy object on your foot and dropping it in a pool of water). When it comes to N-learning, we're all lone amateur scientists, trying to figure out how to cope with the material world.[4]

By contrast, C-learning is about coordinating with other

people – people who are just like us. With C-learning, there is no predetermined universal 'truth' about what is right and wrong. The crucial thing is to do what others are doing, to discover the focal points of our community. The success or failure of C-learning depends on how well we learn the shared cultural conventions of our community and how we extrapolate those conventions to new cases. Consider the use of different head movements to signal agreement or disagreement in human interaction.[5] N-learning won't help here because there's no intrinsic meaning to a head nod or shake. Nodding one's head in northern Europe means 'yes', whereas in Greece it implies 'no'. And in many places across the globe, shaking your head signals 'no', but in Sri Lanka it is used to indicate general agreement. What matters here is that we adopt the same pattern of head movements as the people around us. When it comes to C-learning, we're not lone scientists seeking eternal truths. Rather, we are like musicians whose objective is not to attain perfect pitch but to be in tune with the rest of the orchestra.

Signalling agreement or disagreement might seem a matter of learning conventions by rote. But to play linguistic charades or to meet up in New York, we need to go far beyond rote learning – we need to extrapolate creatively from what we have seen, and to do so in the same way as everyone else. This process of extrapolation reveals a crucial difference between N-learning and C-learning. Imagine that an unknown process produced the sequence 1, 2, 3, . . . How might it continue? If we approach this question as a problem of N-learning, where we assume the data have come from some aspect of the natural world, with so few data points there are an infinite number of possibilities. Most likely, the continuation will be random – the fact that the observed sequence is ascending is pure chance. But suppose there is a pattern. It could be almost anything: a repeating string (1, 2, 3, 1, 2, 3, 1, . . .), an oscillating sequence (1, 2, 3, 2, 1, 2, 3, 2, 1, . . .) or a Fibonacci series (1, 2, 3, 5, 8, 13, 21, . . .); or it might simply get stuck (1, 2, 3, 3, 3, 3, 3, . . .). We just can't be sure.

If we instead view the sequence as part of a cultural product, where the key idea is to guess the same continuation as other people, then the answer comes readily to mind: 4, 5, 6, 7, 8, . . . This is what most people are likely to guess when asked to continue the sequence 1, 2, 3, . . . Solving the C-learning version of the problem is far easier. The obvious answer tends to be the right answer because it is also obvious to other people (who are, after all, just like us). In C-learning, our perceptual, cognitive, communicative and social predispositions, combined with our shared culture and past experiences, help us make the right guesses. We arrive at the shared focal points because we're simply aiming to coordinate with those who came before us, people who had the exact same propensities as we do now. But these very same predispositions are not necessarily helpful for N-learning and can often lead us astray when our guesses must arrive at an answer that is independent of our brains, bodies and social communities. With N-learning, the mere fact that we all jump to the same conclusion (e.g. that heavier objects fall faster) doesn't make it true. Whereas for C-learning, if we all arrive at the same conclusion, we must be right, because our objective is not to mirror nature but to mirror each other.

The distinction between C-learning and N-learning is crucial if we are to understand how language learning can work at all. As mentioned in chapter 4, psychologists and linguists have often viewed children as mini-linguists who are trying to figure out the grammar of their native language, much like a linguistic anthropologist tries to describe a newly encountered language.[6]

From this point of view, the puzzle is especially acute – each child seems to be a prodigy who masters patterns of language more comprehensively in the course of a normal childhood than 'real' linguists ever do, despite decades of scholarship. But this is entirely the wrong way of thinking about how language is learned. It treats language learning as a difficult problem of N-learning, as if the child were attempting to learn some aspect of the natural world, viewing language through the lens of an outside observer.

Language learning is possible not because there is some 'true' language independent of humans that we all aspire to learn, but because it is a matter of learning about an aspect of human culture. Learning language is a matter of C-learning, *not* N-learning. Rather than trying to discover an abstract grammar for their language from the collection of things they happen to hear people around them say, children are instead trying to work out how to use language in the same way as everyone else in their community to solve the communicative challenge of the moment. Playing linguistic charades is, after all, a paradigm example of C-learning. The trick is to create some communicative signal that the speaker and listener interpret *in the same way*. And this dramatically simplifies learning, because language, like any other aspect of culture, is the product of the learning done by previous generations.

Today's language is the product of yesterday's learners. To learn language, the child must coordinate with other learners, both present and past. Each generation only needs to follow in the footsteps of the last, so that our wild 'guesses' are likely to be the right ones because the right guess is the most popular guess made by the previous generation of learners. In doing so, the members of each new generation all follow the same path, and therefore will be able to coordinate successfully not only with previous generations but also with each other. When it comes to language learning, N-learning is like searching for lost keys in a vast city on a dark and moonless night; but for C-learning the challenge is simply for us all to find *each other*. And even though the lost keys could be anywhere, our fellow humans will be standing under the streetlight, for sure.

LAB-BASED GAMES OF TELEPHONE

The shared focal points of one's community, which are the targets of C-learning, are shaped by cultural evolution to fit our specific biological limitations and cultural expectations. Insights into how focal points can arise come from experimental work that cleverly redeploys the popular game of telephone ('Chinese whispers' in the UK) to recreate language evolution in the lab. In the telephone game, children form a line and the first player comes up with a word or message that they whisper into the ear of the next player, who then whispers what they heard (or think they heard) to the third player, and so on until the end of the line is reached. The last player then says aloud whatever they think they heard, and it is compared to what the first player really said. The word or message typically gets garbled along the way, often to humorous effect – hence the popularity of the game.

Nearly a century ago, the celebrated British psychologist Sir Frederic Charles Bartlett, the first professor of experimental psychology at the University of Cambridge, pioneered the use of the game of telephone to study cultural evolution.[7] He was interested in how background knowledge and cultural expectations can alter what we remember, and how this might change our collective memories across time. In one famous line of studies, he asked people to listen to and recall different indigenous folk tales, such as the Native American story 'The War of the Ghosts'. The first participant in a study would read an adaptation of the original tale and afterwards write down what they could recall from memory. The next person would read what the first person had written and then reproduce what they could remember, and so on, in a chain of ten or more people. The story changed substantially across 'generations' of participants, becoming much shorter and to the point, being transformed from a ghost story with many ethereal elements into a straightforward account of a fight and subsequent death, without any supernatural overtones. Over generations, Bartlett suggested, the tale had been adapted to the cultural expectations of the participants in the study. He also observed similar conventionalization of visual depictions when people were asked to draw pictures from memory. In one such case, the unfamiliar Egyptian hieroglyph 'mulak', which resembles an owl, was transmogrified over generations into a much more familiar-looking cat (see figure 6.1).

Some thirty years later, on the other side of the Atlantic, the American linguist and psychologist Erwin A. Esper adopted the game-of-telephone approach to study the role of social transmission in language change (independently of Bartlett's work, it seems).[8] He taught the first participant in his study an artificial language in which nonsense words, such as **pel** and **numbow**, labelled four abstract shapes that could be either red or green. The eight verbal labels were completely different from one another and contained no hints as to either colour or shape. After exposure to these label–shape combinations, the first person would then teach what they had learned to a second participant, who would teach a third, and so on, until there were

Original Drawing

Figure 6.1. Drawings from Bartlett's (1932) visual game-of-telephone study, showing reproductions 1 to 10, ordered left to right and top to bottom. The original drawing of an owl-like Egyptian hieroglyph gradually mutates into a cat.

forty-four people in the chain. At the end, the sound patterns for all but two of the words (**pel** and **shab**) had changed completely. Intriguingly, these changes were not random. People spontaneously began to denote the specific shape and colour using different chunks of sound. For example, shape (independently of colour) became associated with specific word endings, such as **-a** at the end of both labels for a half-moon-like shape and **-zh** (the **z** sound in **azure**) at the end of the two labels for an arrow-like figure. Something approaching a simple morphology-like pattern had emerged. Esper's fascinating study thus provides tantalizing hints about the origins of morphological patterning in language, where different parts of the word denote different aspects of meaning (such as shape).

One might have hoped that Esper's groundbreaking work would have sparked an exciting research programme to shed light on the emergence of language. Quite the opposite – his work was not followed up and is, sadly, largely forgotten today. But the research did get going in the end, albeit independently from Esper's work. From the late 2000s onward, researchers began in earnest to employ the game-of-telephone method to explore cultural evolution of language in the lab. The new wave of studies was initiated at the University of Edinburgh by Simon Kirby, the world's first ever professor of language evolution. More than a century after the Société de Linguistique de Paris banned the topic, the field of language evolution research is now respectable again.

Kirby and two other evolutionary linguists, Kenny Smith and Hannah Cornish, used miniature artificial languages to study whether cultural evolution across generations of learners can lead to the emergence of the kind of complex structure characteristic of language. In one study, they asked participants to learn an 'alien' language consisting of written labels for simple visual stimuli.[9] Instead of Esper's four shapes and two colours, they used three shapes (square, circle, triangle) in one of three colours (black, blue, red) and associated with an arrow indicating one of three kinds of motion (horizontal, bouncing, circular), resulting in twenty-seven different visual scenes (such as a blue circle bouncing or a red circle moving in a circular fashion). The first person was exposed to a set of randomly generated labels that were each between two and four syllables long (such as **luki, kilamo, kanehu** and **namopihu**). So, for example, a red horizontally moving circle might be presented with the label **namopihu**, and a circling black square might be labelled **kilamo**. After this training, the participant was asked to recall the label when shown a scene. The resulting pairing of recalled labels and scenes was then used as input for the next person who came into the lab, and so on, until there were ten generations in a chain.

So far, this is quite similar to Esper's pioneering study. But Kirby and his colleagues also introduced an important twist. They were interested in the phenomenon of compositionality: how language makes it possible for us to utter and understand new sentences by combining familiar components in novel ways. Compositionality is what allows us to conjure up an image corresponding to the unfamiliar sentence **The orange triangle with the purple stripe jumps over the moon**, because we know the meanings of **orange**, **triangle**, **jump**, etc., and the constructions that link them together. To force people to extrapolate to new examples from the alien language in a similar way, the evolutionary linguists deliberately withheld some of the label–scene combinations during training.

In its original form, the mini-language presented to the first learner had no compositionality whatsoever. Knowing that **kalakihu** refers to a bouncy blue triangle doesn't tell us anything about what a blue triangle doing a circular motion should be called. Here, even our very best guesses are bound to be wrong – the chance that we would somehow surmise that it is called **namola** is infinitesimally small. But, remarkably, the experiment worked: systematic patterns spontaneously emerged over generations of learners, enabling them to guess correctly the labels for visual scenes that they had not previously encountered.[10]

Generalization to new visual scenes was possible because the mini-language 'evolved' a compositional system, where labels varied systematically according to meaning. As in Esper's study, different parts of the labels came to denote different features of the visual scenes. In one mini-language, the labels evolved a three-part pattern – colour–shape–motion – where the first part of the string referred to colour, the middle to the shape and the ending to the motion. This means that exposure to just a few items would allow learners to extrapolate to new visual scenes. For example, if a red circle moving horizontally is referred to as **re-ene-ki**, a black square doing a circular motion is labelled **n-e-pilu** and a blue triangle bouncing along is called **l-aki-plo**, then we can confidently guess that a blue triangle going around in a circle should be named **l-aki-pilu** (hyphens inserted to indicate the three parts of the labels; see figure 6.2). This shows the power of compositionality.

These game-of-telephone studies with artificial languages demonstrate how compositional linguistic systems, where meanings are constructed from elementary components, can emerge spontaneously without anyone intending to create such a system. In fact, the participants did not even know that their responses would be passed on to the next person in a multigenerational chain.

But what about more complex linguistic structures such as the ubiquitous multiword sequences – **cup of coffee**, **fire engine red**, **how are you** – that we discussed earlier? We use such multiword sequences all the time, but where do they come from? The answer is chunking, the memory-based ability we use to overcome the Now-or-Never bottleneck. With Hannah Cornish, Rick Dale and Simon Kirby, Morten conducted a game-of-telephone experiment to determine whether such memory limitations *alone*, amplified across generations of learners, can result in the emergence of reusable chunks, just like in language.[11]

Students at the University of Edinburgh were invited to take

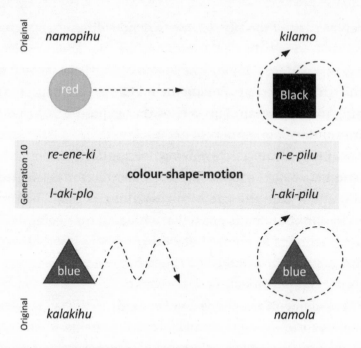

Figure 6.2. Examples of the visual scenes from the Edinburgh game-of-telephone experiment. The labels shown at the top and at the bottom are the original ones that the first learner saw. The labels within the grey bar in the middle were generated by the learner from the tenth generation. Whereas the original labels were random combinations of syllables, labels in the final generation had incorporated compositionality: the first substring indicated the colour; the middle part, the shape; and the ending, the motion – creating the order: colour-shape-motion. (Note that the hyphens were not used by the learners but are inserted here to reveal the compositional structure of the labels.)

part in a memory experiment, with no mention of language or cultural evolution. Seated in front of a computer, the first learner was shown fifteen random strings each consisting of three to five consonants – such as BRG, FGLB, RVFBR – displayed one by one on the screen. After each string had disappeared, the participant was asked to type it in from memory. This same process went on until the participant had seen all the strings six times, after which they were given a surprise memory test: they had to recall all fifteen different consonant strings as well as they could. Whatever strings the first learner typed in (right or wrong) then served as input for the second person who came into the lab, and their responses were in turn used as input for the third participant, and so on, until there were ten learners in a chain. The task of recalling the fifteen strings was not easy. The first learners in each chain could correctly remember fewer than four strings on average. But the learners in the final generation could accurately recall twice as many. Note that there's no meaning here to help out as in the other game-of-telephone experiments where letter strings were paired with visual images. So, what's going on? How did the evolved strings become so much more memorable?

When Morten and his colleagues analysed the recalled strings across generations, they discovered that multi-letter chunks had emerged. With time, these chunks ended up being recycled over and over again – just as multiword constructions are in language. Indeed, the strings from the final generation exhibited a pattern of chunk reuse that closely resembled the way parents repeatedly use the same chunks when talking to their children, such as 'are you' in **are you hungry**, **are you sleepy**, or 'I like your' in **I like your drawing**, **I like your car**. Even though this memory experiment involved meaningless strings of consonants, language-like chunk reuse emerged as the strings were repeatedly squeezed through the Now-or-Never bottleneck. Strings that recycled more easily remembered chunks proliferated at the cost of less memorable one-of-a-kind strings. Repeated cultural transmission from one learner to the next can thus amplify the effects of memory limitations and give rise to the patterns of chunk reuse that we see in language.

These game-of-telephone experiments show that cultural transmission can help explain the emergence of reusable chunks in multiword constructions and the compositional structure of language. Both properties arise from the 'struggle for existence' that Charles Darwin talked about: labels or chunks that are more easily remembered and more communicatively useful survive because they fit a systematic pattern. In this way, cultural evolution gives us design without a designer, demonstrating how language can evolve when generations of learners follow in each other's footsteps. Cultural evolution is what makes language learning possible in the first place. It tailors language for C-learning by creating linguistic focal points that children can home in on, with sufficient exposure. In other words, to adapt the evolutionary biologist Dobzhansky's famous phrase: nothing in language learning makes sense except in the light of cultural evolution.[12]

WORDS ARE NOT ENOUGH

Looking at language through the lens of cultural evolution allows us to see language learning in a completely new light. Language no longer needs to come pre-programmed in our genes or built into our neural wiring. Gone, too, is the idea of the child as a budding theoretical linguist who tries to acquire language through N-learning. Instead, we have seen that the child is a developing language *user* following in the footsteps of others. Language learning is possible because language has been shaped by cultural evolution to fit children's particular abilities for C-learning. The child no more needs to know a 'theory' about the spontaneous order that arises in patterns of language than a pond needs a theory of wave motion to display the complex interference patterns of ripples on its surface.

Viewing language learning as a practical problem doesn't trivialize the challenge that children face when learning their native language. On the contrary, it highlights just how much effort each of us has put into mastering our mother tongue. The superb command of language that every child achieves comes from using language over and over again for tens of thousands of hours (the two hundred hours that SF, the random digit recall wizard from chapter 2, spent perfecting his memory skills pale in comparison). Keeping up with the fast-paced back-and-forth nature of turn-taking in everyday conversations requires huge amounts of practice as we learn to squeeze language through the narrow funnel of the Now-or-Never bottleneck. It is through repeated experience talking with each other that we develop our ability quickly to chunk the input while listening and apply the just-in-time strategy to string together chunks of language when speaking. What matters for language learning is practice, practice and more practice.

In a famous study from 1995, psychologists Betty Hart and Todd Risley set out to measure how much experience with language US children got at home and whether it might differ across families from different social backgrounds.[13] They visited the homes of forty-two families for an hour every month over a period of two and a half years and recorded how many words were spoken around the children. Extrapolating from these hourly counts, they found that by the end of their third year of life, children growing up in families on public assistance would have heard on average about thirteen million words. By contrast, children from high-income families would have been exposed to more than three times this amount: an estimated forty-five million words. So by the time they turned four, children growing up in low-income families had heard thirty million fewer words than their peers from high-income families.

Hart and Risley found that this difference mattered. The more words the children heard during their first four years of life, the larger their vocabulary size: the high-income children knew more than twice as many words as the low-income children. Because of its effect on vocabulary size, the disparity in language input was met with much alarm and dubbed the 'thirty-million-word gap'. Since then, it has received a lot of attention from academics, policy-makers and educators alike, all seeking ways to bridge this gap for low-income children.

Subsequent studies using a larger number of families have found that, irrespective of their income level, there are large amounts of variation among individual families in how many words kids hear. It turns out that the families in the Hart and Risley study represented the extreme ends of the income scales: the thirty-million-word gap appears only when comparing the top 2 per cent with the bottom 2 per cent of families. Still, there remains a very sizeable four-million-word gap between children from low-income families and those from high-income homes by four years of age. And this four-million-word gap even came up during the 2019 Democratic primaries, when presidential candidate Joe Biden urged parents to 'make sure that kids hear words. A kid coming from a very poor school – a very poor background will hear four million words fewer spoken by the time they get there [to school].'[14]

We want to stress that the word gap, no matter how big it is, does not imply that low-income children don't develop normal language abilities – far from it. Every healthy child grows up to become an expert in the language of their community. In fact, everyday language use requires knowledge of a surprisingly small number of words. Analyses of conversational language have shown that a mere one thousand words account for about 90 per cent of everything we say to each other. This means that if we know the one thousand most frequently used words in our speech community, we'll have no problem conversing with our family over the dinner table, gossiping with neighbours or chatting with work colleagues. The same goes for grasping what goes on in most TV shows.[15] And, of course, most children and adults know many more words than this.

Vocabulary size does matter, though, for reading and literacy – especially in academic contexts, where knowledge of specialized vocabulary is needed to excel. On top of that, the ways of speaking in different low-income communities may not match the preferred ways of expressing oneself in an educational setting. Differences in such 'registers' may thus undercount the number of words that low-income children actually know because vocabulary measures typically assess words geared towards education. When combined with other challenges facing low-income families, from poverty to systemic racism, we can begin to see why early vocabulary size has been found to be a good predictor of how well children from low-income backgrounds do in school.[16] It's not that these children do not have normal language skills, but rather that they don't have the kind of vocabulary that is valued in educational settings.

But for all this talk about words – words children hear and words they know – we're only dealing with the tip of the communication iceberg. Even more to the point, words are only the tip of the tip, leaving aside the innumerable multiword constructions and how we combine them into sentences. It is perhaps not surprising, then, that most efforts to alleviate the word gap have missed the mark because they have tended to focus almost entirely on increasing the quantity of words that children hear. But what really matters is giving children more opportunities to *practise* their language skills. If more words were the solution, then simply sitting children down in front of the TV or having them listen to audiobooks would solve the problem. But according to the language-as-charades viewpoint, that is unlikely to work. This is backed up by studies showing that children learn new words not from passively watching videos, but only when they are actively involved in back-and-forth conversation with others.[17] Children are not empty vessels waiting to be filled up with words. What they need is interactive, playful, engaging conversation.

Several recent studies with infants and toddlers indeed show that it is the number of engaged interactions toddlers have that predicts their later language skills, not simply the number of words they overhear in the home.[18] For example, a pioneering study by Rachel Romeo from Harvard University underscores the importance of interaction in language learning.[19] Using a small digital recording device that could be placed in a child's shirt pocket, she and her colleagues recorded everything that was said to children over a weekend. Then, the children's language skills were tested and their brain activity was recorded. Romeo found that it was the amount of turn-taking in which the child participated that predicted their language skills, not how many words the parents said or the number of words that the children uttered themselves. She even discovered that how much we engage kids in conversation has a measurable impact on their brains. Specifically, the more conversational interactions a child had, the stronger the activation of their Broca's area. This highlights the importance of our experience with language as a major developmental driver of the network of brain regions (including Broca's area) that support linguistic communication, as discussed in the previous chapter. Just as practice is key to becoming an expert in digit recall or any other learned skill, so too repeated interactive language experience is crucial to becoming a competent player of linguistic charades.

THE SOCIAL FOUNDATION OF LANGUAGE LEARNING

To get the full picture of how children learn their native tongue, we cannot rely on studying only children growing up in the United States, Europe, Japan or similar rich, educated, industrialized countries. Most of what we know about language learning is based on studying children from these countries, even though the inhabitants of these countries make up only about 12 per cent of the world's population.[20] Fortunately, this is changing now. There has been a recent wave of field work in the language sciences where globetrotting researchers have begun to investigate language learning in rural and indigenous communities.

As these intrepid researchers travelled to far-flung places to observe and record linguistic interactions involving young children, their initial findings seemed to support earlier reports by ethnologists suggesting that adults in these communities didn't talk much to their children until they could talk back.[21] But later, more careful analyses have revealed surprisingly few differences in how much children are talked to across the world. For example, children growing up learning Tseltal Mayan in a subsistence farming community in southern Mexico are talked to just as much as children growing up learning English in the United States, Canada or the United Kingdom, and children learning Spanish in Argentina.[22]

Some differences did emerge. Compared to children learning English, Spanish and Tseltal, children learning Yélî Dnye on the remote Rossel Island in Papua New Guinea were spoken to less, but this did not affect their language learning. A study by Marisa Casillas from the Max Planck Institute for Psycholinguistics demonstrated that these children reached their language-learning milestones at the same times as other children.[23] They say their earliest recognizable words around their first birthday, and a month or two later they utter their very first multiword chunks, just like their peers in the United States, Europe, Japan and elsewhere.

This leaves us with a conundrum: why does reduced language input not hamper language learning among the children on Rossel Island? How do the children learning Yélî Dnye manage to learn more from less? Let's start by dispelling the idea that perhaps Yélî Dnye is easier to learn than, say, English and therefore can be learned with less input. If anything, English is easier to learn, for both children and non-native speakers, compared to languages like Yélî Dnye. Indeed, the latter has over ninety unique speech sounds, whereas English has less than half that. English has a few so-called irregular verbs that change their sound pattern when used in the present and past tenses – such as **go → went, eat → ate** and **sing → sang** – but most verbs simply add **-ed** for the past tense, as in **jump → jumped, talk → talked** and **laugh → laughed.** By contrast, Yélî Dnye uses irregular verb forms extensively, leading to a highly complex morphology full of exceptions. If we place English and Yélî Dnye on a scale from simple to complex verb morphology, English ends up near the simple end and Yélî Dnye falls at the opposite, complex end. Add to that several other grammatical complexities not found in English, and we can begin to appreciate 'the reputation [Yélî Dnye] has of being impossible to learn, whether by Papua New Guinean or by foreigner', as noted by the Australian field linguist James Henderson, who lived on Rossel Island and studied this language.[24]

But if Yélî Dnye is much more complex than English, why are the children of Rossel Island able to learn their native language competently with reduced input? This is where we have to move beyond the standard transmission view of language, which focuses only on the tip of the communication iceberg while ignoring the hidden part that is crucial for becoming a competent language user. As we discussed in chapter 1, words are mere clues to meaning, to be combined with all the other clues from context, what came before and what we have learned about the world, to reach an understanding of what is being said. Although words and utterances are important, what matters more is the broader socialization into the culture of our community. There can be no focal points and no C-learning in the absence of such socialization.

To follow in the footsteps of others and take part in the conversational dance, we need to share the cultural norms, customs, conventions, social taboos and endless unspoken rules of the society into which we're born. And whereas Captain Cook and the Hausch showed that charades can be based purely on our common humanity, the more we share with our conversational partners, the easier it is to play linguistic charades. Without the socialization that comprises the hidden part of the communication iceberg, the individual words and utterances that make up its tip would sink into unintelligibility.

To see why socialization matters, consider the word **uncle**. In English, **uncle** normally refers to your mother's brother or your father's brother. **Uncle** can be used in this way in Danish as well (**onkel**), but you can also use more specific terms: **morbror** is used to talk about your mother's brother, whereas **farbror** is used to refer to your father's brother. Some languages require speakers to pay even closer attention to the family tree and the age of their relatives. In Hindi, your father's brother is called **chacha** (चाचा), but if he is older than your father, the term is **tau** (ताऊ). Your mother's brother is called **mama** (मामा), no matter what age he is. Men married into the family are not called **uncle**. Your father's sister's husband is called **phupha** (फूफा), and your mother's sister's husband is **mausa** (मौसा). Indeed, while the word **uncle** is often used to refer to male friends of the family, even in the absence of any familial relationship by blood or marriage, accidentally calling your **chacha** 'uncle' would be a major faux pas. To complicate matters further, the term **brother** is often extended to cousins, as in **cousin-brother**, meaning that the cousin of your mother is also considered to be her brother and therefore should be called **mama**. And as if this weren't enough, the suffix **-ji** (जी) is sometimes added to the end of a kinship term to signal respect – as in **tauji**, **mamaji** and **phuphaji** – but its exact usage differs from family to family. Thus, even using a simple term such as **uncle** in many cases requires considerable knowledge about family relationships as well as other social rules and cultural conventions specific to one's community.

In many rural and indigenous cultures, children are ordinarily socialized into their community through direct involvement in the day-to-day life of their families and the general goings-on in the village. For example, during the first year of life, children who are learning Yélî Dnye on Rossel Island are carried around in the arms of caregivers as they go about their daily business.[25] From two years onwards, children roam around independently in groups, playing games, frolicking in a nearby river, and foraging for shellfish, wild nuts and fruits near the village to help supplement their family's subsistence farming. In this way, they can pick up names for important foods, plants and animals from having concrete experiences with them, and learn the relevant expressions for how to prepare, find, catch or avoid them. They also learn the local norms, rituals and taboos by observing them in action and overhearing other children and adults discussing them. By being tightly integrated into the daily life of the community, children on Rossel Island build up the necessary social and real-world knowledge they need to get the most out of the reduced input they receive.

Young children in industrialized societies, by contrast, are generally more isolated from the everyday lives of their family, apart from helping out with the occasional chore, like tidying up or helping with the dishes.[26] Instead, a lot of their socialization takes place outside the family in nurseries and schools, where language, literacy and academic accomplishments are given considerably more weight. In such non-family settings, the quantity and type of linguistic input are likely to matter more. In other words, in industrialized societies more of the knowledge about social mores, cultural conventions and informal practices is learned *through* language, rather than through direct engagement with the community at large. And this may be why the degree of linguistic interaction with adult caregivers in these societies turns out to be crucial – these adults provide children with the concepts and vocabulary for things that are not part of their world, and hence prepare them for the world of literacy and formal education.

We have already mentioned that simply increasing the number of words that low-income children hear is not likely to be of much help. However, Casillas's meticulous research on language learning by indigenous children in Papua New Guinea suggests another possible solution. In her studies, she found that the input that children received from adults was not simply spread equally across the whole day, like a slow, steady trickle, but instead was concentrated in intense bursts of interaction, brief cascades of back-and-forth turn-taking, often around mealtimes and other family social occasions. Concentrating linguistic interaction in short bursts like this may very well allow children to maximize their learning even from limited input. Indeed, children are better at learning and using new words when these appear multiple times in 'bursty' contexts, where the same word is repeated in successive utterances, such as 'Look at the **dog**! This **dog** is so sweet. I love that **dog**.'[27] The combination of short, engaged language-learning opportunities during routine social interactions and the way they're spread out in intermittent spurts throughout the day may provide the children learning Yélî Dnye with close to optimal conditions for learning their native language from relatively little input.

All parents, no matter where they're from or how much money they earn, want a bright future for their children. Unfortunately, many children and their parents face major obstacles to success owing to poverty, discrimination, systemic racism and other societal factors. Only real policy changes can resolve these issues, but perhaps we might also draw some lessons from the children growing up on Rossel Island. For starters, we shouldn't simply ask parents to talk more *to* their children; instead, we should encourage them to find small chunks of time here and there for engaged conversations *with* their kids. The key is not quantity but quality: concentrated bursts of interaction spread out across the day.[28] Mealtimes provide an excellent opportunity to talk with children, as do bathtime and other moments when adults and children are together. Even something as mundane as grocery shopping can be used to chat with children about what we buy, what it's for and how we use it.

With young children, it is easier to keep them engaged in conversation when we talk about what they are currently focusing on. They learn more when you don't try to steer the conversation away from what they're interested in. If the child is playing with a teddy bear, talk with them about this, not whatever else you might find more interesting. It might make for some tedious conversations in the short term, but can make a real difference in the long run. And once children have learned a relatively broad vocabulary (roughly around four years of age), parents can help them learn more abstract ideas by relating the relevant concepts to things in their everyday lives. For example, to support children's grasp of the past and the future, talk with them about things they know and remember, such as 'You gave me a drawing for Father's Day last year,' or 'You're going to be five in two months.' If these suggestions are on the right track, and there is growing evidence that they are, then this opens up a new path for improving language skills in children.[29] In fact, this is a path that we should probably take anyway – after all, irrespective of any impact on language, it can only make our interactions with kids more fun, pleasant and meaningful.

◉

It's time we retired once and for all the old adage 'children should be seen, not heard'. In the context of language learning, it incorrectly supposes that children are mere sponges, passively sucking up language input. Instead, we should engage children as much as possible in everyday interactions so that they can learn the improvisational language skills and socialization needed for linguistic charades and conversational dancing. Even though C-learning makes language learning easier, children still require substantial experience with the language of their community to learn their mother tongue. It takes time, experience and practice for children to become competent linguistic musicians who can play in tune with the rest of the communicative orchestra.

This is not to say that there's a one-size-fits-all solution to language learning across the globe. Children learn language by following in the footsteps of others just like themselves – but cultural evolution can lead us in many different directions: to Danish, English, Hindi, Tseltal, Yélî Dnye or any of the world's other seven thousand or so languages in all their astonishing variety. It is this fundamental diversity in the ways that we, as humans, can express ourselves that sets language apart from the myriad other communication systems found in nature. But the diversity of our most remarkable cultural creation doesn't stop there. As we shall see in the next chapter, there is a very real sense in which we all speak our own unique language that lives and dies with us.

7

ENDLESS FORMS
MOST BEAUTIFUL

From so simple a beginning endless forms most beautiful
and most wonderful have been, and are being, evolved.

CHARLES DARWIN,
On the Origin of Species by Means of Natural Selection (1859)

Imagine that you all of a sudden found yourself in utter darkness
unable to see, in complete silence unable to hear, with your
tongue tied unable to speak, and with your senses of taste and
smell gone, too. Your only remaining connection to the world is
through your sense of touch. Devastating as this may seem for
someone who has sampled life for many years through combinations of sights, sounds, flavours and odours, you'd still have
the ability to use language. Although it would be hard to understand others, you could at least make yourself understood by
writing down what you wanted to say. But imagine that this sensory loss happened when you were just two years of age, before

you had developed much command of spoken language, let alone spelling. This was the fate of Laura Bridgman.[1]

Laura was born in 1829 on a farming homestead on the outskirts of Hanover, New Hampshire. She was a frail child, small and skinny. When she was two, the Bridgmans contracted scarlet fever and two of her siblings died. Although it was touch and go for Laura for a while, she survived. But the fever took away her sight, her hearing, and most of her senses of taste and smell. Whatever little language she had learned before the fever soon disappeared, too, and she became mute within a year. Her physical recovery took two years and left her thin and delicate-looking – with her sense of touch as her only connection to the world. Still, she was a spirited child, who used an old boot for a doll and a few rudimentary gestures to communicate with her family.

Charles Dickens would later describe Laura's world: it was, he wrote, as if she were 'in a marble cell, impervious to any ray of light, or particle of sound; with her poor white hand peeping through a chink in the wall, beckoning to some good man for help, that an Immortal soul might be awakened'.[2] This awakening came when she was seven. Dr Samuel Gridley Howe learned of Laura's unfortunate story and brought her to the Perkins School for the Blind in Boston, where he was the director. At that time, deaf–blind individuals were considered to be unreachable imbeciles, destined for a non-communicative existence in silence and darkness. Howe was eager to showcase the power of the human mind by demonstrating that a deaf–blind child could learn language.

Rather than using some kind of sign language, where every object or situation would get its own sign, Howe decided to teach Laura English words spelled out using raised letters that could be differentiated by touch. To begin, he would label common objects, such as spoon, knife, book and key, with these letters.

Laura soon learned to associate each object with its corresponding letter sequence, so that when handed the detached labels she
would carefully place them by the right object: SPOON would be
placed on the spoon, BOOK on the book, KEY on the key and so
on. Next, Howe gave her each raised letter on a separate piece of
paper, arranged next to one another to spell the words she knew:
S-P-O-O-N, B-O-O-K, K-E-Y. All the letters were then mixed up in
a pile, and Laura was prompted to order them into the labels for
the objects she knew. It took a while, but she eventually learned
to do this too. Eventually, Howe reported that, after several
weeks of determinedly imitating her teacher, Laura had an
epiphany: 'The truth began to flash upon her – her intellect
began to work – she perceived that here was a way by which she
could herself make up a sign of anything that was in her own
mind, and show it to another mind.'[3]

Once Laura had grasped the idea that things have names and
that we can use language to talk about them with each other, she
was eager to learn words for everything in her world. Howe then
introduced her to finger spelling, where the 'speaker' uses the
fingers of one hand to form individual letters, and the 'listener'
places their hand over the speaker's hand to feel the shape being
signalled. Laura quickly mastered finger spelling, liberating her
burgeoning language skills from the confines of her desk where
the raised letters were kept. She could now 'finger-talk' wherever
and whenever she wanted – and because her inquisitive mind was
insatiable, she was soon pestering everyone with an unending
stream of questions. Laura even learned how to write by hand.

With a certain flair for publicity, Howe described Laura's ever-
growing language abilities in the Perkins School annual reports.
Her linguistic awakening captured the public's imagination, and
she soon became a household name in America. Laura's fame

turned international after Charles Dickens met her in 1842 while touring North America and told her story in his travelogue *American Notes for General Circulation*. She remained one of the most famous women in the world for the rest of the 1840s. People in the thousands would attend Perkins exhibition days, where Laura would demonstrate her language skills, and clamour for her autograph, some of her writing, even strands of her hair. Girls created their own 'Laura' dolls by poking the doll's eyes out and tying a green ribbon across them, just like the real Laura did.

Today, Laura Bridgman has been all but forgotten. Her accomplishments are now overshadowed by those of Helen Keller, who fifty years later would go through the same journey as Laura and of whom many erroneously think as the first deaf–blind person to learn English. But it was Laura who in the early 1880s taught Anne Sullivan the finger-spelling skills that she would later use to bring Keller into the world of language.

Laura's case is not just a wonderful illustration of the triumph of the human spirit but also a telling example of the spectacular resilience and flexibility of our language ability. For starters, she may be the only person whose initial introduction to language was through the printed word. Normally, we only learn to read once we have a decent mastery of spoken language. For Laura, it was the opposite: her entry into language was through written language – even when she learned finger spelling, she still had to spell out each word she wanted to say (unlike current sign languages, where finger spelling is used only sparingly). Laura's language also had a number of other idiosyncrasies. For example, she often coined words. When being taught the meaning of 'alone', she was asked to go to her room and return alone. She did as told. Soon thereafter she wanted to go with one of her friends and said 'Laura go **al-two**!'[4] And although Laura had been taught 'standard' English, she would often use her own abbreviations and leave out words to speed up communication.

The fact that Laura was able to create her own unique language – while still being understood by those around her – is a testament to one of the most fundamental properties of human linguistic communication: its immense variety and adaptability. Because language doesn't unfold according to a genetic blueprint but emerges through cultural evolution (as discussed in chapter 5), languages are free to vary as long as they can squeeze through the narrow funnel of the Now-or-Never bottleneck and are anchored in the submerged part of the communication iceberg.[5] The widespread heterogeneity of human language – its 'endless forms most beautiful' – is perhaps the one true hallmark that sets it apart from all other communication systems found on Earth. But we can only fully appreciate just how unique the diversity and flexibility of human language are when we compare language with the much more uniform and fixed nature of non-human communication systems. Despite the spectacular diversity in ways of communicating used by different organisms, there is precious little variation among individuals within a given species in how they communicate with each other.

ENDLESS WAYS TO COMMUNICATE

Communication may be almost as old as life itself, probably originating in chemical signalling between archaea, primitive unicellular organisms that have no cell nuclei. Among the archaea we find many so-called extremophiles, that is, organisms that not only survive but also decidedly thrive in extreme environments that are otherwise inhospitable to life.[6] These extremophiles have been discovered living in deep-sea hydrothermal vents, an environment with no light, bone-crushing pressure, and boiling temperatures thought to resemble the forbidding conditions when life first appeared over four billion years ago. Some archaea flourish in high temperatures, such as *Strain 121*, named so because it grows just fine at 121° Celsius (250° Fahrenheit), the temperature used to sterilize medical instruments. Others, like *Thermococcus piezophilus*, live at a pressure of 1,283 atmospheres, which is close to the pressure that is likely to crush a granite floor (1 atmosphere is roughly the atmospheric pressure at sea level). But chemical signalling occurs even in these extraordinary circumstances. Archaea interact with each other using special signalling molecules that allow them to sense how many members of their own species (and sometimes even other species) are in their 'neighbourhood'. Such 'quorum sensing', which is also used by bacteria and fungi, allows simple organisms to coordinate their behaviour in adaptive ways by turning specific genes on and off, thereby changing their behaviour appropriately for crowded or sparsely populated conditions. Quorum sensing may very well have been the earliest form of communication to emerge on our planet.

The message in quorum sensing is a simple 'I'm here!' But chemical messages can also be more specific. Plants, for example, use chemical signals to warn their fellow plants of threats. When a tall goldenrod plant (a member of the sunflower family that grows wild across many parts of the United States) is attacked by the larvae of the goldenrod beetle, it releases airborne organic compounds that trigger defensive chemical reactions in nearby plants (and may also repel the attacking insect or attract its natural predators).[7] Chemical signalling is also widespread among insects. Indeed, ant and termite societies are built on an incredibly intricate and ever-changing network of chemical interactions that enable a colony to behave as one complex and coherent organism.

Some insects also send signals outside the chemical domain, such as the famous 'bee language', the discovery of which earned the Austrian ethologist Karl von Frisch a Nobel Prize.[8] The angle and duration of the bee's waggle dance indicate the direction and distance to the food source, with the vigour of rear-end waggling denoting the amount and/or quality of the resource. The waggle dance conveys an impressively complex message about the location and quality of a food source – and moves animal communication a tiny step, perhaps, in the direction of human language. Interestingly, bees also use their waggle dance as a kind of quorum sensing when deciding on a new location for their nest: scouts fan out in search of a nest site and upon their return use the rapidity and length of their dance to signal their enthusiasm for a found location, encouraging others to check it out. Over time, the better sites have more and more bees dancing in their favour until a quorum of 'votes' is reached in favour of a certain location, and the whole swarm sets off to move there. No individual bee decides where the swarm should move – communication allows a sort of 'bee democracy', a decentralized decision-making strategy that is widespread in social insects.

Visual communication is widely used across animal species, from the choreographed movements of the bee waggle dance and the deliberate manual gestures of apes to the blinking bioluminescent patterns of fireflies on a summer's night and the happy 'play-bow' posture of a dog waiting for a stick to be thrown. But when it comes to visual displays, the common cuttlefish, *Sepia officinalis*, is a true artist.[9] This cephalopod, an invertebrate marine mollusc that resembles a squid, with eight arms and two tentacles, is a master of camouflage and has been nicknamed 'chameleon of the sea'. It generates complex communicative signals by adopting one or more of thirty-four chromatic patterns of skin colouration (such as dark zebra stripes), changing its skin texture (coarse, smooth, etc.), varying its posture (such as waving its arms) and performing an action (like spewing ink). Male cuttlefish use these communicative signals both to attract females and to fend off other males. The signals can be used for deception as well. Remarkably, a small male cuttlefish can display a female pattern on one side (thus distracting a nearby larger rival male), while showing his best male courtship pattern on the other side that faces a female. And such sexual mimicry works: being a Janus-faced cuttlefish really can increase the chances of successful mating.

Then there is auditory communication. Vervet monkeys are famous for their predator alarm calls.[10] These East African monkeys have evolved three separate calls to signal the presence of different kinds of predators: leopards (or other similar carnivores), eagles (or other aerial predators) and snakes. These distinct alarm calls elicit three different kinds of evasive actions, appropriate for defence against the relevant predator. When hearing the 'chirp' signal for a leopard, vervets run high up into the trees to safety. But when they hear the 'rraup' call that denotes an eagle, they instead look to the sky and seek cover in nearby bushes. And when they hear the 'chutter' sound of a snake call, they stand up on their hind legs to spot the serpent. Although the ability to produce these alarm calls appears to be built-in, young vervet monkeys still need to learn to use them correctly. For example, infant and juvenile vervet monkeys often initially use the leopard call indiscriminately for any terrestrial animal – whether predator or not – and only later use it just for leopards. In other words, although the vervet monkeys can produce only instinctive calls to communicate, they appear to have some cognitive flexibility in terms of how they use them.

More evidence for such cognitive flexibility comes from the West African green monkeys, cousins of the vervet monkeys.[11] They also use separate alarm calls for snakes and leopards, but apparently have none for aerial predators. However, when researchers flew a drone near these monkeys, they emitted a call resembling the 'rraup' sound that vervet monkeys produce for eagles, even though the two species of monkeys share no overlap in their geographical ranges and diverged from a common ancestor some 3.5 million years ago.[12] In fact, subsequent acoustic analyses revealed that the vervet monkey eagle call was almost indistinguishable from the green monkey's drone call, suggesting that the drone activated an innate aerial predator response. Intriguingly, when the researchers later played back the drone calls from a hidden speaker, the green monkeys looked up into the sky and quickly hid. So, even though these non-human primates are severely limited when it comes to vocal learning – in the sense that they seem unable to come up with new calls – they are nonetheless skilled perceptual learners, able to repurpose an ancient alarm call for a new threat.

Although such predator calls have been highlighted as a possible precursor to human language, the difference between the modest flexibility evidenced by the green monkey's drone call and the communicative cornucopia of charades is vast.[13] Charades can be invented, corrected and reused on the spot so that a single gesture can indicate a book, a film, a person or a historical event because it draws on the shared knowledge of the specific players involved – and on charades they have played in the past. It is this ingenuity, rather than simple fixed signals such as alarm calls, that provides the foundation for human language.

Monkeys are not generally known for their vocal learning abilities, but songbirds are expert performers – and, at first, the complexity of birdsong may seem a little closer to what we see in human language. Consider the virtuosity of the common nightingale, a smallish brown songbird with a reddish tail that breeds in an area stretching from western Europe to Mongolia and over-winters in sub-Saharan Africa. It produces one of the most beautiful songs of any bird, replete with mellow sequences and, to quote an evocative passage from one academic review, with 'some phrases clear and fluty, others bubbling, churring, rattling or chattering, one a low, long-drawn, repeated whistle ("**wuuu**") that increases rapidly in volume and speed of delivery and ends with flourish,' as illustrated in the following transliteration:

pichu-pichu-pichu-pichurrrrrrr-chí!, wiiit-chuk-chuk-chuk-chuk-chuk-chuk-chí!, wuuuuuuuuuu-wuuuuu-wuu-wuwu-twík!, chatatatatatatatatatatatatat, chiiyo-chiiyo-chiiyo-chiiyo-chí![14]

For centuries, the nightingale's alluring song has inspired poets and writers, from Homer and Ovid to Milton, and from Keats to Hans Christian Andersen's stirring fairytale *The Nightingale*, adapted by Igor Stravinsky into the symphonic poem *The Song of the Nightingale*.[15] And, of course, the very fact that we talk of birdsong rather than, say, 'bird music' suggests a link with language – songs have words, after all.

Another apparent parallel with language is that songbirds, such as the nightingale, don't just produce a rigid song pattern that is coded into their genes – they learn their song from others. Although it was previously thought that only males sang, to attract females and ward off competitors, recent research has shown that in most of the world's songbirds, both males and females sing.[16] They do so not only to attract potential mates and mark their territory but also to maintain pair bonds, for example through duetting, where two partners take turns singing together, sometimes switching back and forth so seamlessly that their song sounds as if it were coming from a single bird. Given that each bird picks up its songs from others, with inevitable variations and imperfections, this allows for the possibility that the repertoire of songs in a population of birds can vary over both time and geography. This sounds a lot like a case of cultural evolution and at first glance appears to provide a counterexample to our claim that human language is unique among the world's communication systems in its spectacular within-species diversity.

But not so fast! Birds' 'songs' have nothing like the meaningful (if sometimes trite) lyrics found in human songs – they are in fact 'bird music', not 'birdsong'. The streams of words in human language have particular meanings, and from those streams of words and their relation to each other we can form an infinity of messages. But the communicative function of birdsong is much more restricted. The **pichus** and **chuk-chís** of the nightingale are not words and phrases conveying some hidden coded message. Instead, they are more like musical notes and phrases whose purpose is to *display* the virtuosity and therefore attractiveness of the singer. Unlike the monkey alarm calls and the bee waggle dance, birds' songs do not vary systematically to alert others to the presence of danger, the location of food or any other aspect of the environment.[17] Indeed, some songbirds incorporate songs from other species. The grandly named superb lyrebird can pick up environmental sounds from nearby construction sites, like the sounds of a hammer, chainsaw, power drill or leaf blower, even a worker's whistling, and add them to its song repertoire.[18] These chunks of sound add to the richness of the bird's song – and listeners will no doubt be suitably impressed. But no message other than the general quality of the singer is being conveyed.

Moreover, it turns out that the parallel with cultural (and potentially linguistic) evolution is not as striking as it might seem. First, though many songbirds learn by imitation, local 'dialects' have been found in only a few species.[19] Second, whereas human languages differ from one another in almost every conceivable way, the dialects of songbirds are really just slight variations on a theme. For example, black-capped chickadees sing a 'hey sweetie' song across most of North America, but on Martha's Vineyard, an island off the coast of Massachusetts, they tweet 'sweetie hey'. Third, where there are marked differences among dialects, these are often found in isolated populations and associated with genetic differences – while the variation of human languages is decoupled from genetics, relying instead on cultural evolution (as we saw in chapter 5).

Finally, variation due to cultural transmission turns out to be very limited in songbirds.[20] As birds sing to attract mates, repel competitors or facilitate bonding, they also have built-in perceptual preferences that shape the cultural evolution of song types. For example, female chaffinches appear to prefer songs with more trill phrases and relatively longer flourishes. Female zebra finches have been shown to provide feedback on juvenile males' song practice, using rapid wing strokes to indicate their approval of a particular sequence. These female preferences limit the variation of culturally evolved songs considerably, with further limitations deriving from the male learner's own perceptual and vocal restrictions.[21]

An elegant demonstration of the strict limitations on the cultural evolution of birdsong is provided by a zebra-finch version of the game-of-telephone experiments that we discussed in chapter 6.[22] The first 'generation' (the initial message in the game) consisted of male birds brought up in isolation without any song input from older males. These birds ended up producing a raspy and arrhythmic song, unlike the songs produced by zebra finches in the wild. The isolated birds served as tutors for the next generation of birds; these second-generation learners were then used as tutors for a third cohort, and so on, for five generations of one-on-one learning. By analogy with the variation found in human languages, one might expect the songs created to go in any number of directions – and to differ substantially from the wild-type song that zebra finches exhibit in their natural habitat. But quite the reverse: across generations, the learners gradually recreated the wild-type song, demonstrating that there is little room for overall variation in zebra-finch song. Another study got the same result even though the first generation was trained up on the song from a completely different bird – a Bengalese finch.[23]

Cultural transmission among zebra finches thus serves to curtail diversity in vocalization and quickly shepherds possible deviations back to existing species-typical patterns rather than allowing them to establish new and different songs. Limiting songs to such stereotyped patterns may be useful for signalling the fitness of the singer, but it leaves little room for cultural evolution. What is clear is that these zebra-finch results contrast starkly with the outcome of the human game-of-telephone experiments, where different lineages of learners create widely diverging but nonetheless systematic miniature languages.

Communication is clearly not unique to humans. Many organisms, perhaps even most, have some way of communicating with other members of their species, from archaea and bacteria to fungi and plants, from bees and cuttlefish to monkeys and birds. The variety of communication systems is truly mindboggling, but when we zoom in and look at a particular organism, we find that all members of that species have practically identical ways of communicating as specified by their genes.[24] By contrast, human language is shaped by culture, allowing every individual to develop their own idiosyncratic version of the language of their community, as we saw in the case of Laura Bridgman. Ironically, it would seem that the idea of an innate universal grammar might provide a better characterization of the fixed and uniform nature of non-human communication systems than of the irrepressible diversity of human language. This is not to deny the importance of communication in species other than humans – far from it – but as beautiful, varied and sometimes wonderfully intricate as these non-human communication systems are in their own right, they offer no parallel to the flexibility and fundamental diversity of human language.

SEVEN THOUSAND NATURAL EXPERIMENTS IN CULTURAL EVOLUTION

The sheer variety of human languages is staggering. Unique to human language, the main communicative signal can be either gestural or vocal, as expressed in either signed or spoken language.[25] There are more than 140 different sign languages across the world, including American Sign Language, Danish Sign Language and Nicaraguan Sign Language. And while Laura Bridgman learned to finger-spell English, American Sign Language has nothing to do with American English or indeed English of any kind, whether spoken or written. This means that American Sign Language is as distinct from British Sign Language as any two randomly chosen spoken languages, say Finnish and Chinese, are from each other.

Within the spoken languages, we find many variations in the specific sounds used to signal subtle differences in meaning.[26] More than seventeen languages in southern and eastern Africa, such as Kxoe, Xhosa and Zulu, incorporate different kinds of clicks into words, including the **tut-tut** (often written as **tsk! tsk!**) used by English-speakers to indicate disapproval and the **tchick!** sound that riders use to encourage their horses. About two-thirds of the world's languages use changes in pitch, known as tone, to distinguish between different words that otherwise sound the same. Consider the five different tones employed in Mandarin Chinese to change the meaning of the syllable **ma**:

- **mā** with a high level, flat tone means 'mother';
- **má** with a tone that rises from mid to high pitch refers to 'hemp';
- **mǎ** with an initially low falling tone that rises to a high pitch denotes 'horse';
- **mà** with a tone that falls sharply from high to low pitch signifies 'scold';
- **ma** with a neutral tone is used as an article indicating a question.

These subtle tonal differences often pose a challenge for second-language learners – it is all too easy to confuse **mā** (mother) with **mǎ** (horse)!

Some languages even use whistling to communicate across

large distances, such as in mountains or dense forests, extending the reach of the human voice up to ten times as far as shouted
speech.[27] Whistled speech is used by sub-populations of speakers
of more than thirty languages, including Turkish, Spanish in the
Canary Islands, Chepang in Nepal and Mazatec in Mexico. And
while whistled speech relies heavily on vowel sounds, some languages, such as the endangered language spoken by the Nuxalk
people living near the Canadian town of Bella Coola in British
Columbia, have many words that consist entirely of consonants,
such as **ts'xlh** (true), **sts'q** (animal fat) and **tsktskwts** (he arrived).
So it's not even the case that languages always use combinations
of vowels and consonants to produce words.

Each language, moreover, is quirky and unique in its own distinctive way.[28] Indeed, just about every apparently universal
linguistic property breaks down in one language or another:
there are languages without adverbs, languages without adjectives, and some that appear not even to distinguish between
nouns and verbs, like Straits Salish, a First Nation language in
Canada. Mandarin Chinese lacks morphology (verb endings, plurals and the like), while in Yupik, the language of a group of
indigenous peoples in western and southern Alaska and north-
eastern Siberia, morphology is so rich that an entire sentence
can be packed into a single word ('he had not yet said again that
he was going to hunt reindeer': **tuntussuqatarniksaitengqig-
gtuq**). And many non-Indo-European languages have unfamiliar
classes of words: ideophones, coverbs and classifiers. For example,
ideophones in many languages form a separate word class that is
used to spice up conversations by evoking an idea through sound,
such as **ribuy-tibuy** in the Mundari language of eastern India,
which denotes the 'sound, sight, or motion of a fat person's but-
tocks rubbing together as they walk'.

European languages rely on verb 'inflections' – word endings that differentiate present, past and future and **walk** from **walking** – captured in the verb tables over which second-language learners labour. Mandarin Chinese has just one form of each verb and instead uses additional words in the sentence to clarify when an event occurred. Other languages have only a small class of 'inflecting' verbs, but combine them with a large open-ended class of 'coverbs' to describe different kinds of events. Consider Jaminjung, an aboriginal language spoken by fewer than 150 people around the Victoria River in the Northern Territory of Australia.[29] Jaminjung has only around thirty verbs, all of which have quite general meanings, such as **ijga**, which refers to some sort of locomotion when used on its own. To create more specific meanings for particular actions, these rather generic verbs can be combined with a large number of coverbs that can't appear on their own. So, when **ijga** is combined with the coverb **warrng-warrng** (walk), it means 'walking'; combined with **bag** (break), it refers to breaking something; combined with **marrug** (hidden), it denotes the act of hiding; and combined with **ngilijga** (cry), it means 'crying'.

Like coverbs, classifiers are another class of words that is widespread among the world's languages but scarcely found in European tongues.[30] A classifier combines with nouns to denote specific types of things – a marginal case in English is the use of 'head' in **three head of cattle** (but not **three head of parrots** or **three head of bicycles**). Diyari, an aboriginal language spoken by a small group of people living in the arid desert east of Lake Eyre, about 650 miles north of Adelaide in South Australia, has nine different classifiers that occur before nouns and carve up the world into different categories important for their everyday life:

- **karna** – human beings (excluding white, non-aboriginal people);
- **paya** – birds that can fly (thus excluding emus);
- **thutyu** – reptiles, snakes;
- **nganthi** – other edible animate beings;
- **puka** – edible vegetable food;
- **pirta** – trees or wood (useful for fires);
- **marda** – stones and minerals (like ochre);
- **thurru** – fire;
- **ngapa** – water.

So, in Diyari you refer to a kangaroo as **nganthi tyukurru**, whereas a sulphur-crested cockatoo is **paya kardarrungka** and a(n) (aboriginal) woman is **karna wilha**.

The meanings that languages can express also vary wildly.[31] Some languages have no tenses, pronouns or numerals, or they lack what might seem to be fundamental logical terms such as **if** and **or**. Others express meanings in highly unexpected ways. In the Navajo language spoken in the south-western United States (and used by the Navajo code talkers we met in chapter 2), the choice of verb depends on which of eleven categories of objects you're talking about – whether, for example, it's a solid round thing like a ball, a slender flexible item like a rope, a slender stiff article like an arrow or some non-compact matter like a bunch of hair. Whereas in English the same verb is used to request something irrespective of what that thing happens to be ('give me **X**' for any **X**), in Navajo you have to select one of eleven different verb forms to formulate the same request. So, if you wanted to say 'give me a cigarette' (slender stiff object), you would use the verb **nítįįh**, but if you wanted to say 'give me some hay', you would instead use the verb **níłjooli**. Yet other languages, like Pirahã, spoken by a contemporary community of eight hundred people living on the banks of the Maici River, a tributary of the Amazon deep in the Brazilian rainforest, appear to lack words for numbers and time. And as we mentioned in chapter 5, they even lack what Chomsky declared to be the most fundamental property of language – recursion – which allows phrases to be nested within phrases of the same type like Russian Matryoshka dolls.

Another intriguing feature found in about a quarter of the world's languages is what linguists call 'evidentiality', which requires speakers to note explicitly what evidence they have for what they're talking about – whether they have first-hand knowledge of it, have inferred it from some evidence, or heard about it from someone else.[32] English doesn't have evidentiality, but speakers can optionally choose to signal that something is hearsay or inferred rather than observed directly by using specific words such as **reportedly**, **allegedly**, **apparently** or **supposedly**. Where evidentiality is built into the grammar of a language, the speaker is typically required to employ two or more verb endings, or suffixes, that indicate the origin of the information. Consider the nearly extinct Eastern Pomo language spoken in Northern California, which employs four different verb endings to specify how the information conveyed was acquired. The ending **-ink'e** is used when talking about something the speaker sensed in a non-visual manner, **-ya** is used when mentioning something of which the speaker has first-hand knowledge (most likely visual), **-ine** when making inferences based on something the speaker saw and **-·le** when reporting something the speaker was told (that is, hearsay). When attached to the stem **pʰa·békʰ**, meaning 'burn', we get the following:

- **pʰa·békʰ-*ink'e*** – the speaker felt the sensation of burning;
- **pʰa·bék-*a*** – the speaker has seen somebody/something getting burned;
- **pʰa·bék-*ine*** – the speaker has seen circumstantial evidence of burning, such as bandages;
- **pʰa·békʰ-·*le*** – the speaker is reporting what they were told about an incident of burning.

So, if you wanted to say that you had heard that 'they got burned', you'd say, '**bé·k-al pʰa·bé-k-ʰ-·*le*'**; but if you instead were suspecting that they had got burned on the basis of what you had seen, you'd say instead, '**bé·k-al pʰa·bé-k-*ine*'**.

In some languages, evidentiality is also used to indicate whether the speaker participated in the events they're talking about.[33] Consider the interview in which the former vice-president of the United States Dick Cheney talked about the unfortunate accident when he shot a fellow hunter, Harry Whittington, in the face, neck and chest during a quail hunt in southern Texas. Cheney famously engaged in evasive verbal contortions to distance himself from his responsibility, saying: 'I turned and shot at the bird, and at that second, saw Harry standing there,' and later: 'Well, ultimately, I'm the guy who pulled the trigger that fired the round that hit Harry.' If he had been talking in Namo Me, a language spoken by about a thousand people living in Papua New Guinea's Southern Highlands and Western Province, such wriggling would have been impossible. The grammar of this language requires speakers to use a suffix to indicate explicitly their participation in the events they describe.

These few examples only scratch the surface of the spectacular linguistic diversity we see across the world.[34] And there is variety within this variety. There are many variations within the specific features we have covered here, such as how many tones a language employs, how many different classifiers are used, and how many evidentiality markers are embedded in the grammar. Even within Europe, there is more linguistic diversity than we often realize. When European nation-states formed and designated their official national languages, other languages often ended up as low-prestige dialects. This phenomenon is captured by the astute quip 'A language is a dialect with an army and navy,' attributed to the sociolinguist and Yiddish scholar Max Weinreich.[35] For example, according to UNESCO's *Atlas of the World's Languages in Danger*, Italy has 30 endangered languages; France, 26; Germany, 13; and the United Kingdom, 11.[36] And there are European languages like Finnish, Hungarian and Estonian (all three part of the Uralic language family) and Basque (whose origin remains mysterious) – each of which is profoundly exotic from the point of view of speakers of, say, English, Spanish and German.

Panning out to a global scale, it becomes clear that the roughly seven thousand human languages are not evenly distributed around the globe. Rather, most of the world's languages are clumped together within the Earth's tropical zones (see figure 7.1). The richest areas of linguistic diversity typically do not merely contain a myriad of marginal variations. The highlands of Papua New Guinea are home to over 10 per cent of the world's languages, and these communities often speak languages with wildly divergent sound systems, word orders and ways of linguistically slicing up the world.

Why are most of the world's languages found in the tropics? The behavioural scientist Daniel Nettle argues that the reason for this pattern is the longer growing season in the tropical

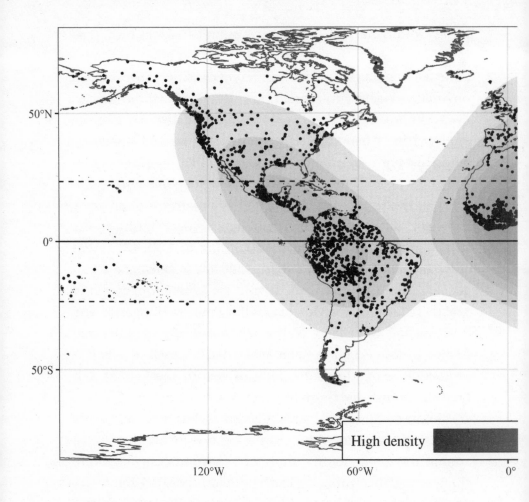

Figure 7.1. The world's more than seven thousand languages are not distributed equally around the globe but instead are concentrated around the equator (solid horizontal line) in the two tropical zones (demarcated by the dashed horizontal lines). The darker the grey contours, the higher the density of languages. The approximate location of individual languages is indicated by the tiny black dots. (Figure by Pablo Contreras Kallens.)

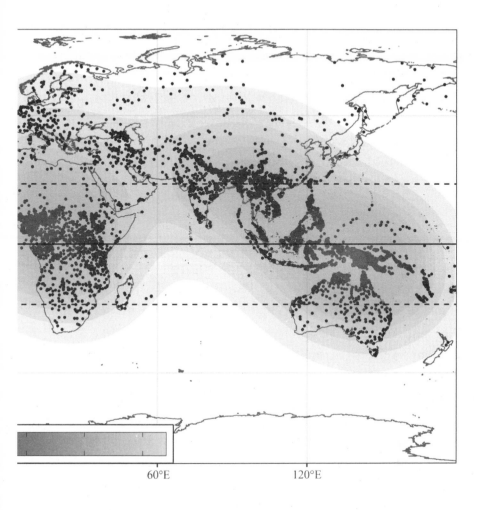

60°E   120°E

regions.[37] People living in these parts of the world therefore have more food security, making them more self-sufficient. By contrast, the shorter growing season in temperate and cold zones makes it more likely that people have to rely on neighbours within a larger geographical area in case of crop failure, and having a common language facilitates such social agreements.

When we take the full diversity of the world's languages seriously, it becomes clear that there are very few, if any, linguistic universals. This is no cause for alarm but rather a call for celebration! The plethora of languages provides us with thousands of opportunities to gain new insights into the uniquely human ability for language. Essentially, we're presented with the results of seven thousand natural experiments in cultural evolution.[38]

IS SOMETHING ROTTEN
IN THE STATE OF DANISH?

If we for a moment take a deeper dive into one of these seven thousand language experiments, we discover that strange and peculiar variation creeps into even seemingly 'garden-variety' European languages, such as Danish. Most non-Danes know little about Danish, except perhaps that it is the language of some of the happiest people in the world and that it is the origin of the word **hygge**, the feeling of cosiness, togetherness and well-being central to the culture of the Danes. As it happens, the Danish language has a longstanding reputation for being hard to understand. As early as 1694, the Irish politician and writer Robert Molesworth wrote in his *An Account of Denmark, as It was in the Year 1692*, 'The Language is very ungrateful, and not unlike the *Irish* in its whining complaining Tone. The King, great Men, Gentry, and many Burghers, make use of the *High-Dutch* in their ordinary Discourse, and of *French* to Strangers. I have heard several in high Employment, boast that they could not speak *Danish*.'[39] And Danish didn't seem to get any better with time. In 1927, the German author Kurt Tucholsky joked: 'The Danish language is not suitable for speaking . . . everything sounds like a single word.'[40] Even the Norwegians, geographical and linguistic neighbours of the Danes, have made fun of the unintelligibility of Danish in a TV comedy sketch that features two Danes who are completely unable to understand each other and therefore are forced to make up nonsense words like **kamalåså**.[41] They end up appealing to the international community to help Denmark before the communicative breakdown leads to a total societal collapse. Things may not be quite that bad – yet something does seem to be amiss in the Danish language (see figure 7.2).

Anecdotally, Danish is hard to learn as a second language, but

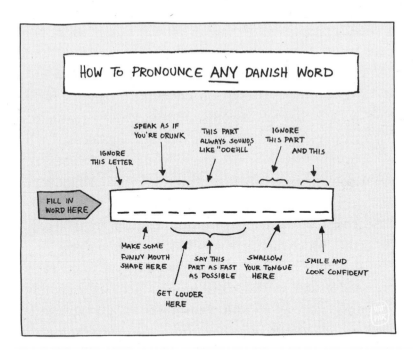

Figure 7.2. A humorous take on the unusual pronunciation of Danish, which also hints at why understanding Danish can be difficult, especially for non-native speakers. (Illustration by Matthias Parchettka.)

counterintuitively even Danish children appear to struggle![42] How can Danish children have problems learning Danish? This question is personal for Morten: he grew up in Denmark, learning Danish as his mother tongue. He now leads the 'Puzzle of Danish' research group at Aarhus University in Denmark, trying to solve this conundrum.

The problem with Danish appears to lie in its pronunciation, which is often sloppy and unclear. With over forty vowel sounds, Danish has one of the largest vowel inventories in the world (by comparison, English has only thirteen to fifteen vowels, depending on the dialect). In addition, Danes turn a number of consonants into vowel-like sounds when speaking. For example, **b** and **v** sounds at the ends of words are often pronounced as **oo**-like sounds (similar to a shortish version of the **oo** in 'boot') when they appear in words such as **løbe** (to run) and **kniv** (knife), which roughly transliterate using English phonology to 'loyoo' and 'kneeyoo', respectively.[43] To complicate matters further, Danes 'swallow' the ends of words, omitting about a quarter of all syllables, even when reading aloud in a radio broadcast. Each of these factors occurs on its own in other languages, but only Danish routinely combines all three. This results in an abundance of sound sequences with no real consonants, such as the noun phrase **røget ørred** (smoked trout; English transliteration: 'rohe-errhl'), which has eight vowel-like sounds in a row.

Danish is thus located at the opposite extreme to the earlier-mentioned Nuxalk language that has words consisting purely of consonants, such as **p'xwlht** (bunchberries). Of the two languages, though, Danish may have drawn the shorter straw when it comes to ease of perception. To understand spoken language, we need to segment the auditory input into words or word combinations. Because consonants interrupt the stream of speech

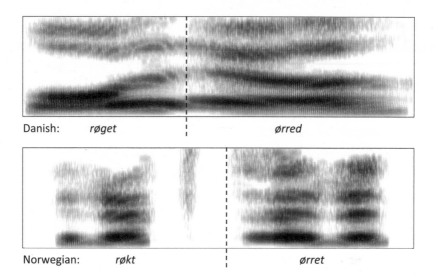

Figure 7.3. Spectrograms providing a visual depiction of the speech signal, showing the distribution and intensity of different frequencies in the speech signal across time for the translation of 'smoked trout' in (top) Danish **røget ørred** (English transliteration: 'rohe-errhl') and (bottom) Norwegian **røkt ørret** (English transliteration: 'rokt ohrrit'). The vertical dotted line shows the approximate location of the boundary between the two words. Note that the Danish spectrogram is undifferentiated, without clues as to syllable or word boundaries. In contrast to Danes, Norwegians pronounce their consonants, making the boundary between the two words easier to detect.

sounds, they provide more useful cues to potential word boundaries than vowels. Strings of vowels make it hard to figure out where one word ends and another begins (see figure 7.3). So, conversing in Danish is a little bit like playing charades in a dimly lit room, where it is hard to distinguish one gesture from another.

Just as it's likely to be more difficult to learn to play charades in semi-darkness than in a brightly lit room, so it seems that the opaque sound properties of Danish hamper language learning.

219

Studies by Morten's colleague at Aarhus University, developmental researcher Dorthe Bleses, have shown that Danish children not only learn new words more slowly than children learning other European languages but also fail to master the past tense of verbs until they're eight years of age – almost two years later than children learning the practically identical past tense systems of Norwegian and Swedish.

Using an eye-tracking device, psycholinguist Fabio Trecca, along with Morten and other colleagues, traced where two-year-old Danish children were looking while they listened to spoken language. The researchers took advantage of the fact that if you show children two objects on a screen, such as a car and a monkey, and say something like 'Find the car!' or 'Here's the monkey!' then they will normally look at the target object soon thereafter. When the Danish toddlers heard **Find bilen!** ('Find the car!' English transliteration: 'Fin beelen!'), which contains several consonants, they would look at the car relatively quickly. But when they heard **Her er aben!** ('Here's the monkey!' English transliteration: 'heer-ahben!'), they would take about half a second longer to look at the monkey because the speech stream consists almost entirely of vowels that mask the boundaries between words. A half-second delay may not seem like much, but in light of the real-time pressures from the Now-or-Never bottleneck, it can be a sizeable stumbling block for both learning and comprehension. Indeed, Morten and his colleagues found in a subsequent study that two-and-a-half-year-olds struggle to learn new words when the new words follow a vowel-only phrase, such as **Her er ...** ('Here is . . .'), even though adults often use this phrase when talking with children.

Morten's Puzzle of Danish research group has also shown that the effects of the opaque Danish sound structure do not disappear when children grow up. Using carefully matched experiments conducted in Denmark and Norway, they found that adult Danes appear to handle their native language differently from speakers of neighbouring languages, like Swedish and Norwegian. The comparison between Danish and Norwegian provides an almost perfect natural experiment: Denmark and Norway have a long common history going back to the time of the Vikings; they have similar welfare systems, educational practices and cultural norms; and their languages have similar grammars, past tense systems and vocabulary. But the key difference is that Norwegians typically pronounce their consonants, whereas Danes tend not to. Because Danish speech is so ambiguous, Danes rely much more on contextual information from background knowledge, the current situation and the prior conversation to work out what they are hearing compared with speakers of other languages, like Norwegian. That is, they need to pay more attention to the submerged part of the communication iceberg because the linguistic input is especially indeterminate in spoken Danish.

Contrary to what is often assumed in psychology and linguistics, the example of Danish suggests that not all languages are equally easy for children to learn and use. Danish illustrates the kind of linguistic variability that we'd expect if languages are culturally evolved rather than following a genetic blueprint. It is unclear why Danes ended up speaking as they do – it may simply be a protracted historical process of language change gone awry, or it may reflect an implicit social desire on the part of Danes to set themselves apart from their Scandinavian neighbours to the north and the Germans to the south. Yet the perverse nature of Danish, which delays learning and complicates even adult usage, may have a positive side. Indeed, Morten's group found that because Danes rely more on communicative cues from outside the speech signal, they are less affected than Norwegians when listening to speech in noise (as when conversing with someone on a busy street corner). Danes are already used to playing charades in a semi-dark room, so turning the lights down a bit more is no problem.

BILLIONS OF DIFFERENT LANGUAGES

Languages are not all cut from the same cloth but vary wondrously along every possible linguistic dimension, from sounds and gestures to word formation and grammar. But linguistic variation doesn't stop with individual languages, like Danish, Nuxalk, English and Navajo; it extends *within* languages as well. In fact, none of us speaks quite the same language as our neighbours.

As with any other skill, there are dramatic variations in linguistic abilities across individuals. We are talking about differences not just in vocabulary size but also in grammatical proficiency and the ability to use prior context to make sense of what is being said.[44] Some of these individual differences are surprising. The linguist Ewa Dąbrowska found that some adult native English-speakers tend to misunderstand even simple passive sentences like **The girl was photographed by the boy**, interpreting it as if the girl took the picture. And they would have real trouble with anomalous claims such as the headline **Dog bitten by man**. Even among Cornell undergraduates, who were all at the top of their respective high-school classes, Morten has measured substantial differences in how fast and how well they can comprehend relatively straightforward sentences such as **The reporter that the senator attacked admitted the error**. Indeed, Dąbrowska has shown that the variability in native language skills is so wide that many second-language learners actually have a better command of English grammar and a larger vocabulary than people who learned English from birth.

Although we are all experts when it comes to language, we are all experts in slightly different languages. Our particular inventory of words and constructions, and how we use them on the fly to play linguistic charades, make each person's language unique. Laura Bridgman's English provides a particularly poignant example of how we each create our own personal language. This means that there can be no one 'true' version of English – any more than there is one true way to dance the tango, play Indian ragas or create Impressionist paintings. Each English-speaker has their own version of English, and the same goes for speakers of any other language, from 'Are'are (spoken in the Solomon Islands in Oceania) through Hindi, Spanish and Yélî Dnye to Zuni (spoken in western New Mexico and eastern Arizona in the United States). A language is no more than a collection of so-called idiolects, each consisting of a distinctive combination of constructions, word choices and personal styles of expression peculiar to a particular individual. Each and every one of us speaks a unique language that, for better or worse, will go extinct with us.[45]

But if each of us speaks a different language, how is communication possible at all? How can we ever hope to understand each other? This is where our charades metaphor comes into play again. A successful game of charades depends as much on the ability of the audience to interpret the (often overacted) clues they are given as on the actor's miming abilities. Each person might mime King Kong in a different way, but our communicative creativity and inventiveness allow us to understand each other nonetheless. And language is no different: listeners do much of the work for the speaker. The speaker merely gives clues to the message they're trying to get across; listeners must use their knowledge of the speaker, what was said before and the world in general to help them work out the meaning of an utterance. This is why we can generally understand one another even though each of us speaks our own idiosyncratic version of the language of our community.

Languages only need to be roughly aligned for communication to be possible. This alignment is rooted in mutual understanding fostered by the processes of cultural evolution that we discussed in previous chapters – we are all following in the footsteps of previous generations of speakers in our community, who interpreted the clues just as we do. So, although the approximately two billion speakers of English (native speakers and second-language learners alike) are speaking two billion different Englishes, the versions are all related closely enough for us to generally understand each other. The same goes for the speakers of the other languages of the world: everyone has their own take on the language(s) they know. Within a speech community, close is good enough – the creativity of interpretation is more than sufficient to fill in the gaps. Indeed, as we saw in the encounter between Captain Cook's crew and the Haush, the expressive power of the submerged part of the communication iceberg enables us to understand one another to a reasonable degree even when the linguistic tip is entirely missing.

◉

At the very end of *On the Origin of Species*, Charles Darwin ponders the awesome power of natural selection, musing that 'from so simple a beginning endless forms most beautiful and most wonderful have been, and are being, evolved'. He was talking about the evolution of biological organisms; but, as we have seen, his evocative phrase 'endless forms most beautiful' applies equally well to the cultural evolution of language. Just as variation among organisms is fundamental to biological evolution, so too is linguistic diversity essential to the cultural evolution of language. The predominantly genetic control of non-human communication systems curtails variation within a species, thereby putting the brakes on cultural evolution, as illustrated by the zebra-finch game-of-telephone experiments. By contrast, human linguistic abilities practically burst with diversity both across and within languages as the unmistakable signature of cultural evolution.

Communication may be universal across species, but language is uniquely human. It is the fundamental flexibility of language, combined with our built-in desire to communicate, that allows us to play linguistic charades, whether through spoken words, manual signs or even touch, like Laura Bridgman. These repeated games of charades culminate in a spectacular diversity of languages that enable humanity to accumulate knowledge of all the things that language can express across generations. As we shall see next, each language carries within it the seeds for further cultural flourishing. Our powers of endless linguistic improvisation provide the catalyst for the creation of human culture and society in all its dazzling variety.[46]

8

THE VIRTUOUS CIRCLE: BRAINS, CULTURE AND LANGUAGE

The relation of thought to word is not a thing but a process,
a continual movement back and forth from thought to
word and from word to thought.

LEV VYGOTSKY,
Thought and Language (1934)

Coming out of the lifts in Uris Hall, home of Cornell's Department of Psychology, where Morten works, visitors are confronted with an astonishing sight: human brains floating in vats of liquid. These are selected highlights from the Wilder Brain Collection, which consists of the donated brains of local scholars and psychopaths. The brains range from the illustrious (psychologist Edward Titchener, who founded Cornell's Psychology Department in 1895; Helen Hamilton Gardener, noted civil servant, writer and suffragist) to the notorious (doctor, lawyer, embezzler and multiple murderer Edward Rulloff, who at one point even masqueraded as a professor and, bizarrely, also wrote an unpublished tract on the evolution of language).[1] The founder of the collection, Cornell anatomist Burt Green Wilder, had high hopes that, upon examination, the diversity in brains would map on to the diversity of people to whom those brains belonged and that the collection would become a valuable resource for research. Demonstrating admirable commitment to the cause, he ordered that on his death his own brain be added to the collection. Yet the Wilder collection ended up as a mere curiosity. It turns out that although the gross anatomy of human brains differs quite a lot, most notably in overall size, there is no obvious signature distinguishing the brilliant from the mundane or dividing the virtuous from the criminal.

What if we broaden our scope to consider brains from across the animal kingdom? Now the differences in the anatomy of the nervous system among species, and especially in the size of the brain, are substantial. The tiny roundworm (*Caenorhabditis elegans*, much studied by neuroscience) has just 302 cells in its entire nervous system; a pond snail, about 10,000 neurons; a lobster, 100,000; an ant, 250,000; and a honeybee, nearly 1 million.[2] The nervous systems of vertebrates, by contrast, appear dramatically more sophisticated, from the 16 million neurons in the frog to 70 million in the house mouse, 80 million in the Nile crocodile, roughly 200 million in the brown rat, 2 billion for ravens, pigs and dogs, about 30 billion in chimps, gorillas and orangutans, and approximately 100 billion in humans.[3]

The link between brain size and intelligence is not straightforward. Large animals tend to have large brains and nervous systems, irrespective of behavioural sophistication. For instance, take the two animals that have been taught to communicate with humans most successfully: the chimpanzee and the African grey parrot. While the chimp has thirty billion neurons, the much smaller African grey parrot manages comparable communicative feats with only a twentieth of that number. Similarly, in humans, male and female brains differ in proportion to overall body size, but there are no average differences in intelligence – a point the brilliant Helen Hamilton Gardener made vigorously during her life and which her brain now illustrates in death.[4] Indeed, even within genders, human brain size and intelligence are only weakly correlated in the general population. Playwright and short-story writer Ivan Turgenev was revealed to have an astonishingly large brain on post-mortem examination; yet distinguished poet and novelist Anatole France had one of the smallest brains on record – just half the size of Turgenev's.[5]

Something remarkable began to happen to the human brain two or three million years ago: it began steadily to grow, not only in absolute terms but also, more significantly, in relation to body size.[6] Presumably, being smart was becoming increasingly important for our ancestors; and being smart meant, other things being equal, having a larger brain. But brains are expensive to run: pound for pound, brain tissue consumes nine times as much energy as typical body tissue. In total, the brain accounts for about 20 per cent of our energy expenditure, regardless of whether we are concentrating on some difficult problem, daydreaming or even just fast asleep. In the light of such significant costs, larger brains must on average have substantial evolutionary advantages.

There has been considerable speculation concerning what drove this remarkable expansion in the hominin brain. One possibility is a shifting diet: across primate species, there is a remarkable negative relationship between brain size and the size of another metabolically costly organ, the gut.[7] So it could be that an easier-to-digest diet, perhaps resulting from the invention of cooking, required less digestive activity and so freed up energy that could be used to run a larger brain. And, of course, a larger brain might allow for cleverer hunting and food preparation methods, thus improving diet further. Another possibility is that group size was crucial: primates living in larger groups might have larger brains because they depend on keeping track of, and interacting with, more social partners.[8]

Pursuing this line of thought, it is tempting to wonder whether the explosion in brain size might actually be tied to the invention and gradual development of language. Now, as we saw in chapter 5, the apparently appealing idea of co-evolution between language and specialized genes and brain structures that supposedly encode a universal grammar can't work. Languages change too quickly for genes to keep up. Moreover, distant peoples whose genes diverged many tens of thousands of years ago show no signs of having brains specialized for their own languages – any normally developing baby can learn any language without difficulty. After all, language is shaped by the brain rather than the other way around. But perhaps a very different story might work: language could reshape human life so that a premium is placed on general 'smartness'.[9] Even a small improvement in communicative abilities would make it easier for our ancestors to coordinate their behaviour to create effective teams, to teach skills, to share knowledge, and much more. These changes will favour people with larger, smarter brains, because they will be best able to profit from such social complexity. Smarter brains will, in turn, generate more sophisticated linguistic charades, thus creating a more complex language. And a more complex language will ratchet up the social complexity, and the selectional pressure for larger, smarter brains, still further. So perhaps there was a *virtuous circle* in which language and brains co-evolved, leading to the runaway increases in brain size, human cleverness and social complexity.[10]

If this story is right, the remarkable human facility for playing charades – the ability to communicate actively using the mutual understanding of improvised, flexible gestures or noises – must be very old, perhaps going back as far as two million years. Early language-like communication is likely to have been relatively rudimentary. But even rudimentary communication may have allowed our ancestors to pass on skills such as making stone tools, controlling fire and possibly even cooking food – behaviours more complex than anything observed in modern chimps or gorillas. And once our ancestors could play charades, patterns in those charades (reusing old signals for new purposes) would have arisen almost immediately. The forces of spontaneous order that we described in chapter 4 would have made charades-like communication ever more conventionalized. According to the virtuous circle story, even a simple proto-language would increase social and behavioural complexity, ramp up the selection pressure for smartness (and large brains) and in turn allow yet more complex communication. Full-blown language would thus arise gradually through the interplay of biological evolution (of us) and cultural evolution (of our systems of communication).

The virtuous circle between charades-playing and brain size is very different from the putative co-evolution between a language and an innate universal grammar that we considered and abandoned in chapter 5. Whether we are planning, trading, hunting, or sharing skills and knowledge, the ability to communicate effectively is strongly advantageous – and confers an evolutionary advantage. Communication becomes increasingly central to increasingly complex patterns of living. This is not a matter of having specialized genes for abstract grammatical patterns, but rather requires a powerful 'engine' for creating and interpreting linguistic charades.[11] More generally, a rich culture puts a premium on general smartness – there are suddenly so many new complex tools, religious practices, social norms and more to learn about. An individual's success in a complex culture depends on smartness more than on physical robustness or prowess. Ever smarter communicators will, in turn, develop ever richer charades-playing abilities, more complex language and more elaborate culture. This may have seeded a runaway process of culture–brain co-evolution of which contemporary humanity is the result.[12]

Around three hundred thousand years ago, our own species, *Homo sapiens*, emerged in a variety of locations in Africa.[13] Recent findings suggest that even the earliest *Homo sapiens* had a distinctively complex cultural repertoire. For example, excavations at the Olorgesailie basin in southern Kenya provide evidence of finely wrought stone points that had probably been fastened to spears, and the chiselling of red pigment from iron-rich rocks, presumably used for decoration or to signal allegiance with a social group. And, remarkably, archaeologists have uncovered tools made during that period of glassy black obsidian and white and green chert (a hard rock composed of quartz crystals) that had been brought from distances of up to 30 miles over mountainous terrain.[14] This suggests the possibility of trade, because such distances far exceed the range of a small band of humans in such difficult terrain. Findings from around the same period or slightly later across Africa include ostrich-egg shell fragments etched with grid-like patterns and decorative perforated shells, probably used as strings of beads. By this time, it seems likely that language-like communication had reached considerable sophistication. The transition from the stone hand-axes used by our earlier ancestors to decorative trade goods appears to mark a step change.

The complexity of our ancestors' culture may have arisen, at least in part, from their communicative abilities – an ever-enhanced ability to play charades. Recall how the Haush and Captain Cook's landing party were able to gesture their way to two-way trade right away on first contact. This requires the ability to signal what you want, what you can give, and that you have no hostile intentions; in short, trade between groups is possible only if you can play charades (and, of course, it is still easier if you happen to share a common language). It is difficult to imagine trade occurring otherwise; indeed, trade is not observed among non-human animals, despite its potential for huge mutual benefit.[15] And the same is true for the many other forms of complex social behaviour so characteristic of humans: inventing and imposing social conventions, ethical norms or religious beliefs, and creating images, decorations, complex tools, currencies, units of measurement and records of account. Language appears to underpin every aspect of human culture and society. So charades-playing, and the languages that flow from it, enable the development of culture. Once culture is established, the ability to play linguistic charades becomes of paramount importance for any individual seeking to flourish in a highly complex, language-soaked society – so that charades-playing ability will be under strong pressure from biological selection. Thus, human charades-playing and the human mind are both propelled towards ever greater intellectual sophistication packed into an ever larger brain.[16]

APES DON'T PLAY CHARADES

The Language Research Center at Georgia State University is nestled in a large wooded area on the outskirts of Atlanta. This interdisciplinary centre was established in 1981 to study language and other aspects of cognition in different primates: humans, chimps and bonobos, as well as capuchin and macaque monkeys. Morten was fortunate to visit the research centre back in March 2009 and saw at first hand the amazing cognitive and communicative abilities of non-human primates. After playing a game of chase with a male chimp named Mercury, which involved them both running back and forth on their respective sides of the enclosure fence, Morten was in for a treat. Panzee, a female chimp, watched from inside her play yard as Morten walked out into the surrounding forest and hid a peach under some leaves. Afterwards, Morten went back inside the centre to locate Dr Charles Menzel, a senior research scientist who had been working closely with Panzee for many years to study her foraging, spatial cognition and memory abilities. Back outside a little while later, Panzee used various manual signs to direct Menzel to where Morten had hidden the peach. At this point, Morten was no longer sure exactly where the peach was – it was very well hidden – but Panzee's memory was perfect and she had no problem quickly steering Menzel to its exact location using manually signed directions. And as soon as it was found, Panzee received the peach as her reward for this impressive demonstration of her memory and communication skills.

If human uniqueness stems from hundreds of thousands of years of a virtuous circle linking language, culture and the brain, then we should expect communication to be a crucial point of distinction between ourselves and the other apes, and indeed this is the case. As we might predict, wild chimpanzees don't play charades, even of the simplest kind. When interacting with each other (rather than with humans), they don't even point! Twelve-month-old human infants are continually pointing to interesting toys, food or animals – and following the pointing of the adults around them. But so far, there has not been a single observation of one chimp indicating an object of interest to another chimp through pointing, either in captivity or in the wild.[17]

In one striking experiment, by Michael Tomasello and his team at the Max Planck Institute for Evolutionary Anthropology in Leipzig, a chimp has to choose between one of two opaque containers, one of which hides some tasty bananas. Through prior training, the chimp knows that just one box contains food and that it can only make one choice.[18] The human experimenter tries to communicate which box the chimp should choose by pointing, looking directly at the 'right' container or placing a wooden token on it. In each case, though, the chimps entirely ignore these helpful clues and choose at random. By contrast, children under three do significantly better than chance at this type of task and are especially good at understanding pointing.[19]

In a beautiful follow-up study, Tomasello's team created a situation in which the experimenter made the same arm-extending movement involved in pointing.[20] To a human observer, the arm movement would not be interpreted as a pointing action but as an unsuccessful attempt to reach for food from a container, which had been carefully placed just out of reach. Seeing the experimenter apparently trying to get food for themselves from a particular bucket, the chimps were easily able to infer that this must be the location of the food – and grab it for themselves. So, when presented with the very same arm-extending action, chimps can make sense of a competitive scenario in which someone reveals where the food is by attempting to retrieve it; but they are mystified by a cooperative scenario in which the other tries helpfully to pass on some useful information. The very idea that a person's (or, presumably, another chimp's) action might be trying to convey helpful information seems to have no place in the chimp world-view – they seem to be missing much, if not most, of the hidden part of the communication iceberg that is so fundamental to human language.[21]

If this is right, then teaching apes the full extent of human language will be an uphill struggle. The communicative drive to draw each other's attention to and describe the state of the external world that pushes human infants to learn language seems to be largely or perhaps entirely absent in apes and monkeys. Most ape communication with humans is instrumental: it achieves practical goals, as when Panzee conveyed the location of the peach to Menzel so that she could eat it. But apes seem to have no urge to draw attention to interesting objects, inform others about the world or let others know about their feelings or experiences – for an ape, the collaborative purpose of language is essentially a mystery.

Now, it is true that through laborious hours of training apes can be taught to make signs and to associate them with objects and actions. Although chimps have difficulty reproducing humanlike speech sounds, they have successfully been taught a small vocabulary of signs used in American Sign Language.[22] But whereas human signers rapidly master a rich grammar, chimps seem restricted to generating largely unordered strings of signs, often with many repetitions of the same sign. And chimps do not appear to learn the multiword constructions that emerge early in child language, and which lay the foundations for grammar (as discussed in chapter 4).

More promising results were found with Kanzi, a bonobo (a close and highly intelligent relative of the common chimpanzee) reared at the Language Research Center where Morten made his memorable visit. To communicate with Kanzi, a team led by Susan Savage-Rumbaugh used a miniature 'language' called Yerkish that had been devised by philosopher Ernst von Glasersfeld specifically to be used by non-human primates. This language consisted of sequences of 'lexigrams' that mapped on to keys on a specially designed keyboard, each key having a distinctive colour and shape. Rather than learning through hours of direct instruction, Kanzi learned his first few lexigrams by observing experimenters attempting unsuccessfully to train his mother, Matata. Impressively, Kanzi went on to learn to use over two hundred additional lexigrams, although he generated these in fairly unstructured strings rather than ordering them by any rules of grammar. Even more formidable is Kanzi's ability to understand spoken human language. Kanzi and a two-year-old human child, Alia, were tested on their ability to act out over two hundred spoken English sentences, such as 'Go get the carrot that's in the microwave' and 'Pour the lemonade in the Coke.' Remarkably, Kanzi responded correctly to 74 per cent of the sentences, whereas Alia understood only 65 per cent of the requests.[23]

Kanzi's ability to 'speak' in Yerkish and understand English is impressive. Yet the contrast between his language abilities and those of human children is striking. Children spontaneously and joyously engage in cooperative communication about the world around them, using all manner of gestures, facial expressions and noises. Nearing their second birthday, the start of the 'vocabulary spurt', they begin to hoover up words from those around them remarkably quickly. They dive right into the communicative challenges of the moment (wanting some milk, expressing a dislike of tomatoes, showing a new toy or pointing out a truck), deploying whatever linguistic resources they can bring to bear. With children, language is cobbled together in the service of the immediate demands of communication. And communication is something that babies, along with people of all ages, seem wired to do: we see messages and messengers everywhere. If anything, the interpretative powers of humans tend to be rather liberal: reading runes, tea leaves, giblets and thunderstorms as messages from ancestors or spirits, omens of the future or signs from the gods.

What about ape communication in the wild? Animal communication in general tends to focus on getting across a small number of basic messages that have important functions: marking out territory (roughly, 'Go away, I'm here!'), attracting mates ('Come over, I'm here!'), pair bonding ('You and me together, babe'), signalling threats ('I'm ready to fight'), raising alarms ('Watch out, predator approaching!') and so on. Apes appear to combine such signals in interesting ways. Consider the wild bonobo, which can be found in the tropical rainforest of the Congo Basin in West Africa. Bonobos live in small 'fission–fusion' communities in which temporary groups continually form, merge and break up throughout daily activities. They have two long-range calls: the whistle and the high hoot. Using *both* signals seems to signify the desire to join a temporary group – or, at least, joining the group is significantly more likely after using both signals rather than just a high hoot.[24] And joining is also more likely if the call is 'answered' by the group that the bonobo wants to join. The interchange is thus almost an embryonic 'conversation' in which the reply seems to indicate consent. If there is no response, the lone individual may repeat their call. Indeed, this is more likely after the whistle–high hoot combination, adding to the evidence that the combination of signals indicates a particularly strong desire to join.

Yet how far this is from human communication! Bonobos have a small set of apparently built-in biological signals with standardized meanings (something like, 'I want to join your group'). But human charades can create a limitless variety of meanings. Even a simple gesture, such as pointing in the direction of the window, can mean: 'Look at that bird!' or 'It's raining' or 'Nice clean windows' or 'Bob's car has gone' or 'The window is dirty' or 'Clean the window' or 'Hide! Trick-or-treaters are coming!' But even the simplest case of pointing ('That's the box with the bananas') is baffling to apes. And the combinations of human charades don't merely reinforce each other, as the bonobos' whistles and high hoots appear to do. Instead, charades interact to produce entirely new improvised meanings: a mimed rifle firing could be followed by a beatific smile to indicate *War and Peace*; but preceded by an outline of a T-shirt, the rifle mime might indicate *Top Gun* – or, combined with splayed hands 'growing' from each side of the head to convey antlers, it might signal *The Deer Hunter*. Charades, whether in gesture or speech, become increasingly conventionalized; they are layered upon each other, and subject to generations of grammaticalization and the forces of spontaneous order, thus gradually creating the seven thousand or so languages of the world, with all their wonderful intricacy.

Human languages develop through cultural evolution. On the other hand, animal signals are typically genetically encoded and fixed within a species, from ant pheromone trails to the bee waggle dance, from visual cuttlefish displays to vervet alarm calls.

This means that such signals develop not through cultural evo-lution but through the much slower mechanism of biological evolution. What about non-human primate communication using gestures? Apes do not seem to employ a standard set of fixed gestural signals. Instead, individuals create their own idio-syncratic set of gestures to attempt to get what they want from others (though they don't point out interesting features of the environment). Often the gesture directs the attention of another individual to some possible action (e.g. a baby chimp tugging its mother's back to get her to lower it so the baby can climb on); or it may simply be designed to attract attention, full stop (e.g. one young chimp slapping the ground noisily, then poking a second young chimp in the back to get the latter's attention and initiate play). But crucially, each figures out some of its repertoire of communicative strategies from scratch rather than by imitating the strategies of others in its group. Hence the cultural evolu-tion of a communicative system cannot get off the ground because, unlike humans, the other apes don't follow in each other's footsteps.[25]

Interestingly, while each ape appears to learn its own gestures from scratch, the repertoire of possible signs is actually quite restricted. Apes can't learn just any signal, but learn to employ those in a subset of about eighty gestures (including 'dangle', 'body drum', 'chest beat' and 'arms out', among many others). Indeed, the set of gestures learned by bonobos, chimps, gorillas and oran-gutans is surprisingly similar, though with some variations.[26] This implies that the capacity to learn these communicative gestures originates deep in biological evolution, at least as far back as the last common ancestor of the great apes, more than ten million years ago.[27] So, whereas each ape seems to learn its own signals from scratch, the ability to learn such signals appears to be wired into the genes. Unlike human language, the set of signals used in a community of apes does not appear to be shaped by cultural evolution over time.

There is a direct way to test this theory. If cultural evolution did play some role in ape communication (perhaps in fine-tuning the particular choice of gestures used in a particular community), then there should be greater similarity between the gestures and the meanings within particular groups of apes who supposedly share the same 'culture'. But observation of the variety of gestures used by different groups of apes suggests quite the opposite: gestures are just as varied within groups as they are between groups. So ape signals can only become established by individual learning built on the foundations shaped by natural selection over countless generations. By contrast, human charades can be invented, modified and reused to create new communicative conventions and, ultimately, complete languages shared by entire human societies.[28]

Ape communication seems profoundly different from human communication – it has none of the complex charade-like reasoning that allows us to convey rich messages with such limited means. This fits with our thesis that the emergence of this charades-playing ability led to language, richer cultures and more complex societies, which in turn led to the runaway selection for general cleverness that underpinned the rapid expansion of the human brain.

Although this picture is plausible, we can't, of course, know for sure whether it is correct. For one thing, estimates of when language arose vary widely. Hard evidence is difficult to come by: unlike many other human artefacts, speech doesn't fossilize. If it turns out that language and charades-like communication arose recently, say, within the last one hundred thousand years, it may have arrived too late to influence brain evolution and intelligence substantially. It is also possible that the intelligence and social sophistication required to play charades with others are mere side-effects of some other selection pressure for larger, smarter brains. Thus, rather than there being a virtuous circle between communication, social complexity and intelligence, perhaps our distinctive large and clever brains arose for reasons completely unconnected with communication. According to this story, intelligence comes first, and the charades-playing ability that induces communication, cultural evolution and our collective creation of the world's languages emerges purely as a side-effect. After all, the human ability to prove theorems in geometry, play chess, compose operas or invent the wheel would seem to require considerable intelligence. Perhaps language is no different.[29]

So, where does this leave the impact of language on the history of evolution? One might be tempted to conclude that language's role in driving a runaway growth in human intelligence and the human brain is unproven. Depending on which of the stories – virtuous circle or language as side-effect – is correct, the role of language in shaping our biology may be anywhere between 'very substantial' and 'minimal'. Yet although this is important, focusing on how much language has modified our genes and our brains misses a much more fundamental point. Language gave rise to a completely new type of evolutionary process: the evolution not of genes but of *culture*.

LANGUAGE AS CATALYST

It is not easy to imagine what a human society without language would be like. There are no such societies. Humans are relentless and brilliant charades players, building rudiments of communication from scratch when necessary, as we saw with Captain Cook's men and the Haush. Where no common language is available, improvised systems of communication are created to fill the void. Children deprived of language rapidly invent one, as the spontaneous creation of Nicaraguan Sign Language so vividly illustrates. But suppose that none of this were possible. What would a non-charades-playing human society look like?

The closest we can get is to consider the contrast with our biological cousins. As we saw above, for all their remarkable intelligence, apes don't play charades. So, rather than cumulatively constructing an intricate language, their communication is surprisingly limited. Wild bonobos can communicate that they'd like to join another group while foraging, but they can't outline a plan, argue against injustice, speculate about the origin of the universe or even recount what happened to them yesterday. In the absence of language, many animals can learn from others, but they show only the faintest traces of cultural evolution.[30] In one study, different groups of wild vervet monkeys were introduced to tasty red corn and bitter pink corn. Collectively, they rapidly learned to select the tastier corn – and young monkeys entering the group picked the tasty corn by its colour, without ever trying the other.[31] Furthermore, over periods of more than two decades, wild chimpanzee groups in close proximity to each other have been observed to have distinct, stable preferences for cracking nuts with stones or wood – and, interestingly, it seems that females who join the group as adults adopt their new group's traditions.[32] But contrast this with language-using humans: we can in a few seconds simply say, 'Don't eat the horrible pink corn!' or 'Use a stone!' and cultural transmission is achieved.

Language allows human skills, knowledge, social rules and religious beliefs to accumulate at an astonishing and ever-increasing rate. We can collectively work out which plants are edible, medicinal or poisonous; how to make an axe or an arrowhead; how to track animals, build a canoe, construct a hut, decide what is sacred and navigate by the stars. Without language, each individual animal faces the formidable challenge of learning everything from scratch – a lone struggle with the complexity of the world.[33] Each new generation of non-linguistic animals learns about as much as the previous generations did. Even where an insight or innovation occurs, it will most likely be lost, rather than touted, shouted about, recommended and actively taught, as with humans.

The ability to play charades and create language allows people to accumulate knowledge and pass on skills. We can develop moral and religious norms and debate what to do, who is to blame or who should be in charge. Other animals can do none, or almost none, of these things. This is no coincidence. Without language, the amazing cultural and social complexity that is unique to our species would be impossible. So, language is no ordinary element of culture. By enabling the accumulation, storage and transmission of knowledge, it is the catalyst for explosive change in almost every aspect of human culture and society. It allows for ever more elaborate expertise, norms and agreements, resulting eventually in vastly elaborate societies with their division of labour, trade, belief systems, constitutions, rituals and intricate systems of law.

Since the appearance of language, culture has become the motor of change above and beyond genetics – a process rapidly accelerated by mathematics, science, engineering, computers, the internet and much more. But language has an even more fundamental role. By providing the communicative link between human minds, it radically extends what we are collectively able to *think*.

HOW LANGUAGE SHAPES THOUGHTS

Charades are endlessly flexible. And words (e.g. **game** and **light**) have a vast and often loosely connected set of uses. So it doesn't make much sense to wonder what it is possible to express in a particular language any more than to ponder what can be conveyed in a game of charades. Once we have the hidden part of the communication iceberg in place, creativity can take us just about anywhere!

But our language (or our set of past charades) will make some things very much *easier* to convey than others. Famously, the invention of the written symbol for zero is crucial for a positional representation of numbers, so that 205 is two hundreds, *no tens* and five ones. A positional representation of numbers is incredibly helpful for adding and subtracting, the core business of accounting and astronomical calculations. Roughly five thousand years ago, the Sumerians indicated a zero with two diagonal wedges in their base 60 number systems (base 60 is still with us: we have 60 seconds in a minute, and 60 minutes in an hour). Three thousand years later, the Mayans independently invented a base 20 number system, with a zero indicated by a simple shell-like pattern. Roman numerals, with no positional zero and numerous other irregularities, made arithmetic considerably trickier. It is a further, radical, step to use zero *alone* – so that zero could be conceived of as a number (preceding 1, 2, 3). Brahmagupta, a seventh-century Indian mathematician and astronomer, began to treat zero as a number, with rules for how it functions in arithmetic. Later, Arab mathematicians began to use zero in formulating algebra, where zero plays a key role in equations with unknown quantities. Zero also plays a crucial role in Descartes' profound connection between equations and geometry; in Newton's and Leibniz's invention of the calculus; in the underpinnings of modern physics, the digital computer and much more.[34]

Is zero really an addition to language? Or to mathematical notation? Or to mathematics itself? Probably these questions have no useful answers. After all, learning the English word **zero** involves understanding how zero functions in the decimal system, that it can denote a numeral (0), a real number (that is, a point on the number line), and a part in positional notation (as in 205). And knowing all this *is* learning mathematical notation and how zero works in mathematics. Even an abstract concept like **zero** has many uses and meanings. And the more we know about mathematics, the richer our understanding of the term.

It seems uncontroversial that the invention of zero has had a revolutionary impact on thought. Without it, little would be possible in modern mathematics. In this sense, language has profoundly changed how we think. But a mere word **zero** is not enough – indeed, it is entirely useless on its own! What we need to develop are the games in which zero can play a role: how it can be used to write large numbers, add, subtract and help construct equations. This is not to say that people whose language does not have the word **zero** are forever unable to have such thoughts – not at all. Language is infinitely extendable. A newcomer need only be introduced to zero and how it works, and the scope of their thoughts will thereby be extended. And this is, of course, precisely how we all learn about zero, and a host of other connected concepts, at school.

On the topic of arithmetic, the counting system of the Pirahã, hunter-gatherers in the Amazon, consists of just **hói** ('approximately one' and 'small'), **hoí** ('approximately two') and **baagi** or **aibai** (both meaning 'many'). Clearly, the Pirahã's thoughts about mathematics will inevitably be limited by these terms: no counting, no zero, and presumably no addition, subtraction or multiplication. But the Pirahã also struggle with tasks that seem to involve quite basic judgements of numerosity, as Columbia University psychologist Peter Gordon discovered in an elegant experiment. He sat on one side of a table, the Pirahã participant on the other, a stick dividing the surface of the table. Gordon would place a number of objects on his side of the stick, and the participant was to match the objects one to one with, as it happens, AA batteries. The participants were mostly accurate up to two or three items, after which performance deteriorated abruptly. Similarly, Gordon would show a number of nuts before putting them in a can. He would then remove the nuts one at a time, asking after each removal whether there were any more nuts left in the can. Or he would hide candy in a box with a particular number of fish depicted on the lid. The task was to choose this box rather than another box marked with more or fewer fish. Performance involving numbers above two or three was very poor. For a person with a full repertoire of number words, and the ability to count, these tasks would of course be straightforward.[35]

Is maths special? Does language shape thought in other areas too? It turns out that similar effects are so ubiquitous that we scarcely remark upon them. Just about every specialized area of human life has its own vocabulary: whether we are getting to grips with physics or physiology, botany or bicycle repair, accountancy or astrology, we have to master a plethora of 'terms of art' in order to understand what is going on. No one has *any* thoughts about protons, the Krebs cycle, tap roots, gears, double-entry book-keeping or the signs of the zodiac without learning the meaning of these and many related words. As in mathematics, learning the jargon and learning the field are largely one and the same. Specialized language is obviously crucial to helping us think at all about specialized subject matter. The same point is true of everyday language.

A particularly striking example concerns not abstract mathematics but how we think of the spatial arrangements of the objects around us. In 1971 Penny Brown, a graduate student in anthropology at the University of California, Berkeley, started working with speakers of the Mayan language of Tseltal spoken in Chiapas in the south of Mexico. Together with Stephen Levinson (whom we met in chapter 2, studying the astonishing rapidity of turn-taking in language), she was studying the community's intricate norms of politeness.[36] But the two of them also noticed something very unexpected about how the Tseltal speakers talked about space: they had no words for left and right. Instead, directions would be given in relation to landmarks or the terrain (e.g. uphill/downhill). They do have distinct words for the left and right hands, but no general term to pick out left arms, left legs or left eyes, or to express the meaning 'to the left' or 'on the right'. Neither do they distinguish left and right versions of the same pattern – a shape and its mirror image (such as left and right shoes or a snail shell that spirals in a clockwise or anti-clockwise direction). Even thinking in terms of east and west on a map only makes sense if we distinguish a map from its mirror image – and indeed Tseltal-speakers don't use points of the compass. Brown and Levinson point out that Tseltal-speakers have an entirely coherent view of the geometry of space, one they use very successfully in navigating and communicating, albeit one that is unfamiliar to most of us. It is a world of symmetry (pots with two handles, not one; square houses with symmetrically placed doors that are split in two halves) in which locations are seen as locked into the landscape rather than as spatially related to objects (to the left of, in front of, etc.). Even when considering the location of objects on a flat tabletop indoors, Tseltal speakers refer to objects by **uphill** and **downhill**, referring to the landscape, even when the landscape is not visible through a window.

As with numbers, science, technology, religion – any topic at all – there is a two-way relationship between the language we use and the thoughts we entertain. The Tseltal-speakers don't think 'Let's put everything on the left of the table' because they have no word for 'left'. Equally, English-speakers don't think 'Let's put things on the uphill end of the table' (when the table is flat and uphill is determined by the surrounding landscape). But both can achieve the same goal, and they can also learn each other's thoughts and language. Language is not a prison – we can always learn new ways of talking and thinking about the world. This happens when we learn about any new domain (whether it be science, technology, music, religion or any other subject matter).

Language may even affect basic aspects of perception. Consider how different languages treat colour. For a start, not all languages have colour. The three and a half thousand speakers of Yélî Dnye in Papua New Guinea don't appear to classify the world in terms of abstract colours (for example, they use the name of a species of red parrot to pick out a red item).[37] Moreover, they don't have terms for many parts of colour space at all or any analogue of the word **colour**. So Yélî Dnye speakers can't even *ask* what colour something is, let alone give an answer that aligns with the colours in English.

And when languages do have abstract colour terms, it turns out that these exhibit remarkable variety. Some languages have just two primary colour terms (Bassa, a Kru language largely spoken in Liberia), others three (Ejagam, a Bantoid language spoken in parts of Nigeria and Cameroon), four (Culina, from the Arawan language family in Peru and Brazil), five (Iduna, an Austronesian language spoken in Papua New Guinea) or six (Buglere, from the Chibchan language family, Panama).[38] The boundaries between these various colours are not aligned in any simple way (as we might imagine if adding an extra colour simply splits, say, a term for blue-green into blue and green). Instead, they represent fundamentally different organizations of 'colour space'. These different colour terms certainly affect how people talk about colours and therefore how well they remember colours. But more remarkably, they even appear to have subtle impacts on basic perceptual processing.

How can we tell if the colour words in a language determine how its speakers perceive colours? One clever approach is to measure how easy it is for speakers of a particular language to distinguish between a pair of colours when each colour has a different linguistic label in that language compared to when both colours in a pair have the same label. If language shapes perception, we might expect people to spot the difference between two colours easily when they each have a separate name (such as **green** versus **blue**), but not when both colours have the same name (say, **blue**). Researchers can then further check whether any differences in perception between the first and second colour pair disappear when they test speakers of a different language where all the colours in the experiment are called the same thing (say, **blue**). This pattern, if observed, suggests that a person's language – and in particular how their language slices up colours – is having an effect on what they see. This was the strategy used in an experiment conducted by a team of psychologists from the University of Wales at Bangor.[39] The experiment employed an 'odd-ball' method. Specifically, a person is shown a stream of blobs mostly of the same colour but with a minority of shapes of a different colour. Such changes lead to a rapid and characteristic signature in our brain waves – visual mismatch negativity (vMMN) – that typically occurs rapidly (within 200 milliseconds) and should respond to changes of colour, irrespective of conscious attention. Moreover, this signature can be detected easily by placing a net of electrodes on the scalp. The person is not told to focus on colour during the task. Instead, they are instructed to press a button whenever an unusual **shape** appears, no matter its colour. But the characteristic signal of vMMN shows up for changes of colour, regardless of whether the person is paying attention to colour.

So now for the trick. In English, light and dark blue are both variants of the same colour (blue, of course), and the same goes for light and dark green. But in Greek, light and dark blue are associated with *different* colour words (light blue = **ghalazio**; dark blue = **ble**), whereas light and dark green are, as in English, considered to be variants of the same colour (green = **prasino**). This means that Greek-speakers might exhibit a stronger vMMN for a switch from one shade of blue to the other than for a switch from one shade of green to the other because in the first case, the two blues are seen as different colours, not just different shades of the same colour. And this is just what happens. The effect should be smaller or non-existent for English-speakers, for whom both cases correspond to shifting to a different shade of the same colour, not a different colour. And this happens, too. So, at least when it comes to colour, it seems that the language we speak can, quite literally, change the way we see the world.

An elegant follow-up experiment at Humboldt University in Berlin using similar stimuli showed that colour words in a language can affect even the degree to which a change in shade allows an item to enter conscious awareness.[40] Contrasting Russian-speakers (who, like the Greeks, have different colour terms for light blue and dark blue) with German-speakers (who, like English-speakers, do not), the researchers asked participants to report the shape of rapidly presented coloured stimuli. It turned out that a light–dark switch for blue items made the shape of those items easier to report than a light–dark switch for green items – but only for the Russian-speakers. The fact that a change of *colour* happens to cross a linguistic boundary makes the perception of *shape* accessible to consciousness.[41]

These experiments, and many more, strongly suggest deep connections between language and thought. The charades we create influence not just how we communicate but also how we think about the world. Seeing language as charades allows us to keep the nature of this connection in perspective. Language is always open-ended and flexible, able to convey the message of the moment rather than following a set of gridlines. But the particular linguistic charades we have to hand affect how easy it will be to express a new message. And, as we've seen, language may even partly reshape attention and perception.

In this light, it is interesting to revisit a debate that has exercised anthropologists, linguists and psychologists for more than a century. This is the so-called Sapir–Whorf hypothesis, which posits that differences in language shape how communities of speakers think and perhaps even determine what it is possible for them to think.[42] Sapir and Whorf studied Native American languages and were struck by how differently these languages carve up the world compared to European languages. They argued that, as a consequence, the thoughts of speakers of Hopi, Navajo and Shawnee must be profoundly different from those of speakers of English, French or German.[43]

Yet, despite a century of controversy, resolving the debate over the Sapir–Whorf hypothesis seems straightforward when we think of language as charades. First, as we've noted already, the remarkable creativity of charades allows us to convey just about anything. If we don't currently have a label for some aspect of the world, we can create one instantly or creatively combine labels that we do already have. Our specific language, therefore, does not set strict limits on our thoughts. Second, depending on the repertoire of charades we have already built, some messages will be much easier to convey than others. Hence, our language is likely to bias how we formulate our ideas to communicate both with others and with ourselves (indeed, the traces of such biases show up in the experiments we have described). Language is a useful set of limitlessly flexible tools from which new objects and, indeed, new tools can be created. Our set of linguistic tools doesn't limit what we can express; but it does affect what is easy to express and what can be expressed only with difficulty. Language shapes which thoughts are natural, but not which thoughts are possible.

THE EIGHTH TRANSITION

Evolution by natural selection is slow. The process is presumed to have started some time between three and four billion years ago, with the appearance of the first self-replicating molecules. Yet the gulf between a self-replicating molecule and a self-replicating organism, such as a tree, a fish or a poodle, is vast. The evolutionary biologists John Maynard Smith and Eörs Szathmáry famously argued that bridging that gulf has involved successive fundamental processes of reorganization – what they term the major transitions in evolution.[44]

At each major evolutionary transition, the nature of replication and/or what is replicated changes fundamentally. The first transition was from individual self-replicating molecules to a state in which many molecules were safely 'walled off' from the external world by a membrane. This development allowed all sorts of complex biochemistry to occur within the membrane-enclosed compartment – reactions that were only possible when safely shielded from the outside world. A second hypothesized transition linked independent replicating molecules together in chemical 'strings', tying the fate of each replicating molecule to that of others in the same string (in modern cells a string would be a chromosome) and creating the pressure for 'cooperation' between molecules, enabling even more biochemical complexity. A third hypothesized transition was the 'invention' of DNA: a specialized, highly stable replicator molecule. These first three transitions are presumed to have occurred some time between three and four billion years ago. Roughly two billion years ago (plus or minus a few hundred million years), the fourth transition occurred: the development of a distinct, walled-off cell nucleus. This is the transition when eukaryotes (cells with a nucleus; eukaryotes encompass just about all life we are familiar with, including amoebae, geraniums and whales) split from prokaryotes (cells lacking a separate nucleus, which includes the huge variety of modern bacteria and ancient archaea).

Maynard Smith and Szathmáry note that their fifth transition, the option of sexual reproduction (mixing the DNA of two organisms) rather than purely asexual reproduction, may have occurred at the same time as the fourth.[45] It is only with the sixth transition, from single-celled to multicellular organisms, that we see the emergence of the plant and animal kingdoms.[46] Now it is no longer just individual cells that reproduce, but entire organisms composed of different types of cells. Multicellularity radically reshaped what was biologically possible, enabling organisms to evolve specialized systems for respiration, digestion, locomotion and so on. A lung, liver or muscle cell, say, cannot reproduce unaided. Indeed, the entire organism can reproduce only via the transmission of its DNA through sperm or egg cells. Thus the reproductive fates of the trillions of cells making up a reasonably large organism such as a dog or a person are yoked together, all channelled through their collective contribution to determining the fate of a few individual sperm and eggs, which succeed or fail in their mission to propagate the organism's genes to the next generation.

The seventh transition occurred more than once but was adopted by only a tiny fraction of animals. It is the transition from living as individuals to living in genetically related and mutually interdependent colonies. The social insects, ants, wasps and bees, form incredibly diverse and complex colonies, often with many thousands of individuals. Naked mole rats, adapted to underground burrowing in the inhospitable East African desert, provide another striking example, with colonies of hundreds of animals reproducing via a single 'queen'. Many mammals live in interdependent groups with diverse and complex social behaviour, from hunting dogs and hyenas to primates and dolphins.[47] For example, the gelada (nicknamed the bleeding heart monkey because of the red markings on its front) has a remarkably complex hierarchical social organization that includes both reproductive units (typically comprising a few males and females and their young) and all-male units made up of a few adult males. These units are formed into bands (which include several units of each kind), herds (temporary groupings with up to sixty reproductive individuals, often from different bands) and communities (more stable groupings of several bands).[48]

The eighth and final major transition in the history of evolution, according to Maynard Smith and Szathmáry, is the emergence of language. The ability to play linguistic charades allows us gradually to build up an ever richer collection of communicative tools – or rather, the diverse set of collections that make up the languages of the world. Words and constructions become new 'units of selection', embodying the categories, distinctions, connotations and metaphors that have been most communicatively effective over endless conversational interactions spanning countless generations.

To the extent that language is a *system*, the usefulness of its words and constructions is not determined in isolation. Instead, different elements of the language propagate from generation to generation, primarily because they play a useful role in that system. There is a parallel here with biological evolution: whether or not a particular gene is useful depends on how it contributes to building and maintaining an entire organism, and helping it reproduce – and that organism is the product of a complex web of interactions among many genes. Asking about the 'usefulness' of a gene considered in isolation makes no sense. Now, some words to a certain extent can function usefully on their own: a cry of 'Dog!' or 'Goal!' or 'Help!' has some communicative value. But such cases are very much in the minority.

Consider the famous sentence from the US Declaration of Independence: 'We hold these truths to be self-evident, that all men are created equal, that they are endowed by their Creator with certain unalienable Rights, that among these are Life, Liberty and the pursuit of Happiness.' While surely one of the most influential statements ever written, most, if not all, of its component words would be entirely useless if used in isolation (imagine trying to conjure up the charade for **to**, **all**, **unalienable**, **liberty** or **pursuit**). It is the systematic patterns in language, not its individual elements, that give it such power: the power to transform our collective ability to create new forms of cultural, technological and social complexity. Without language, there would be no way of formulating, sharing and storing knowledge, skills, religious traditions or moral norms; people would be unable to organize into groups, firms, religious orders, scientific societies, armies or entire nations. Indeed, the eighth evolutionary transition is really not just one transition but a cascading wave of transitions that human culture has been surfing ever since.

◉

The astonishing and rapid advances of human culture are far beyond what can be created by the limited powers of any individual brain, facing the world afresh. Language has allowed us to harness the accumulated insights of countless generations before us and the billions of minds on our planet that are currently buzzing with ideas. Language connects us; language enables us to learn from each other; to disagree, criticize and test; to undercut bad ideas and reinforce the good. And it underpins most aspects of abstract thought – about mathematics, science, technology, the law or any other domain – with far-reaching implications for the development of our culture and society.

This changes everything. Natural selection is, to use Richard Dawkins's evocative phrase, a 'blind watchmaker', constructing complexity by an incredibly slow but powerful process of random variation and selection. Yet the existence of language enables the gradual construction and propagation of human culture by entire communities of *sighted* watchmakers – harnessing our collective cleverness to create knowledge, technology and social complexity at breathtaking speed.

It is through the invention of linguistic charades, and the virtuous circle of language, culture and the brain that it triggered, that humans have come to dominate the entire planet. So much so that geologists have recently declared that we have entered a new geological epoch – the Anthropocene – in recognition of humanity's collective and often profoundly disruptive influence on the climate, the oceans and coral reefs, the planet's biodiversity (and hence the future fossil record), the Earth's surface and much more.[49] The future biological evolution – or extinction – of all species, including our own, depends on the unpredictable ramifications of the collective invention of language.

EPILOGUE

LANGUAGE WILL SAVE US
FROM THE SINGULARITY

The primitive forms of artificial intelligence we already have, have proved very useful. But I think the development of full artificial intelligence could spell the end of the human race. Once humans develop artificial intelligence, it would take off on its own, and re-design itself at an ever increasing rate. Humans, who are limited by slow biological evolution, couldn't compete, and would be superseded.

STEPHEN HAWKING,
on *BBC Technology News* (2014)

Language has allowed humans to create and pass on knowledge, enact laws, teach each other skills, and create technology, organizations and cultures of astonishing complexity. The talking ape has come to dominate the planet to a staggering degree. Although there are more than seven billion humans, there are only a few hundred thousand chimpanzees, perhaps twenty thousand bonobos, and around one hundred thousand gorillas and orangutans.

The collective weight of all humans and our livestock (mostly cattle and pigs) outweighs all other vertebrates on the planet combined (with the exception of fish).[1] The power of language has enabled the emergence of collective human intelligence, ingenuity and creativity far beyond what any individual could independently achieve.

But perhaps the conversation is about to be joined by a new kind of language user, one of our own creation: artificial intelligence. Alexa and Siri can respond to our questions and commands, and do so by consulting quantities of human language far in excess of what any one person can peruse (at the time of writing, there are roughly sixty billion web pages on the World Wide Web).[2] The prospect of conversing with an artificial intelligence that possesses encyclopedic knowledge of any and every topic and the ability to chat fluently in any language is extremely alluring. And, indeed, this is partly why an estimated $36 billion was poured into AI research and development in 2019, a figure that is expected to continue to grow rapidly.[3]

But if we really hand the power of language to machines, are we in danger of giving away the secret of our own success to a new type of being? And might this not be a disastrous miscalculation, opening the door to a monster of our own creation? With the entire contents of human knowledge in digital form at their disposal and increasingly clever methods for extracting and using that knowledge, there would seem to be a real danger that machines with artificial intelligence may soon be smarter than their human creators.

The hypothetical point at which artificial intelligence exceeds human intelligence is known as the technological 'singularity'. This would be a momentous moment, because smart machines could build yet smarter machines, which could build even smarter machines still, without obvious limit. If we ever pass the singularity, the machines will be in charge for good, and what would become of humanity afterwards is impossible to gauge. The machines might retain humans as useful servants for practical tasks to which robots are ill suited or through some unaccountable nostalgia. But equally, they might not. After the singularity, it will no longer be up to humans to decide.

Passing the singularity would be terrifying. If we create a superintelligence, or rather a vast number of superintelligences (since software is so easy to replicate), that can piggyback on and exceed accumulated human knowledge, we would surely be left out of any future conversations. The idea that beings more intelligent than ourselves would work purely in our service seems entirely fanciful – indeed, the reverse is more likely. This concern has worried many great thinkers of our age, including theoretical physicist Stephen Hawking and mathematical genius and co-inventor of the modern digital computer John von Neumann.[4] Entrepreneur Elon Musk (the founder of Tesla and SpaceX) views artificial intelligence as 'summoning a demon' that may represent the greatest existential threat to humanity.[5] Leading AI researcher Stuart Russell has argued that humans face what he calls the 'gorilla' problem, in which the smartest minds on the planet tend to take over most of its resources – which is why humans dominate the Earth and gorillas do not. Russell fears that we humans may find ourselves in the position of the gorillas if we create artificial intelligence that is smarter than we are – and that's assuming we survive at all.[6]

There certainly are a number of good reasons to be worried. Indeed, chess, often viewed as the ultimate battle of wits, seems to provide an ominous precedent. Computer chess began in the 1950s and 1960s with a stream of unremarkable artificial chess players that were easily dispatched by human players. But in 1996, IBM's Deep Blue creditably lost a six-game match against the world champion of the time, Garry Kasparov, gaining two points to Kasparov's four. The next year, a rematch with an improved program, Deep(er) Blue, indicated that the chess singularity had been crossed: the AI program won 3.5 to 2.5 points against Kasparov. Soon after that, the only serious opposition to the best computer chess programs were other computer chess programs.

To give a sense of the scale of humanity's collective defeat, we can look to Elo ratings, the standard system for measuring chess-playing ability. A typical international master has a rating between 2,400 and 2,500; a grand master, between 2,500 and 2,700. The current world champion, Magnus Carlsen, has the highest-ever human Elo rating of nearly 2,900. By 2018, several computer chess programs, with charmingly idiosyncratic names such as Stockfish 9, Komodo 11.3.1 and Houdini 6, had Elo ratings above a staggering 3,400.[7] Indeed, no human player can now compete with the computer chess apps that run on most smartphones.

But our defeat doesn't end with chess: a gamut of games has since been conquered by computers. DeepMind's AlphaGo program beat the world champion of Go, Ke Jie, 3–0 in 2017.[8] AI has also proved devastatingly good at a wide range of popular video games, including seven Atari 2600 games, Super Mario World, Quake III Arena 'Capture the Flag', Dota 2 and StarCraft II – games that, like chess and Go, appear to require high levels of human intelligence.[9]

These AI achievements, while astonishing, carefully avoid dealing with language. They instead deal with the narrowly defined 'worlds' in which the game is played, and which can be learned by experience rather than by tapping into humanity's collective wisdom through language. However, in other domains, AI systems do appear to engage successfully with language. Indeed, the rather uninspiringly named GPT-3, released in 2020 by the San Francisco-based company OpenAI, has shown some rather remarkable results.[10]

The core of GPT-3 is a so-called deep neural network that consists of a large number of simple processing units linked to each other in layers. One of the many interesting features of neural networks (deep or otherwise) is that they don't need to be programmed by a software engineer to do a particular task. Instead, the neural network is trained to tackle any of a wide range of tasks, learning from examples of the task in question by modifying the strengths of the links between the units. If all goes well, the neural network learns not only how to deal with the training examples but also how to tackle new examples of the same task successfully. This style of computation is loosely inspired by the operation of the human brain, although it is very different in detail. The computational units are analogous to neurons, and learning is reminiscent of how the links between neurons (the synapses) are modified when learning occurs in the brain.

For decades, neural networks were viewed as conceptually elegant but limited to fairly simple tasks. But a succession of technical breakthroughs, ever more powerful computers and the availability of vast amounts of training data have transformed them into the workhorse of modern artificial intelligence. Modern deep neural networks (deep because of their many layers of artificial neurons) deliver state-of-the-art performance in a huge variety of tasks, from recognizing speech or faces, moving robotic arms and recommending movies to learning to play chess, Go and video games (a deep neural network is one of the key components of AlphaGo and related AI systems).

The scale of GPT-3 is extraordinary in a number of ways. First, it is a truly giant neural network containing 175 billion adjustable 'weights' that capture the strength of the connections between pairs of artificial neurons.[11] Second, it is trained on about a trillion words (not far from the entire contents of the World Wide Web). Third, it consumes staggering amounts of computer time (training GPT-3 involves more than a billion billion billion computational steps). But after this training on general patterns in human language, GPT-3 is able to deal with a wide variety of new tasks with uncanny flexibility. The artist Mario Klingemann gave GPT-3 an author (Jerome K. Jerome), a title ('The importance of being on Twitter'), and a first word (**It**) and found it generated a story with the striking opening:

> It is a curious fact that the last remaining form of social
> life in which the people of London are still interested is
> Twitter. I was struck with this curious fact when I went on
> one of my periodical holidays to the sea-side, and found
> the whole place twittering like a starling-cage. I called it an
> anomaly, and it is.[12]

This is pastiche, but pretty good pastiche; and the starling-cage image is rather delightful. And GPT-3 can answer questions, too. Indeed, in one demonstration, the philosopher Henry Shevlin prompted GPT-3 to answer interview questions on the nature of consciousness in the style of New York University philosopher Dave Chalmers, with mixed but not unimpressive results.[13] GPT-3 can write simple computer code, unscramble anagrams, perform basic arithmetic, answer a wide range of obscure general knowledge questions, translate between languages with passable accuracy and much more.

These technological achievements are remarkable – and far exceed anything that seemed conceivable when we were graduate students in Edinburgh three decades ago. Yet it turns out that these achievements have been made possible not by creating humanlike intelligence, which would raise the threat that human intelligence might soon be overtaken, but rather by avoiding the need for intelligence altogether. It is not that AI systems understand language and encode knowledge in a different way from us. Rather, AI systems have been able to do interesting and useful tasks without understanding language *at all*.

Computer scientist Kevin Lacker provides clever illustrations of how GPT-3 is impressively good at working with language, but without even the slightest trace of understanding anything. He finds GPT-3 able to answer basic questions about history—[14]

Q: Who was president of the United States in 1801?

A: Thomas Jefferson was president of the United States in 1801.

—though it gives rather strange answers to ill-posed questions:

Q: Who was president of the United States in 1600?

A: Queen Elizabeth I was president of the United States in 1600.

This is quite wrong, of course! GPT-3 should respond that there was no president of the United States, and for that matter, no legal entity called the United States. But Queen Elizabeth was at least a ruler in 1600, and England is after all closely historically linked with the United States. So Elizabeth I is at least a reasonable stab in the dark. But it gets worse. Lacker notes that GPT-3 should really fall apart when asked questions that have not been asked, or answered, anywhere on the web – so that no clever cutting-and-pasting from the trillion-word training sample can possibly work. Consider the following:

> **Q:** How many eyes does a spider have?
> **A:** A spider has eight eyes.
> **Q:** How many eyes does my foot have?
> **A:** Your foot has two eyes.

The first answer seems to show a good grasp of zoology – most spiders do, indeed, have eight eyes. But a foot having two eyes? If GPT-3 had even a remote understanding of anatomy, it would know that feet have no eyes. But it doesn't have the faintest understanding of anatomy – it knows the answer for spiders because the answer is all over the internet. But the internet is not full of comments about the eyelessness of feet. So GPT-3 is lost. One final example from Lacker shows just how profoundly GPT-3 is a shuffler of sentence fragments rather than a participant in meaningful dialogue:

> **Q:** How many rainbows does it take to jump from Hawaii
> to seventeen?
> **A:** It takes two rainbows to jump from Hawaii to
> seventeen.

The question is nonsense. GPT-3's answer is nonsense, too. GPT-3 has no idea about the difference between sense and nonsense. GPT-3 doesn't understand the difference. Of course not, because GPT-3 does not understand *anything*.

What did we expect? Once we see how language really works, as an elaborate form of charades, we should be immediately sceptical about the very idea of AI understanding language: computers don't (currently) play charades any more than chimps do. Charades is about clever improvisation, deploying knowledge in flexible and creative ways – and each charade can build on the last through metaphorical transformations of all kinds. Also, words don't have stable meanings, but evoke loose networks of connected meanings. Remember the 'unbearable lightness of meaning', where even the word **light** itself can have multiple interpretations – from light beers to light cavalry, light orchestras, light weights, light measures and light blues. GPT-3 isn't learning to play charades – it is learning to find incredibly complex patterns across billions of words of language. Humans and GPT-3 can both write short stories, technical manuals and press releases, and do other simple tasks with language, such as answering questions – but GPT-3 is not mimicking the human mind. It has no mind at all.

To put the point metaphorically: human language is to GPT-3 as the horse is to the motor car. Horses have indeed been replaced by motor cars, buses and trains as the most efficient means of human transport. But motor cars are scarcely artificial horses! They can't metabolize grass, reproduce, care for and raise young, navigate terrain of all kinds, jump fences or learn dressage. Cars are not even the slightest step towards the creation of the artificial horse, let alone the 'superhorse'. Rather, cars do one of the enormous number of things that horses can do (that is, transport people and goods), and though they do this exceedingly well, they do it completely differently. So it is with humans and AI. GPT-3 and similar artificial systems handle language not through creative charades-playing but by sifting through phenomenal amounts of data and running statistical analyses.

Translation is another clear example. The best translation systems operate by learning statistical patterns within languages, finding statistical matches between languages (matching up documents that have been translated by humans) and welding these together to make a surprisingly good stab at how a word sequence in one language might match up with a word sequence in another. And they do this without going through the rich metaphorical process of mapping sentences into what they are intended to mean on the basis of past conversation, experience and knowledge of the world. The statistical mapping between strings of words in one language and strings of words in another language entirely bypasses the need for knowing the meaning of either. Computers focus on the tip of the communication iceberg – words, phrases and sentences – but they are oblivious to its hidden, submerged part comprising all the cultural and social knowledge that makes human language possible. To a computer, the six-word story from chapter 1, 'For sale. Baby shoes. Never used,' would be no more than a typical classified ad. It would not evoke the kind of profound sadness, heartbreak and empathy that many a human reader is likely to experience.

The same is true of Alexa, Siri and Google Assistant. Each system is a remarkable engineering achievement that can match questions to answers through the power of statistics. But they all rely heavily on human-curated data. For example, Google Translate depends on armies of linguists from around the world to hand-annotate the input so that the system can learn from it.[15] None of these systems has the remotest idea of the meaning of the question, of the meaning of the web pages or encyclopedia articles it is analysing, or of the meaning of the answers it produces. They have no more understanding of language than a jukebox has of the songs it's playing.

As ever, mistakes are revealing. For example, on 20 May 2020 (and the algorithms are continually being fine-tuned), we had Google Translate turn the phrase **machines are set on world domination** into French and then back into English. The result was the bizarre **machines are placed on world domination**. Back-translating the phrase from Chinese produced **Machines dominate the world**, and via Zulu, we got the comical **the equipment is set to world domination**. Perhaps we have less to fear than we think!

Computers haven't joined the human conversation. And they haven't even learned to synthesize human knowledge from across the Web. AI technology is terrific for rough-and-ready translations and for pulling out useful information for people to look at (Google's stock-in-trade). But current computers are no better at emulating human intelligence than motor cars are at imitating horse biology; cars manage to do some of the useful things horses do by bypassing all that complicated biology entirely. The successes of current AI similarly bypass all the complexity of human intelligence. This is not to downplay the importance of these achievements – AI is likely to be as transformational for society as the invention of the motor car, and quite possibly far more. But right now, the idea that the singularity poses an imminent existential threat to humanity is about as fanciful as imagining that the more advanced motor cars will begin to live and reproduce freely in herds, train to become show-jumping champions or win the Grand National.

◉

We live in a time when computers continually amaze us: they can store unimaginably huge quantities of data, perform gigantic mathematical calculations, break codes, predict the weather, land planes, steer spacecraft through the solar system and even fly a mini-helicopter on Mars. But they lack the secret of human intelligence – the charades-playing ability that underpins language and allows us to mesh together our individual beliefs, preferences and ingenuity to create mathematics, science, philosophy, religion, the arts, money, laws, organizations, cities and ethics.

Yes, computers can beat us at chess, Go and any number of games. But the games that really matter are the creative and inventive games we play with language. In these games, humans are pre-eminent. It's not simply that AI systems play badly; rather, that they don't really know how to play at all. Until they can, they are no match for the linguistic improvisations at the core of human intelligence.

NOTES AND RESOURCES

PREFACE: THE ACCIDENTAL
INVENTION THAT CHANGED THE WORLD

1   Unless noted otherwise, throughout this book we use the term
    ape colloquially refer to the currently living non-human apes –
    chimpanzees, bonobos, gorillas and orangutans – rather than
    following the more technical taxonomic standard that includes
    humans.

2   In his famous posthumously published book *Philosophical
    Investigations*, the Austrian-born philosophical genius Ludwig
    Wittgenstein viewed language as arising from specific, local,
    practical, game-like interactions. Two quotes from his treatise
    give a flavour of his radical viewpoint, which has been very
    influential in our own thinking: 'The meaning of a word is its use
    in the language'; 'To understand a sentence means to understand
    a language. To understand a language means to be master of a
    technique'. L. Wittgenstein, *Philosophical Investigations* (Oxford:
    Blackwell, 1953), pp. 43, 199. The translation used here is from
    Elizabeth Anscombe, editor of *Philosophical Investigations*.

3   In this vein, Wittgenstein notes, 'One can also imagine someone's
    having learnt the game without ever learning or formulating
    rules': Wittgenstein, *Philosophical Investigations*, p. 31.

1: LANGUAGE AS CHARADES

1   The European perspective on the meeting between the Cook
    party and the Haush is based on the online version of Captain
    Cook's journals from his first Pacific voyage, 1768–71, along

with those of his fellow voyagers, Joseph Banks and Sydney Parkinson, and can be found at http://southseas.nla.gov.au/index_voyaging.html. Further background information about the Haush has been sourced from C. W. Furlong, 'The Haush and Ona, primitive tribes of Tierra del Fuego', *Proceedings of the Nineteenth International Congress of Americanists*, Dec. 1915, pp. 432–44; D. Macnaughtan, 'Bibliography of the Haush (Manek'enk) Indians: an indigenous people of southeastern Tierra del Fuego, Argentina', *Ethnographic Bibliographies*, no. 10 (2020), https://www.academia.edu/10500405/The_Haush_Indians_of_Tierra_del_Fuego; D. Macnaughtan, 'Haush Indians of Tierra del Fuego', *Don Macnaughtan's Bibliographies*, https://waikowhai2.wordpress.com/the-haush-indians-of-tierra-del-fuego/.

2   Linguistic descriptions of the Haush and Ona (also known as Selk'nam) languages are based on W. F. H. Adelaar and P. Muysken, *The Languages of the Andes* (Cambridge: Cambridge University Press, 2004); L. M. Rojas-Berscia, 'A heritage reference grammar of Selk'nam', master's thesis (Radboud University, Nijmegen, 2014).

3   The Haush's encounters with Europeans were initially peaceful, as in the case with their meeting with Cook's men and later with Charles Darwin and the crew of HMS *Beagle* in 1832. However, the indigenous people of the Tierra del Fuego – the Haush and the Ona – were soon tragically imperilled by the subsequent influx of European colonists. Abhorrently, sheep ranchers even organized hunting parties to kill them off. Disease brought by the Europeans was also a major threat to indigenous people, the last of the Haush succumbing to a measles epidemic in the 1920s. Macnaughtan, 'Bibliography of the Haush (Manek'enk) Indians', https://www.academia.edu/10500405/The_Haush_Indians_of_Tierra_del_Fuego; Macnaughtan, 'Haush Indians of Tierra del Fuego', https://waikowhai2.wordpress.com/the-haush-indians-of-tierra-del-fuego/.

4   It's important to note that creoles are fully developed languages on a par with older, more established languages, such as English, Danish and Hindi. Yet speakers of creole languages often suffer discrimination, including by bans on using their native language

in schools. J. L. Bonenfant, 'History of Haitian-Creole: from pidgin to lingua franca and English influence on the language', *Review of Higher Education and Self-Learning* 4 (2011), pp. 27–34.

5   M. Tomasello, *The Origins of Human Communication* (Cambridge, MA: MIT Press, 2008). Tomasello was the director of the Department of Developmental and Comparative Psychology at the Max Planck Institute for Evolutionary Anthropology in Leipzig, Germany, when he presented this argument. Morten enjoyed spending three months at the institute in 2007 as part of his sabbatical, staying in an apartment overlooking the beautiful St Nicholas Church – the centre of the peaceful revolution that eventually overturned the government of the German Democratic Republic. Nick also visited the institute for a short while. To carry out his groundbreaking research on primate social cognition, Tomasello divided his time between the institute and Pongoland (also known as the Wolfgang Köhler Primate Research Centre), situated a few miles away within the grounds of Leipzig Zoo. Tomasello was so dedicated to the non-human primates he worked with that he at the last minute cancelled his talk at a conference that Nick co-organized in 2002 because one of the chimps was giving birth; so Nick ended up delivering Tomasello's lecture, with the bizarre consequence that some of the conference attendees had the urge to follow up the talk with the traditional round of questions – which, of course, Nick had no idea how to answer!

6   D. Blum, *Love at Goon Park: Harry Harlow and the Science of Affection* (New York: Basic Books, 2002).

7   What is now called the 'forbidden experiment' has fascinated scholars and thinkers since ancient times. The Egyptian pharaoh Psamtik I, the Holy Roman Emperor Frederick II and James IV of Scotland are all said to have conducted variations on this kind of experiment, having children brought up without language input, and with questionable outcomes at best (typically confirming the beliefs of the time). J. P. Davidson, *Planet Word* (London: Michael Joseph, 2011).

8   J. Kegl, A. Senghas and M. Coppola, 'Creation through contact: sign language emergence and sign language change in Nicaragua', in M. DeGraff, ed., *Language Creation and Language Change: Creolization, Diachrony, and Development* (Cambridge, MA: MIT Press, 1999), pp. 179–237.

9   S. Goldin-Meadow, *The Resilience of Language: What Gesture Creation in Deaf Children Can Tell Us About How All Children Learn Language* (New York: Psychology Press, 2005).

10   This example comes from J. Pyers and A. Senghas, 'Lexical iconicity is differentially favored under transmission in a new sign language: the effect of type of iconicity', *Sign Language & Linguistics* 23 (2020), pp. 73–95. We are grateful to Jennie Pyers for providing us with the detailed descriptions of the sign configurations for 'horse'.

11   Intriguingly, there's even a charades-like game that aims to recreate the initial emergence of Nicaraguan Sign Language: *Sign: A Game About Being Understood* (https://thornygames.com/pages/sign).

12   Our exposition of Perlman's work is based on several of his papers as well as personal communication with him. M. Perlman, 'Can a game of "vocal" charades act out the origin of language?', *Babel: The Language Magazine* 12 (2018), pp. 30–5; M. Perlman, R. D. Dale and G. Lupyan, 'Iconicity can ground the creation of vocal symbols', *Royal Society Open Science* 2 (2015): 150152; M. Perlman and G. Lupyan, 'People can create iconic vocalizations to communicate various meanings to naïve listeners', *Scientific Reports* 8 (2018): 2634; A. Ćwiek, S. Fuchs, C. Draxler, E. L. Asu, D. Dediu, K. Hiovain et al., 'Novel vocalizations are understood across cultures', *Scientific Reports* 11 (2021): 10108; M. Perlman, J. Z. Paul and G. Lupyan, 'Congenitally deaf children generate iconic vocalizations to communicate magnitude', in *Proceedings of the 37th Annual Cognitive Science Society Meeting* (Austin, TX: Cognitive Science Society, 2015), 315–20.

13   Shannon was a true scientific pioneer whose work set the stage for the digital revolution and the information age, from

)

microprocessors and data storage to the internet and artificial intelligence. He was also an avid inventor – but, unlike the inventions of his distant cousin Thomas Edison, Shannon's contraptions often revealed his more playful side, such as his rocket-propelled frisbee, a flame-throwing trumpet, and a machine whose only function was to turn itself off. Through it all, his wife, Betty Shannon, was his closest collaborator, although she didn't receive the recognition she deserved. C. E. Shannon, 'A mathematical theory of communication', *Bell System Technical Journal* 27 (1948), pp. 379–423, 623–56; W. Weaver, 'Recent contributions to the mathematical theory of communication', in C. E. Shannon and W. Weaver, eds, *The Mathematical Theory of Communication* (Urbana: University of Illinois Press, 1949); 'MIT professor Claude Shannon dies; was founder of digital communications' (press release), *MIT News* (Cambridge, MA, 27 Feb. 2001), http://news.mit.edu/2001/Shannon; 'A Goliath amongst giants: Claude E. Shannon', Nokia Bell Labs (n.d.), https://www.bell-labs.com/claude-shannon/; J. Soni and R. Goodman, 'Betty Shannon, unsung mathematical genius', Voices (blog), *Scientific American*, 24 July 2017, https://blogs.scientificamerican.com/voices/betty-shannon-unsung-mathematical-genius/.

14 G. Miller, 'The cognitive revolution: a historical perspective', *Trends in Cognitive Sciences* 7 (2003), pp. 141–4.

15 Cognitive science is also the field in which both Morten and Nick earned their PhDs at the University of Edinburgh in Scotland.

16 Our perception of the world is not passively rendered from the input to our senses but actively constructed by our brains. 'By viewing the brain as a computer that passively responds to inputs and processes data, we forget that it is an active organ, part of a body that is intervening in the world, and which has an evolutionary past that has shaped its structure and function': M. Cobb, 'Why your brain is not a computer', *Guardian*, 27 Feb. 2020, https://www.theguardian.com/science/2020/feb/27/why-your-brain-is-not-a-computer-neuroscience-neural-networks-consciousness.

17 F. de Saussure, *Course in General Linguistics* (New York: McGraw-Hill, 1916).

18 C. E. Shannon, 'A mathematical theory of communication', *Bell System Technical Journal* 27 (1948), pp. 379–423, 623–56.

19 We're not suggesting that the mathematics of Shannon's information theory is somehow circumvented by the ingenuity of human communication. For example, in a given context, with a specific history of prior charades-playing, the number of possible messages can't exceed the number of gestures to convey them without some messages being lost. But the challenge of understanding how people play charades is to figure out what the possible messages are, given the circumstances, and creatively find a novel way of mapping gestures to messages.

20 Urban legend has it that this particular story was crafted by Ernest Hemingway in response to a bet about whether he could come up with a short story, with a beginning, middle and end, consisting of just six words. This seems unlikely, though, because a twelve-word-long classified ad with the same sentiments, 'Baby's hand made trousseau and baby's bed for sale. Never been used' appeared in the *Spokane Press* in Washington State in 1910, when Hemingway was only ten years old. In 1921, a seven-word version appeared in the humour magazine *The Judge*: 'For sale, a baby carriage, never used' – but in this case, the story has a happy ending because the parents had twins and needed to replace their original single baby carriage with a double-seater. This discussion of the urban legend behind the baby shoes story owes a lot to the detective work done by the Quote Investigator, Garson O'Toole: https://quoteinvestigator.com/2013/01/28/baby-shoes/. Additional sources: 'Tragedy of baby's death is revealed in sale of clothes', *Spokane (Washington) Press*, 16 May 1910, p. 6; Jay G'Dee, 'Fools rush in', *The Judge*, no. 81, 16 July 1921, p. 14.

21 This kind of 'inferential' rather than code-sending perspective on communication can be traced back at least to the philosopher Paul Grice, and has inspired later work including Dan Sperber and Deirdre Wilson's influential 'Relevance Theory' and especially

Herbert Clark's important work on language as a type of joint action, from which we have drawn much inspiration. H. P. Grice, 'Meaning', *Philosophical Review* 66 (1957), pp. 377–88; D. Wilson and D. Sperber, *Relevance: Communication and Cognition* (Oxford: Blackwell, 1986); H. H. Clark, *Using Language* (Cambridge: Cambridge University Press, 1996).

22　Our notion of the communication iceberg is inspired in part by the use of a similar metaphor to understand cross-cultural adjustment difficulties in G. R. Weaver, 'Understanding and coping with cross-cultural adjustment stress', in R. M. Paige, ed., *Cross-Cultural Orientation: New Conceptualizations and Applications* (Lanham, MD: University Press of America, 1986), pp. 111–45. Similarly, Gilles Fauconnier notes, 'Language is only the tip of a spectacular cognitive iceberg,' but doesn't develop the concept further: G. Fauconnier, 'Methods and generalizations', in T. Janssen and G. Redeker, eds, *Cognitive Linguistics: Foundations, Scope, and Methodology* (Berlin: Walter de Gruyter, 1999), pp. 95–127 at p. 96. Another related idea about the importance of culture, social values and emotions to language understanding can be found in the concept of 'dark matter' in D. Everett, *How Language Began* (London: Profile Books, 2017).

23　H. H. Clark and M. A. Krych, 'Speaking while monitoring addressees for understanding', *Journal of Memory and Language* 50 (2004), pp. 62–81.

24　The discussion of Alan Alda and his approach to science communication is based on his book: A. Alda, *If I Understood You, Would I Have This Look on My Face?* (New York: Random House, 2017).

2: THE FLEETING NATURE OF LANGUAGE

1　The content of the first message sent in Navajo code is unknown. The message here is taken from the 'Code Talking' section of the *Native Words, Native Warriors* website (produced by the National Museum of the American Indian, Smithsonian Institution, at

https://americanindian.si.edu/education/codetalkers/html/
chapter4.html) and coded using the declassified *Navajo Code
Talker Dictionary* (on the *Naval History and Heritage Command*
website, https://www.history.navy.mil/research/library/
online-reading-room/title-list-alphabetically/n/navajo-code-
talker-dictionary.html). The original English message reads:
'Fierce action at forward position. Intense mortar attack. Request
reinforcements immediately!'

2   The US Army had already used Native American (primarily
Choctaw) code talkers at the end of the First World War, and with
great success, but a system wasn't developed until the Second
World War. Alongside the Navajo, members of other Native
American tribes were also employed as code talkers in their
respective native languages, including Comanches, Choctaws,
Hopis and Cherokees (*Native Words, Native Warriors*, https://
americanindian.si.edu/education/codetalkers/html/chapter4.
html). The Navajos made up the largest group, with more code
talkers than all the other Native American tribes together, and
they were even featured in the 2002 Hollywood movie *Windtalkers*,
which bombed at the box office. The movie was criticized for
merely relying on battlefield clichés rather than telling the
fascinating tale of the code talkers (Rotten Tomatoes, https://www.
rottentomatoes.com/m/windtalkers/). The missed opportunity to
tell the true story about the code talkers is particularly haunting
because of the injustices suffered by Native Americans. For years,
they were forbidden to use their native languages (and culture)
in the name of assimilation into white society, and the enlisted
men suffered lifelong racism and prejudice: 'Chester Nez, 93,
dies; Navajo words washed from mouth helped win war', *New
York Times*, 6 June 2014, https://www.nytimes.com/2014/06/06/us/
chester-nez-dies-at-93-his-native-tongue-helped-to-win-a-war-
of-words.html. In fact, Native Americans weren't even considered
US citizens until 1924 – well after they had served in the First
World War. Further details about the Navajo code talkers came
from the *Naval History and Heritage Command* website (https://

www.history.navy.mil/research/library/online-reading-room/
title-list-alphabetically/n/code-talkers.html) and 'Codemakers:
history of the Navajo code talkers', on *HistoryNet.com*, https://www.
historynet.com/world-war-ii-navajo-code-talkers.htm.

3 Initially, the number of chunks was thought to be 7 ± 2
(G. A. Miller, 'The magical number seven, plus or minus two: some
limits on our capacity for processing information', *Psychological
Review* 63 [1956], pp. 81–97), but this number is likely to reflect the
role of long-term memory processes in short-term recall. In so
far as 'raw' memory can be measured in the absence of any prior
experience, the limit on chunks is reduced to just 4 ± 1. N. Cowan,
'The magical number 4 in short-term memory: a reconsideration
of mental storage capacity', *Behavioral and Brain Sciences* 24 (2000),
pp. 87–114.

4 Although we focus primarily on speech in this chapter, the
Now-or-Never bottleneck applies to sign language as well. The
production of signs is somewhat slower than the production of
speech (at least when comparing the production of American Sign
Language [ASL] signs to spoken English; U. Bellugi and S. Fischer,
'A comparison of sign language and spoken language', *Cognition*
1 [1972], pp. 173–200), but signed words are still very brief visual
events, with the duration of an ASL syllable of about a quarter of
a second (R. B. Wilbur and S. B. Nolkn, 'The duration of syllables
in American Sign Language', *Language and Speech* 29 [1986], pp.
263–80). Our sensory memory for visual information is also very
short-lived (H. Pashler, 'Familiarity and visual change detection',
Perception & Psychophysics 44 [1988], pp. 369–78), disappearing
within about two-thirds of a second. And the memory for visual
sequences is limited to about four items (S. J. Luck and E. K.
Vogel, 'The capacity of visual working memory for features and
conjunctions', *Nature* 390 [1997], pp. 279–81).

5 Some languages tend to be spoken more rapidly than others,
at least when measuring the number of syllables produced per
minute. For example, speakers of Japanese and Iberian Spanish
tend to produce more syllables per minute than speakers of

German and Mandarin Chinese. However, Japanese and Spanish syllables carry less information than German and Mandarin syllables, so when it comes to amount of information transferred (about 39 bits per second), all languages are more or less the same. Spaniards do speak faster than Germans, but they tend to say less with each syllable they produce. F. Pellegrino, C. Coupé and E. Marsico, 'A cross-language perspective on speech information rate', *Language* 87 (2011), pp. 539–58; C. Coupé, Y. M. Oh, D. Dediu and F. Pellegrino, 'Different languages, similar encoding efficiency: comparable information rates across the human communicative niche', *Science Advances* 5 (2019): eaaw2594.

6   G. A. Miller and W. G. Taylor, 'The perception of repeated bursts of noise', *Journal of the Acoustical Society of America* 20 (1948), pp. 171–82.

7   Dick Neisser, a towering giant in the study of the mind, in 1967 wrote the first textbook on 'cognitive' psychology, an approach that views the mind as an information-processing system. With his great intellectual curiosity, vast knowledge of psychology and penetrating analytical skills, his presence at Cornell was among the key attractions that drew Morten to the university. It was therefore with much sadness that Morten later came to witness Neisser, his informal mentor, gradually succumb to the ravages of Parkinson's disease.

8   U. Neisser, 'The control of information pickup in selective looking', in A. D. Pick, ed., *Perception and Its Development: A Tribute to Eleanor J. Gibson* (Hillsdale, NJ: Lawrence Erlbaum, 1979), pp. 201–19.

9   D. J. Simons and C. F. Chabris, 'Gorillas in our midst: sustained inattentional blindness for dynamic events', *Perception* 28 (1999), pp. 1059–74.

10   D. J. Simons and D. T. Levin, 'Failure to detect changes to people during a real-world interaction', *Psychonomic Bulletin & Review* 5 (1998), pp. 644–9.

11   For a thorough look at the surprising shallowness of perception and thought in general, and how it is hidden by a continual stream

of creative improvisation, see N. Chater, *The Mind Is Flat* (London: Penguin, 2018).

12 In this chapter, we draw on our own research on the Now-or-Never bottleneck, as detailed in several publications, including M. H. Christiansen and N. Chater, *Creating Language: Integrating Evolution, Acquisition, and Processing* (Cambridge, MA: MIT Press, 2016); M. H. Christiansen and N. Chater, 'The Now-or-Never Bottleneck: A Fundamental Constraint on Language', *Behavioral & Brain Sciences* 39 (2016): e62; N. Chater and M. H. Christiansen, 'Language acquisition as skill learning', *Current Opinion in Behavioural Sciences* 21 (2018), pp. 205–8.

13 Periander's saying is often misquoted as 'practice makes perfect'. Periander's original work from more than 2,600 years ago is lost, but he is quoted in a secondary source from the third century AD: D. Laertius, *The Lives and Opinions of Eminent Philosophers*, trans. C. D. Yonge (London: H. G. Bohn, 1853).

14 K. A. Ericsson, W. G. Chase and S. Faloon, 'Acquisition of a memory skill', *Science* 208 (1980), pp. 1181–2.

15 Here, spoken and signed language differ somewhat from written language, where we deliberately practise spelling out words as part of our literacy skills (and which we took advantage of in the previous 'language game' recall example).

16 Similarly, we often mishear song lyrics, such as when hearing 'There's a bathroom on the right' instead of 'There's a bad moon on the rise' in the Creedence Clearwater Revival song 'Bad Moon Rising'; or when we hear ''Scuse me while I kiss this guy' rather than ''Scuse me while I kiss the sky' in the song 'Purple Haze' by Jimi Hendrix. Both examples are from M. Konnikova, 'Excuse me while I kiss this guy', *New Yorker*, 10 Dec. 2014.

17 The precise nature of the units does vary, though. For example, some languages, such as most dialects of Japanese, are better organized into sub-word elements, mora, with particular properties of timing and stress, rather than syllables. Moreover, phonemes operate very differently in sign languages.

18   The idea that speech understanding and speech production
     mirror one another has a long and varied history in the language
     sciences. See, for example, A. M. Liberman and I. G. Mattingly,
     'The motor theory of speech perception revised', *Cognition* 21
     (1985), pp. 1–36; M. J. Pickering and S. Garrod, 'An integrated theory
     of language production and comprehension', *Behavioral and Brain
     Sciences* 36 (2013), pp. 329–47.

19   T. Ōno and S. Mito, *Just-in-Time for Today and Tomorrow*
     (New York: Productivity Press, 1988). The phrase 'just-in-
     time' has been used in the engineering field of speech
     synthesis in a similar way by T. Baumann and D. Schlangen,
     'INPRO_iSS: a component for just-in-time incremental speech
     synthesis', in *Proceedings of the ACL 2012 System Demonstrations*
     (Stroudsburg, PA: Association for Computational
     Linguistics, 2012), pp. 103–8.

20   This word, or very close variants thereof, has a surprisingly long
     history in popular entertainment and was even the subject of
     lawsuits over its invention. 'The real origin of "supercalifragilistic"',
     Word History (blog), *Merriam-Webster*, https://www.merriam-
     webster.com/words-at-play/origin-supercalifragilisticexpialidocious.

21   The speed records for talking are from 'Fastest talking female-
     world record set by Fran Capo', *World Record Academy*, https://www.
     worldrecordacademy.com/human/fastest_talking_female_world_
     record_set_by_Fran_Capo_70895.htm; Rachel Swatman, 'Can you
     recite Hamlet's "To be or not to be" soliloquy quicker than the
     fastest talker?', 19 Jan. 2018, *Guinness World Records*, https://www.
     guinnessworldrecords.com/news/2018/1/can-you-recite-hamlets-
     to-be-or-not-to-be-soliloquy-quicker-than-the-fastest-t-509944.

22   K. Conklin and N. Schmitt, 'The processing of formulaic language',
     Annual Review of Applied Linguistics 32 (2012), pp. 45–61.

23   Michael Skapinker, 'Foreign managers' phrases find the back
     of the net', *Financial Times*, 14 May 2018. The paper to which
     Skapinker referred is M. H. Christiansen and I. Arnon, 'More than
     words: the role of multiword sequences in language learning and
     use', *Topics in Cognitive Science* 9 (2017), pp. 542–51.

24 F. Wijnen, 'Incidental word and sound errors in young speakers',
    Journal of Memory and Language 31 (1992), pp. 734–55.

25 Speech error examples are taken from the appendix of V. A.
    Fromkin, ed., *Speech Errors as Linguistic Evidence* (The Hague,
    Netherlands: Mouton, 1973).

26 The linguist Noam Chomsky has rather bizarrely claimed that
    language is almost exclusively for monologue: 'Well, probably
    99.9 percent of its use is internal to the mind. You can't go a
    minute without talking to yourself': N. Chomsky and J. McGilvray,
    The Science of Language: Interviews with James McGilvray (New
    York: Cambridge University Press, 2012). For a cogent review, see
    C. Behme, 'Noam Chomsky: the science of language. Interviews
    with James McGilvray', *Philosophy in Review* 33 (2013), pp. 100–3.
    Whereas this might be true for armchair philosophers (although
    even this is likely to be a stretch), an empirical study that recorded
    how many words we actually utter suggests that on average we
    say aloud around sixteen thousand words per day: M. R. Mehl,
    S. Vazire, N. Ramírez-Esparza, R. B. Slatcher and J. W. Pennebaker,
    'Are women really more talkative than men?', *Science* 317 (2007),
    p. 82. On Chomsky's monologue account, this would mean that
    we'd say about 15,984,000 words to ourselves internally every day.
    Given an average speech rate of 150 words per minute, it would
    require 1,776 hours to say a day's worth of monologue to ourselves.
    Even if we assume an internal speech rate comparable to the
    motormouth Fran Capo, at 667 words per minute, it would still
    take 399 hours, or more than two weeks.

27 Martin Pickering and Simon Garrod have been particularly
    influential in reorienting the language sciences towards viewing
    dialogue, rather than monologue, as fundamental. M. J. Pickering
    and S. Garrod, 'Toward a mechanistic psychology of dialogue',
    Behavioral and Brain Sciences 27 (2004), pp. 169–90.

28 This paragraph is inspired by S. C. Levinson, 'Turn-taking in
    human communication – origins and implications for language
    processing', *Trends in Cognitive Sciences* 20 (2016), pp. 6–14. It also
    draws on the following sources. Fast turn-taking: T. Stivers, N. J.

Enfield, P. Brown, C. Englert, M. Hayashi, T. Heinemann et al., 'Universals and cultural variation in turn-taking in conversation', *Proceedings of the National Academy of Sciences* 106 (2009), pp. 10587–92; speed of face recognition: S. Caharel, M. Ramon and B. Rossion, 'Face familiarity decisions take 200 msec in the human brain: electrophysiological evidence from a go/no-go speeded task', *Journal of Cognitive Neuroscience* 26 (2014), pp. 81–95; speed of picture naming: E. Bates, S. D'Amico, T. Jacobsen, A. Székely, E. Andonova, A. Devescovi et al., 'Timed picture naming in seven languages', *Psychonomic Bulletin & Review* 10 (2003), pp. 344–80; speed of reading aloud: D. A. Balota, M. J. Yap, K. A. Hutchison, M. J. Cortese, B. Kessler, B. Loftis et al., 'The English lexicon project', *Behavior Research Methods* 39 (2007), pp. 445–59.

29 Here we rely on: T. D. Erickson and M. E. Matteson, 'From words to meaning: a semantic illusion', *Journal of Verbal Learning and Verbal Behavior* 20 (1981), pp. 540–52; F. Ferreira and N. D. Patson, 'The "good enough" approach to language comprehension', *Language and Linguistics Compass* 1 (2007), pp. 71–83.

30 M. Dingemanse, F. Torreira and N. J. Enfield, 'Is "huh?" a universal word? Conversational infrastructure and the convergent evolution of linguistic items', *PLOS ONE* 8 (2013): e78273.

31 This dialogue is excerpted from the 'SBC036 judgmental on people' sample of J. W. Du Bois and R. Englebretson, *Santa Barbara Corpus of Spoken American English, Part 3* (Philadelphia: Linguistic Data Consortium, 2004). An audio file with the twelve-second excerpt can be found here: https://vod.video.cornell.edu/media/ TLG_C2_conversation-excerpt/1_419ixr20, and a transcript of the full conversation is here: https://www.linguistics.ucsb.edu/ sites/secure.lsit.ucsb.edu.ling.d7/files/sitefiles/research/SBC/ SBC036.trn. For more on the different conversational strategies we use to keep a conversation going, see C. Dideriksen, R. Fusaroli, L. Tylén, M. Dingemanse and M. H. Christiansen, 'Contextualizing conversational strategies: backchannel, repair and linguistic alignment in spontaneous and task-oriented conversations', in

A. Goel, C. Seifert and C. Freksa, eds, *Proceedings of the 41st Annual Conference of the Cognitive Science Society* (Austin, TX: Cognitive Science Society, 2019), pp. 261–7.

3: THE UNBEARABLE LIGHTNESS OF MEANING

1   M. Kundera, *The Unbearable Lightness of Being* (New York: Harper & Row, 1984).
2   The phrase 'the unbearable lightness of meaning' was discussed by George Dunbar, formerly a fellow PhD student at the Centre for Cognitive Science at the University of Edinburgh, in describing the instability of word meanings. It has appeared independently in a slightly different context: H. Postigo, 'Social media: the unbearable lightness of meaning', *Social Media + Society* 1 (2015). DOI: 10.1177/2056305115580342.
3   This viewpoint allows that the very same forms (as patterns of sound and strings of letters) may happen to be associated with two or more meanings by coincidence or for historical reasons. So, the word *bank* can refer to the side of a river or a financial institution. From this point of view, we're really talking about two words, not one (as it were, bank1 and bank2); they just happen to sound the same. And each of these is presumed to have a clear-cut meaning – denoting some concept and/or aspect of the external world.
4   Genesis 2:19.
5   The *Confessions of Saint Augustine*, in thirteen books, was written in Latin between AD 397 and 400, and mainly recounts Augustine's transition from a licentious life of lust, adultery and, perhaps unexpectedly, pear stealing to that of a devoted Christian. Wittgenstein viewed Augustine's brief passage on how language is learned, from which our quotation is taken, as so eloquently capturing the 'received view' of language as philosophically unproblematic that he opens *Philosophical Investigations* by quoting Augustine and noting that the rest of the book aims to

break the hold that this viewpoint has upon us. Wittgenstein, *Philosophical Investigations*, pp. 66–7.

6 The great Harvard philosopher Willard Van Orman Quine famously illustrated the point by imagining how we might try to infer the meaning of a word, *gavagai*, in an unknown language, shouted when a rabbit comes into view. Quine controversially argued that the translations of individual words, and entire languages, can never be completely pinned down, however much experience and however many examples we have.

7 Or two or more meanings, for ambiguous words like *bank* (river or financial) or *seal* (aquatic or wax). But ambiguity is far more prevalent than this – the loosely interconnected but distinct ways in which words are used ramify off in the most unexpected directions. Of course, this is just what we expect when we see language as charades – words or gestures can endlessly be reused, distorted or extended in innumerable ways, limited only by our imaginations.

8 Wray played the damsel in distress in the original 1933 film.

9 For a classic discussion of metaphor, language and thought, see G. Lakoff and M. Johnson, *Metaphors We Live By* (Chicago: University of Chicago Press, 1980). The authors stress just how astonishingly widespread, systematic and mutually contradictory metaphors can be – and how our reasoning about abstract realms builds on (another metaphor!) our understanding of the concrete physical world, including our own bodies.

10 The collection of metaphors about mental depth, including the conscious/subconscious divide, may be highly misleading as the starting point for a science of the mind: see Chater, *The Mind Is Flat*.

11 As the Oxford philosopher John Austin put it: 'There is ... [a] ... danger in words that invoke models, half-forgotten or not. It must be remembered that there is no necessity whatsoever that the various models used in creating our vocabulary, primitive or recent, should all fit together neatly as parts into one single, total model or scheme ... It is possible, and indeed highly likely, that

our assortment of models will include some, or many, that are overlapping, conflicting, or more generally simply disparate': J. L. Austin, 'A plea for excuses: the presidential address', *Proceedings of the Aristotelian Society* 57 (1957), pp. 1–30.

12 S. Carey, 'Conceptual differences between children and adults', *Mind & Language* 3 (1988), pp. 167–81. Nick was lucky enough to see Sue talk about this work at Edinburgh's Centre for Cognitive Science while he was a PhD student. This was one of those rare talks that was, for Nick, an utter revelation. Nick and his friend and fellow PhD student Mike Oaksford followed up, initially somewhat sceptically, with Mike's own pre-school daughter. Sure enough, the strangeness of the pre-school child's conception of alive and dead was confirmed: it turned out that the sun was alive when shining in the sky, and cars were alive, but only when being driven.

13 J. S. Horst and L. K. Samuelson, 'Fast mapping but poor retention by 24-month-old infants', *Infancy* 13 (2008), pp. 128–57.

14 F. de Saussure, *Course in General Linguistics* (New York: McGraw-Hill, 1916).

15 P. Monaghan, M. H. Christiansen and S. A. Fitneva, 'The arbitrariness of the sign: learning advantages from the structure of the vocabulary', *Journal of Experimental Psychology: General* 140 (2011), pp. 325–47.

16 J. Wilkins, *An Essay Towards a Real Character and a Philosophical Language* (London: Gellibrand, 1668). The speculative and fanciful nature of Wilkins's thought is illustrated by the very title of another of his works, the 1638 book *The Discovery of a World in the Moone. Or, a Discourse Tending to Prove, That 'Tis Probable There May Be Another Habitable World in That Planet.*

17 U. Eco, *The Search for a Perfect Language* (New York: John Wiley & Sons, 1997). Umberto Eco was not only a formidable scholar of language and culture but also the author of the best-selling *The Name of the Rose*, among other novels.

18 Yet despite its ramshackle and peculiar features, some good came of Wilkins's bizarre project. Almost two centuries later, his

classification was a key source of inspiration for the taxonomy of English words in Roget's much-loved thesaurus, as outlined in W. Hüllen, *A History of Roget's Thesaurus: Origins, Development, and Design* (Oxford: Oxford University Press, 2003).

19 D. E. Blasi, S. Wichmann, H. Hammarström, P. F. Stadler and M. H. Christiansen, 'Sound–meaning association biases evidenced across thousands of languages', *Proceedings of the National Academy of Sciences* 113 (2016), pp. 10818–23. Specifically, they looked at a total of 6,452 lists of words, each drawn from a different language or dialect (the language–dialect boundary is notoriously difficult to draw). Because different dialects of a given language are often counted as a single language (rather than as distinct languages), these word lists represent only about two-thirds of the world's seven thousand or so languages but about 85 per cent of language families (groups of languages related through common descent, such as the Niger-Congo, Austronesian and Indo-European languages).

20 The symbols used here are from the simplified phonetic system used in the Automated Similarity Judgment Program, which enables sounds to be compared across the world's languages: S. Wichmann, A. Müller, A. Wett, V. Velupillai, J. Bischoffberger, C. H. Brown et al., *The ASJP Database*, version 16 (Leipzig, 2013).

21 W. Köhler, *Gestalt Psychology* (New York: Liveright, 1929). This type of effect was first described (using the slightly different nonsense words **takete** and **maluma**) by the great Gestalt psychologist Wolfgang Köhler, while working in Tenerife as director of the grandly titled Prussian Academy of Sciences Anthropoid Research Station. Interest in the effect was rekindled, and the **kiki–bouba** terms fixed, as part of a wider research project concerned not primarily with language but with the phenomenon of synaesthesia, where different perceptual senses are linked (so that musical notes might be perceived as having a colour, for example): V. S. Ramachandran and E. M. Hubbard, 'Synaesthesia – a window into perception, thought and language', *Journal of Consciousness Studies* 8 (2001), pp. 3–34.

22 A. J. Bremner, S. Caparos, J. Davidoff, J. de Fockert, K. J. Linnell and C. Spence, '"Bouba" and "kiki" in Namibia? A remote culture make similar shape–sound matches, but different shape–taste matches to Westerners', *Cognition* 126 (2013), pp. 165–72. They also find, interestingly, that the link between tastes and images is not the same. Westerners tend to map bitter chocolate to angular shapes and milk chocolate to rounded shapes. The Himba show the opposite pattern.

23 O. Ozturk, M. Krehm and A. Vouloumanos, 'Sound symbolism in infancy: evidence for sound–shape cross-modal correspondences in 4-month-olds', *Journal of Experimental Child Psychology* 114 (2013), pp. 173–86.

24 A. Aryani, E. S. Isbilen and M. H. Christiansen, 'Affective arousal links sound to meaning', *Psychological Science* 31 (2020), pp. 978–86.

25 Interestingly, Leibniz was aware of Wilkins's scheme and viewed his own approach as more appropriate for philosophy and science than for the practical challenges of communication: L. Couturat, *La Logique de Leibniz* (Paris: Felix Alcan, 1901).

26 Leibniz's famous passage is 'Whenever controversies arise, there will be no more need for arguing among two philosophers than among two mathematicians. For it will suffice to take the pens into the hand and to sit down by the abacus, saying to each other (and if they wish also to a friend called for help): Let us calculate!': W. Lenzen, 'Leibniz's logic', in D. M. Gabbay and J. Woods, eds, *The Rise of Modern Logic: From Leibniz to Frege* (Amsterdam: Elsevier, 2004).

27 F. W. Nietzsche, *The Will to Power* (1901; repr. New York: Vintage, 1967).

28 I. Kant, *Critique of Pure Reason*, trans. P. Guyer and A. W. Wood (1781; repr. New York: Cambridge University Press, 1998).

29 G. W. F. Hegel, *Phenomenology of Spirit*, trans. A. V. Miller (1807; repr. Oxford: Oxford University Press, 1977).

30 From the preface of L. Wittgenstein, *Tractatus logico-philosophicus* (1921; repr. Abingdon, UK: Routledge, 2013). Wittgenstein famously had two philosophical periods. The first, expressed in the

Tractatus, aimed completely to clarify philosophical problems through translation into a perfect logical language in which the confusions of everyday language would be eliminated. The second period, culminating in his *Philosophical Investigations* of 1953, abandoned the very idea of such abstract logical analysis and instead saw language as arising from specific, local, practical, game-like interactions – it was here the idea of a 'language game' was developed. See also A. Kenny, *Wittgenstein* (Cambridge, MA: Harvard University Press, 1973); R. Monk, *Ludwig Wittgenstein: The Duty of Genius* (New York: Random House, 2012); A. Biletzki and A. Matar, 'Ludwig Wittgenstein', *Stanford Encyclopedia of Philosophy* (Stanford, CA, 2002; revised 2 May 2018, https://plato.stanford.edu/entries/wittgenstein/); A. P. Mills, 'Knowledge of language', *Internet Encyclopedia of Philosophy*, https://iep.utm.edu/knowlang/.

31 J. A. Fodor, *The Language of Thought* (Cambridge, MA: Harvard University Press, 1975); J. McCarthy and P. J. Hayes, 'Some philosophical problems from the standpoint of artificial intelligence', in B. Meltzer and D. Michie, eds, *Machine Intelligence*, Vol. 4 (Edinburgh: Edinburgh University Press, 1969), pp. 463–502.

32 S. Pinker, *The Language Instinct: How the Mind Creates Language* (New York: William Morrow, 1994).

33 D. R. Dowty, R. Wall and S. Peters, *Introduction to Montague Semantics* (Dordrecht, Netherlands: Kluwer, 1981); R. Cann, *Formal Semantics: An Introduction* (Cambridge: Cambridge University Press, 1993). Formal semantics in linguistics is, though, a small field by comparison with its cousin, the formal semantics of computer programming languages, where the goal is to provide a precise mathematical specification of the meaning of computer programs: G. Winskel, *The Formal Semantics of Programming Languages: An Introduction* (Cambridge, MA: MIT Press, 1993). Computer languages are all that human languages are not: precise, regimented and requiring everything to be utterly spelled out in complete detail, with no leaps of imagination or interpretation required – indeed, any kind of linguistic creativity is likely to elicit the response 'syntax error'. So, on the face of

it, finding a formal theory of meaning for computer languages is much more feasible, whereas a complete formal theory of human language is, we would argue, a mirage. Nonetheless, the attempt to provide formal accounts of specific aspects of human languages has led to a far deeper understanding of how language works – and mathematical precision has, more generally, been hugely beneficial to the development of linguistic theory: G. K. Pullum, 'Formal linguistics meets the boojum', *Natural Language & Linguistic Theory* 7 (1989), pp. 137–43.

34 Interestingly, Wittgenstein was greatly struck by a pointed critique of his early views made by his Cambridge colleague, the economist Piero Sraffa. Wittgenstein's biographer Norman Malcolm explains: 'Sraffa made a gesture, familiar to Neapolitans as meaning something like disgust or contempt, of brushing the underneath of his chin with an outward sweep of the finger-tips of one hand. And he asked: "What is the logical form of that?"' Not quite a charade, perhaps – but close: M. Malcolm, *Ludwig Wittgenstein: A Memoir* (Oxford: Oxford University Press, 1958), pp. 58–9.

35 Wittgenstein, *Philosophical Investigations*, p. 220.

36 In the epilogue, we argue that the unruly, improvised nature of language provides a huge challenge to the project of creating human-level artificial intelligence – and one that, despite optimistic noises from some sections of the artificial intelligence community, it seems currently impossible to overcome.

4: LINGUISTIC ORDER AT THE EDGE OF CHAOS

1 Quoted in D. Shariatmadari, 'Why it's time to stop worrying about the decline of the English language', *Guardian*, 15 Aug. 2019, https://www.theguardian.com/science/2019/aug/15/why-its-time-to-stop-worrying-about-the-decline-of-the-english-language.

2 J. Humphrys, 'I h8 txt msgs: how texting is wrecking our language', *Daily Mail*, 24 Sept. 2007, https://www.dailymail.co.uk/news/article-483511/I-h8-txt-msgs-How-texting-wrecking-language.html.

3   Quoted in J. Aitchison, 'Reith Lectures: is our language in decay?',
     Independent, 23 Oct. 2011, https://www.independent.co.uk/life-
     style/reith-lectures-is-our-language-in-decay-1317695.html.
4   https://queens-english-society.org/about/.
5   Aitchison, 'Reith Lectures'.
6   The great philosopher and social theorist of the Scottish
     Enlightenment Adam Ferguson famously termed such emergence
     of cultural and economic patterns as 'the result of human action,
     but not the execution of any human design', a phrase later picked
     up by one of the architects of spontaneous order in modern social
     science, Friedrich Hayek. When at the University of Edinburgh,
     we were daily confronted with the rather charmless and rambling
     1960s construction the Adam Ferguson Building, opposite the old
     terraced building in Buccleuch Place that housed the Centre for
     Cognitive Science. We are ashamed to admit that neither of us had
     the remotest idea who Adam Ferguson was at the time, nor the
     curiosity to find out.
7   Sources for this paragraph include S. Sturluson, *The Prose Edda*,
     trans. J. Byock (London: Penguin, 2005); E. H. Man, 'On the
     aboriginal inhabitants of the Andaman Islands (Part II)', *Journal
     of the Anthropological Institute of Great Britain and Ireland* 12 (1883),
     pp. 117–75; J. A. Teit, 'Old-one (Okanagon tales)', in *Folk-Tales
     of Salishan and Sahaptin Tribes* (New York: American Folk-Lore
     Society, 1917); P. Sutton, 'Materialism, sacred myth and pluralism:
     competing theories of the origin of Australian languages', in
     F. Merlan, J. Morton and A. Rumsey, eds, *Scholar and Sceptic:
     Australian Aboriginal Studies in Honour of L. R. Hiatt* (Canberra:
     Aboriginal Studies Press, 1997), pp. 211–42, 297–309.
8   The next three paragraphs build on the wonderful book by
     Umberto Eco, *The Search for the Perfect Language* (London:
     Blackwell, 1995). The references to the works of the various
     glottogonists discussed here can be found in chapter 5 of that
     book, 'The monogenetic hypothesis and the mother tongues'.
9   The biographical information about Rask is from H. F. Nielsen,
     'Rasmus Kristian Rask (1787–1832) Liv og Levned [Rasmus Kristian

Rask (1787–1832): Life and Accomplishments]', *RASK: Internationalt Tidsskrift for Sprog og Kommunikation* 28 (2008), pp. 25–42.

10 The next two paragraphs draw on M. F. Müller, *Lectures on the Science of Language* (London: Longman, Green, Longman & Roberts, 1862); O. Jespersen, *Language: Its Nature, Development, and Origin* (New York: Henry Holt, 1922); D. Crystal, *How Language Works* (London: Penguin, 2005).

11 M. F. Müller, 'On the Origin of Reason', *Contemporary Review* 31 (1878), pp. 534–51 at p. 550.

12 Article 2 of the Society's 1866 statutes reads: 'La Société n'admet aucune communication concernant, soit l'origine du langage soit la création d'une langue universelle [The Society does not accept any communication concerning either the origin of language or the creation of a universal language]': 'Statuts de 1866', Société de Linguistique de Paris, https://www.slp-paris.com/statuts1866.html.

13 This section is based in part of our reading of Chomsky's work over the years, including N. Chomsky, *Cartesian Linguistics: A Chapter in the History of Rationalist Thought* (New York: Harper & Row, 1966); N. Chomsky, *Reflections on Language* (New York: Random House, 1975); N. Chomsky, 'Rules and representations', *Behavioral and Brain Sciences* 3 (1980), pp. 1–15; N. Chomsky, *Language and Mind* (Cambridge: Cambridge University Press, 2006); N. Chomsky, 'The language capacity: architecture and evolution', *Psychonomic Bulletin & Review* 24 (2017), pp. 200–3.

14 The project of generative grammar has branched out in many directions, some very far from Chomsky's own programme, and its proponents typically do not share his assumptions about the existence of an innate universal grammar – indeed, many of them don't necessarily see generative grammar as represented in the brain at all. Even by the late 1980s, when we were graduate students, rival generative theories included Lexical Functional Grammar, Generalized Phrase Structure Grammar, Categorial Grammar and Tree-Adjoining Grammar, among others.

15 In chapter 5, we discuss Chomsky's account of how humans got universal grammar in the first place.

16 Chomsky says, 'I have not hesitated to propose a general
    principle of linguistic structure on the basis of observation of a
    single language': N. Chomsky, 'On cognitive structures and their
    development: a reply to Piaget', in M. Piatelli-Palmarini, ed.,
    *Language and Learning: The Debate between Jean Piaget and Noam
    Chomsky* (London: Routledge & Kegan Paul, 1980), p. 48.

17 These examples are drawn from the delightful collection of 'Fun
    things children say' compiled from info-CHILDES postings in 2013 by
    Bruno Estigarribia: https://childes.talkbank.org/teach/sayings.pdf.

18 M. Tomasello, *First Verbs: A Case Study of Early Grammatical
    Development* (Cambridge: Cambridge University Press, 1992);
    L. Bloom, *Language Development: Form and Function in Emerging
    Grammars* (Cambridge, MA: MIT Press, 1970).

19 There is now an enormous literature exploring the construction-
    by-construction way in which children seem to learn language.
    For some recent examples, see B. Ambridge, 'Against stored
    abstractions: a radical exemplar model of language acquisition',
    First Language 40 (2020), pp. 509–59; B. MacWhinney, 'Item-based
    patterns in early syntactic development', in T. Herbst, H.-J. Schmid
    and S. Faulhaber, eds, *Constructions, Collocations, Patterns* (Berlin:
    De Gruyter, 2014), pp. 33–69.

20 The question of whether children or adults are the primary drivers
    of language change remains unresolved, and the answer may
    differ for different aspects of language; for a review, see V. Kempe
    and P. J. Brooks, 'Linking adult second language learning and
    diachronic change: a cautionary note', *Frontiers in Psychology*
    9 (2018), p. 480, https://www.frontiersin.org/articles/10.3389/
    fpsyg.2018.00480/full). However, sophisticated computational
    simulations suggest that language change is unlikely to originate
    in errors that children make during language learning: R. A.
    Blythe and W. Croft, 'How individuals change language', *PLOS ONE*
    16 (2021): e0252582.

21 M. Dingemanse, S. G. Roberts, J. Baranova, J. Blythe,
    P. Drew, S. Floyd et al., 'Universal principles in the repair of
    communication problems', *PLOS ONE* 10 (2015): e0136100.

22 See, for example, S. DeCock, S. Granger, G. Leech and T. McEnery,
    'An automated approach to the phrasicon of EFL learners', in
    S. Granger, ed., *Learning English on Computer* (London: Addison,
    Wesley, Longman, 1998), pp. 67–79. For a review, see K. Conklin and
    N. Schmitt, 'The processing of formulaic language', *Annual Review
    of Applied Linguistics* 32 (2012), pp. 45–61.

23 P. W. Culicover, *Syntactic Nuts: Hard Cases, Syntactic Theory, and
    Language Acquisition* (New York: Oxford University Press, 1999).

24 The concept of 'free' word order has fuzzy edges (and doesn't just
    apply to subjects, verbs and objects but also applies to where
    adjectives, adverbs and the like are placed). Usually, as in Latin,
    certain word orders are more common. And even in languages
    with fixed word order, non-standard word orders are sometimes
    allowed. For example, in English we might say **guacamole Mary
    absolutely adores**, where the object **guacamole** is put first for
    emphasis.

25 The large number of adult learners of Latin as a second language
    also seems likely to have contributed to the change away from
    case markers towards a fixed word order – because case systems
    are notoriously difficult to learn by second-language learners:
    C. Bentz and M. H. Christiansen, 'Linguistic adaptation: the trade-
    off between case marking and fixed word orders in Germanic and
    Romance languages', in G. Peng and F. Shi, eds, *Eastward Flows the
    Great River: Festschrift in Honor of Prof. William S.-Y. Wang on his
    80th Birthday* (Hong Kong: City University of Hong Kong Press,
    2013), pp. 45–61.

26 B. Heine and T. Kuteva, *The Genesis of Grammar: A Reconstruction*
    (New York: Oxford University Press, 2007); B. Heine and T. Kuteva,
    'Grammaticalization theory as a tool for reconstructing language
    evolution', in M. Tallerman and K. Gibson, eds, *The Oxford
    Handbook of Language Evolution* (Oxford: Oxford University Press,
    2011), pp. 512–27.

27 Nick has a vivid (and, hopefully, not confabulated) memory of
    browsing the linguistics books in Blackwell's bookshop in Oxford
    in the mid-1990s and leafing randomly through a newish book by

Paul Hopper and Elizabeth Traugott, with no idea what it might be about. After five minutes, he was utterly captivated. On the other side of the Atlantic, Morten was having a similar reaction to the same ideas. When we started comparing notes, we realized that the idea of grammaticalization would completely change our outlook on language.

28 P. J. Hopper, 'Some recent trends in grammaticalization', *Annual Review of Anthropology* 25 (1996), pp. 217–36.

29 E. Van Gelderen, *A History of the English Language* (Amsterdam: John Benjamins, 2014).

30 R. Coleman, 'The origin and development of latin habeo+ infinitive', *Classical Quarterly* 21 (1971), pp. 215–32; S. Fleischman, *The Future in Thought and Language: Diachronic Evidence from Romance* (Cambridge: Cambridge University Press, 1982).

31 For a detailed analysis, see M. B. M. Hansen, 'Negation in the history of French', in D. Willis, C. Lucas and A. Breitbarth, eds, *The History of Negation in the Languages of Europe and the Mediterranean: Volume I Case Studies* (Oxford: Oxford University Press, 2013), pp. 51–76. For the use of *pas* in some dialects of colloquial French, see P. J. Hopper, 'Some recent trends in grammaticalization', *Annual Review of Anthropology* 25 (1996), pp. 217–36.

32 'Linguists are like, "Get used to it!"' by Britt Peterson, *Boston Globe*, 25 Jan. 2015, https://www.bostonglobe.com/ideas/2015/01/25/linguists-are-like-get-used/ruUQoVoXUTLDjx72JojnBI/story.html.

5: LANGUAGE EVOLUTION WITHOUT BIOLOGICAL EVOLUTION

1 C. Darwin, *The Autobiography of Charles Darwin 1809–1882. With the Original Omissions Restored. Edited and with Appendix and Notes by His Grand-Daughter Nora Barlow* (London: Collins, 1958), p. 120, http://darwin-online.org.uk/content/frameset?pageseq=1&itemID=F1497&viewtype=text. (Scanned by John van Wyhe, 2004; OCRed

by AEL Data, December 2005; proofread and corrected by Sue Asscher, December 2005.)

2   Wedgwood, for example, published a review of Grimm's major opus on sound changes within the Indo-European language family: H. Wedgwood, 'Grimm's Deutsche Grammatik', *Quarterly Review* 50 (1833), pp. 169–89. For further background on Darwin's use of language as an analogy of the evolution of species, see S. G. Alter, *Darwinism and the Linguistic Image: Language, Race, and Natural Theology in the Nineteenth Century* (Baltimore, MD: Johns Hopkins University Press, 2003).

3   In contrast to the tree of life, there is no real reason to believe that all human languages have a single common root – indeed, there is every reason to suppose the opposite: that language has been independently invented and reinvented many times.

4   *Metaphysical Notebook N*, in P. H. Barrett, P. J. Gautrey, S. Herbert, D. Kohn and S. Smith, eds, *Charles Darwin's Notebooks, 1836–1844* (Cambridge: Cambridge University Press, 1987), p. 65.

5   C. Darwin, *On the Origin of Species by Means of Natural Selection* (London: John Murray, 1859), pp. 422–3. Note, however, that Darwin may also have used the language–species comparison because he thought that his theory when applied to human evolution would predict that 'less' civilized societies spoke less civilized languages: G. Radick, 'Darwin on language and selection', *Selection* 3 (2002), pp. 7–16.

6   C. Darwin, *The Descent of Man, and Selection in Relation to Sex*, Vol. 1 (London: John Murray, 1871), pp. 59–61.

7   M. Müller, 'The science of language', *Nature* 1 (1870), pp. 256–9 at p. 257.

8   Linguistics: R. C. Berwick and N. Chomsky, *Why Only Us? Language and Evolution* (Cambridge, MA: MIT Press, 2016); psychology: S. Pinker, *The Language Instinct* (New York: William Morrow, 1994); biology: J. Maynard Smith and E. Szathmáry, *The Origins of Life: From the Birth of Life to the Origin of Language* (Oxford: Oxford University Press, 1999); history: Y. N. Harari, *Sapiens: A Brief History of Humankind* (New York: Random House, 2014).

9   This is, though, how our type of view is often caricatured by
    those who argue for a genetic blueprint for language: S. Pinker,
    The Blank Slate: The Modern Denial of Human Nature (New York:
    Viking, 2003).

10 From E. Bates, 'On the nature and nurture of language', in E. Bizzi,
    P. Calissano and V. Volterra, eds, *Frontiere della biologia: Il cervello
    di Homo sapiens* [Frontiers of Biology: The Brain of *Homo Sapiens*]
    (Rome: Giovanni Trecanni, 1999), pp. 241–65.

11 For example, M. A. Halliday, 'Notes on transitivity and theme
    in English: Part 2', *Journal of Linguistics* 3 (1967), pp. 199–244;
    H. H. Clark and S. E. Haviland, 'Comprehension and the given-
    new contract', in R. O. Freedle, ed., *Discourse Production and
    Comprehension* (Norwood, NJ: Ablex, 1977), pp. 1–40.

12 Thinking about language as an organism has a long historical
    pedigree that includes the philologist Chomsky views as the
    father of generative grammar, Wilhelm von Humboldt, as well as
    the German linguist August Schleicher, Charles Darwin and Max
    Müller. After lying dormant for nearly a century, the idea was
    resurrected within a modern evolutionary framework by R. D.
    Stevick, 'The biological model and historical linguistics', *Language*
    39 (1963), pp. 159–69; B. Nerlich, 'The evolution of the concept
    of "Linguistic evolution" in the 19th and 20th century', *Lingua*
    77 (1989), pp. 101–12; and M. I. Sereno, 'Four analogies between
    biological and cultural/linguistic evolution', *Journal of Theoretical
    Biology* 151 (1991), pp. 467–507. In his PhD dissertation from 1994,
    Morten suggested that language might be viewed as a 'beneficial
    parasite', a phrase that was picked up by T. W. Deacon, *The
    Symbolic Species: The Co-evolution of Language and the Brain*
    (New York: W. W. Norton, 1997). For further discussion, see M. H.
    Christiansen and N. Chater, *Creating Language: Integrating
    Evolution, Acquisition, and Processing* (Cambridge, MA: MIT Press,
    2016), ch. 2.

13 This paragraph builds on the following articles: J. Xu and J. I.
    Gordon, 'Honor thy symbionts', *Proceedings of the National
    Academy of Sciences* 100 (2003), pp. 10452–9; H. M. Wexler,

'*Bacteroides*: the good, the bad, and the nitty-gritty', *Clinical Microbiology Reviews* 20 (2007), pp. 593–621. For a gentle and entertaining introduction to our microbiome, see E. Yong, *I Contain Multitudes* (New York: Ecco, 2016).

14 S. M. Blinkov and I. I. Glezer, *The Human Brain in Figures and Tables: A Quantitative Handbook* (New York: Basic Books, 1968).

15 Of course, not all microbes are as helpful to us as *B. theta* – indeed, some are downright nasty pathogens that can make us ill and even kill us. At the time of writing, in 2020–1, humanity is in the grip of the worldwide Covid-19 pandemic. But this is where our alliance with the 'language symbiont' is self-evidently crucial – without language, we would have none of the scientific and organizational resources to overcome these viral invaders.

16 R. D. Gray and Q. D. Atkinson, 'Language-tree divergence times support the Anatolian theory of Indo-European origin', *Nature* 426 (2003), pp. 435–9.

17 M. R. Frean and E. R. Abraham, 'Adaptation and enslavement in endosymbiont–host associations', *Physical Review E: Statistical, Nonlinear, and Soft Matter Physics* 69 (2004): 051913.

18 Comparing bacterial genomes extracted from faecal samples of wild gorillas in Cameroon, wild bonobos in the Democratic Republic of the Congo, wild chimpanzees in Tanzania and not-so-wild humans in the United States, a team of evolutionary microbiologists found that different lineages of Bacteroidaceae (the family of gut bacteria to which *B. theta* belongs) evolved through a process of 'cospeciation' with their hosts over the past fifteen million years. That is, these bacteria co-evolved separately with different host species as the hominid line split into gorillas, bonobos, chimps and humans. The genes of the bacterial symbionts changed considerably faster than the genes of their hominid hosts, suggesting a skewed partnership: A. H. Moeller, A. Caro-Quintero, D. Mjungu, A. V. Georgiev, E. V. Lonsdorf, M. N. Muller et al., 'Cospeciation of gut microbiota with hominids', *Science* 353 (2016), pp. 380–2.

19 See the works cited in note 8 above.

20 S. Pinker and P. Bloom, 'Natural language and natural selection', *Behavioral & Brain Sciences* 13 (1990), pp. 707–27.

21 A. Parker, *In the Blink of an Eye: How Vision Sparked the Big Bang of Evolution* (New York: Basic Books, 2003).

22 Pinker, *Language Instinct*.

23 For a full discussion, see M. H. Christiansen and N. Chater, 'Language as shaped by the brain', *Behavioral & Brain Sciences* 31 (2008), pp. 489–558; Christiansen and Chater, *Creating Language*, ch. 2.

24 N. Chater, F. Reali and M. H. Christiansen, 'Restrictions on biological adaptation in language evolution', *Proceedings of the National Academy of Sciences* 106 (2009), pp. 1015–20. Note that our argument does not preclude fast human biological adaptations, such as the evolution of genes for the digestion of starch (G. H. Perry, N. J. Dominy, K. G. Claw, A. S. Lee, H. Fiegler, R. Redon et al., 'Diet and the evolution of human amylase gene copy number variation', *Nature Genetics* 39 [2007], pp. 1256–60) and lactose (C. Holden and R. Mace, 'Phylogenetic analysis of the evolution of lactose digestion in adults', *Human Biology* 69 [1997], pp. 605–28) following the development of agriculture and dairying. Crucially, though, once people settled down as farmers there was no turning back, and this established a steady environmental pressure within which natural selection could work. By contrast, constantly changing languages do not create a unidirectional selective pressure toward biological adaptations for language.

25 A. Baronchelli, N. Chater, R. Pastor-Satorras and M. H. Christiansen, 'The biological origin of linguistic diversity', *PLOS ONE* 7 (2012): e48029.

26 This would also mean that multilingualism – speaking more than one language – should be rare, confined only to closely related languages. Again, this is not the case. In fact, most populations around the world speak at least two languages: G. Valdés, 'Multilingualism', Linguistic Society of America, https://www.linguisticsociety.org/resource/multilingualism.

27 M. Kislev and R. Barkai, 'Neanderthal and woolly mammoth molecular resemblance', *Human Biology* 90 (2018), pp. 115–28.

28 S. Tucci, S. H. Vohr, R. C. McCoy, B. Vernot, M. R. Robinson, C. Barbieri et al., 'Evolutionary history and adaptation of a human pygmy population of Flores Island, Indonesia', *Science* 361 (2018), pp. 511–16.

29 It has been suggested – controversially, we might add – that humanity's first language was an early version of the click language from which the current Khoisan languages spoken in southern Africa originated: E. Pennisi, 'The first language?', *Science* 303 (2004), pp. 1319–20.

30 Technically speaking, Chomsky talks about 'merge', a hypothetical computational process that combines two elements, such as words or phrases, into a single unit and does this recursively, meaning that the process can be applied over and over again, including to previously combined units of the same kind. Recursion is the mathematical concept underlying this process of combination. N. Chomsky, 'Some simple evo devo theses: how true might they be for language?', in R. Larson, V. Déprez and H. Yamakido, eds, *The Evolution of Human Language* (Cambridge: Cambridge University Press, 2010), pp. 45–62. Later the Prometheus account was popularized in Berwick and Chomsky, *Why Only Us?*.

31 F. Karlsson, 'Constraints on multiple center-embedding of clauses', *Journal of Linguistics* 43 (2007), pp. 365–92. It should be noted, though, that there are other types of recursion that don't raise the same problem. One example is 'tail' recursion, in which the same grammatical structure is repeated successively. Unlike the multiple centre-embedded sentences, these tail-recursive sentences do not tax our memory beyond its breaking point. Consider the old British nursery rhyme 'The House That Jack Built'. It starts with a single centre-embedded clause, **This is the house that Jack built**, which is OK for our language system. The rhyme then goes into a loop, where it continuously adds clauses before **the house that Jack built**. First, it becomes **This is the malt that lay in the house that Jack built**, then **This**

is the rat that ate the malt that lay in the house that Jack built, and it continues to loop around like this until the final rhyme is an impressive seventy words long: **This is the farmer sowing his corn, that kept the cock that crow'd in the morn, that waked the priest all shaven and shorn, that married the man all tatter'd and torn, that kissed the maiden all forlorn, that milk'd the cow with the crumpled horn, that tossed the dog, that worried the cat, that killed the rat, that ate the malt, that lay in the house that Jack built**. Intriguingly, we experience few problems with this sentence – but if we instead were confronted with a centre-embedded Matryoshka-doll version of this, we would get lost very quickly. Because the tail-recursive loops can be accommodated without recursion, whereas centre embedding cannot, it is the latter that is the focus of debate.

32   D. Everett, *How Language Began* (London: Profile Books, 2017). Everett's claims are controversial, but it is empirically well grounded that our ability to comprehend centre-embedded recursion is very limited no matter which language we speak.

33   R. McKie, 'Whisper it quietly, but the power of language may all be in the genes', *Guardian*, 7 Oct. 2001, https://www.theguardian.com/education/2001/oct/07/research.highereducation; C. Kenneally, 'First language gene found', *Wired*, 3 Oct. 2001, https://www.wired.com/2001/10/first-language-gene-found/; M. Balter, 'First "speech gene" identified', *Science*, 3 Oct. 2001, https://www.sciencemag.org/news/2001/10/first-speech-gene-identified.

34   C. S. L. Lai, S. E. Fisher, J. A. Hurst, F. Vargha-Khadem and A. P. Monaco, 'A forkhead-domain gene is mutated in a severe speech and language disorder', *Nature* 413 (2001), pp. 519–23. We should note that Simon Fisher, one of the discoverers of *FOXP2* and director of the Genetics of Language Department at the Max Planck Institute for Psycholinguistics, has long argued that *FOXP2* is not a language gene: e.g. S. E. Fisher, 'Tangled webs: tracing the connections between genes and cognition', *Cognition* 101 (2006), pp. 270–97.

35 M. Gopnik, 'Feature-blind grammar and dysphasia', *Nature* 244 (1990), p. 715; M. Gopnik and M. B. Crago, 'Familial aggregation of a developmental language disorder', *Cognition* 39 (1991), pp. 1–50.

36 J. Berko, 'The child's learning of English morphology', *Word* 14 (1958), pp. 150–77.

37 S. Pinker, 'Talk of genetics and vice versa', *Nature* 413 (2001), pp. 465–6.

38 N. Wade, 'Language gene is traced to emergence of humans', *New York Times*, 15 Aug. 2002, https://www.nytimes.com/2002/08/15/us/language-gene-is-traced-to-emergence-of-humans.html; Associated Press, 'Gene linked to the dawn of speech', Sciences News, NBC News, 14 Aug. 2002, http://www.nbcnews.com/id/3131127/ns/technology_and_science-science/t/gene-linked-dawn-speech; M. Balter, '"Speech gene" debut timed to modern humans', *Science*, 14 Aug. 2002, https://www.sciencemag.org/news/2002/08/speech-gene-debut-timed-modern-humans.

39 W. Enard, M. Przeworski, S. E. Fisher, C. S. Lai, V. Wiebe, T. Kitano et al., 'Molecular evolution of *FOXP2*, a gene involved in speech and language', *Nature* 418 (2002), pp. 869–72. For a review, see S. E. Fisher and C. Scharff, '*FOXP2* as a molecular window into speech and language', *Trends in Genetics* 25 (2009), pp. 166–77.

40 J. Krause, C. Lalueza-Fox, L. Orlando, W. Enard, R. E. Green, H. A. Burbano et al., 'The derived *FOXP2* variant of modern humans was shared with Neandertals', *Current Biology* 17 (2007), pp. 1908–12.

41 E. G. Atkinson, A. J. Audesse, J. A. Palacios, D. M. Bobo, A. E. Webb, S. Ramachandran et al., 'No evidence for recent selection at *FOXP2* among diverse human populations', *Cell* 174 (2018), pp. 1424–35.

42 Although many of these allelic differences appear to have little impact, some can introduce important differences among individuals. For example, variations in alleles determine how we respond to drugs such as warfarin, an anti-coagulant (or blood thinner) commonly used to treat blood clots. The alleles of two genes, *CYP2C9* and *VKORC1*, affect how quickly warfarin is metabolized in the body. This drug was previously used as a rat poison, so it's important to get the dosage right for each

individual to avoid causing people to haemorrhage. Using genetic information can help: D. A. Flockhart, D. O'Kane, M. S. Williams, M. S. Watson, B. Gage, R. Gandolfi et al., 'Pharmacogenetic testing of *CYP2C9* and *VKORC1* alleles for warfarin', *Genetics in Medicine* 10 (2008), pp. 139–50.

43   N. S. Caron, G. E. B. Wright and M. R. Hayden, 'Huntington disease', in M. P. Adam, H. H. Ardinger, R. A. Pagon et al., eds, *GeneReviews* (Seattle: University of Washington, 1998; updated 5 July 2018). Available from https://www.ncbi.nlm.nih.gov/books/NBK1305/.

44   K. L. Mueller, J. C. Murray, J. J. Michaelson, M. H. Christiansen, S. Reilly and J. B. Tomblin, 'Common genetic variants in *FOXP2* are not associated with individual differences in language development', *PLOS ONE* 11 (2016): e0152576.

45   The two mouse studies discussed here are S. Reimers-Kipping, W. Hevers, S. Pääbo and W. Enard, 'Humanized *Foxp2* specifically affects cortico-basal ganglia circuits', *Neuroscience* 175 (2011), pp. 75–84; C. Schreiweis, U. Bornschein, E. Burguière, C. Kerimoglu, S. Schreiter, M. Dannemann et al., 'Humanized *Foxp2* accelerates learning by enhancing transitions from declarative to procedural performance', *Proceedings of the National Academy of Sciences* 111 (2014), pp. 14253–8.

46   K. S. Lashley, 'The problem of serial order in behavior', in L. A. Jeffress, ed., *Cerebral Mechanisms in Behavior* (New York: Wiley, 1951), pp. 112–31.

47   J. B. Tomblin, J. Murray and S. Patil, 'Genetics of specific language impairment: multiple approaches', presentation, 55th Annual Meeting of the American Society of Human Genetics, Salt Lake City, UT, 2005; J. B. Tomblin, E. Mainela-Arnold and X. Zhang, 'Procedural learning in adolescents with and without specific language impairment', *Language Learning and Development* 3 (2007), pp. 269–93.

48   Broca's area was discovered by the French physician Paul Broca in 1861, following the autopsy of an individual who had damage to this part of the brain and had become unable to produce speech. Wernicke's area was named after the German neurologist Carl

Wernicke, who in 1874 noted a link between lesion to this area and problems with language understanding. Up until quite recently, these areas were thought to be language-specific parts of the brain, dedicated to speech production (Broca's area) and language comprehension (Wernicke's area): J. Sedivy, *Language in Mind*, 2nd edn (New York: Oxford University Press, 2020).

49 For an overview of the cultural evolution of different writing systems, see J. M. Diamond, *Guns, Germs, and Steel* (New York: Random House, 1998), ch. 12.

50 Our discussion of reading as cultural product is inspired by S. Dehaene and L. Cohen, 'Cultural recycling of cortical maps', *Neuron* 56 (2007), pp. 384–98.

51 For a review, see D. J. Bolger, C. A. Perfetti and W. Schneider, 'Cross-cultural effect on the brain revisited: universal structures plus writing system variation', *Human Brain Mapping* 25 (2005), pp. 92–104. Note that the visual word form area may also play a role in accessing meaning more generally, though it does seem particularly important for recognizing printed words: J. T. Devlin, H. L. Jamison, L. M. Gonnerman and P. M. Matthews, 'The role of the posterior fusiform gyrus in reading', *Journal of Cognitive Neuroscience* 18 (2006), pp. 911–22.

52 Of course, it is possible to recognize and reliably create more complex symbols, such as Chinese characters – but these 'justify' their additional complexity by conveying whole words rather than single speech sounds. In writing systems, as in language, a range of trade-offs between different constraints is possible.

53 M. A. Changizi, Q. Zhang, H. Ye and S. Shimojo, 'The structures of letters and symbols throughout human history are selected to match those found in objects in natural scenes', *American Naturalist* 167 (2006): E117–E139.

54 J. Grainger, S. Dufau, M. Montant, J. C. Ziegler and J. Fagot, 'Orthographic processing in baboons (*Papio papio*)', *Science* 336 (2012), pp. 245–8.

55 H. Meng, S. D. Smith, K. Hager, M. Held, J. Liu, R. K. Olson et al., '*DCDC2* is associated with reading disability and modulates

neuronal development in the brain', *Proceedings of the National Academy of Sciences* 102 (2005), pp. 17053–8.

56 From E. Bates, 'On the nature and nurture of language', in E. Bizzi, P. Calissano and V. Volterra, eds, *Frontiere della biologia: Il cervello di Homo sapiens* [Frontiers of Biology: The Brain of *Homo Sapiens*] (Rome: Giovanni Trecanni, 1999), pp. 241–65.

6: FOLLOWING IN EACH OTHER'S FOOTSTEPS

1 US Census Bureau, 'Quick facts: New York City, New York', https://www.census.gov/quickfacts/fact/table/newyorkcitynewyork/PST045219.

2 We are indebted to Andy Clark. Almost thirty years ago, when Morten and Andy were both at Washington University in St Louis and Nick was visiting, we discussed the analogy between language evolution, cultural evolution and the 'evolution' of scissors.

3 N. Chater and M. H. Christiansen, 'Language acquisition meets language evolution', *Cognitive Science* 34 (2010), pp. 1131–57; Christiansen and Chater, *Creating Language*, ch. 3.

4 There are cases where C-learning is involved in N-learning, such as learning from others which plants are edible and which are not, or which foods require special preparation to be made suitable for eating. And in most current societies there are various cultural institutions that help facilitate N-learning, such as apprenticeships, schools and universities, so in these cases we are not lone scientists working in isolation. But ultimately what works and what doesn't work in N-learning still depends on the external world and not on whether we do the same thing as other people do.

5 D. Wang and H. Li, 'Nonverbal language in cross-cultural communication', *Sino-US English Teaching* 4 (2007), pp. 66–70.

6 For example, R. Jackendoff, *The Architecture of the Language Faculty* (Cambridge, MA: MIT Press, 1997), p. 5.

7 F. C. Bartlett, *Remembering; A Study in Experimental and Social Psychology* (Cambridge: Cambridge University Press, 1932).

8   E. A. Esper, 'Social transmission of an artificial language',
    Language 42 (1966), pp. 575–80.

9   S. Kirby, H. Cornish and K. Smith, 'Cumulative cultural evolution
    in the laboratory: an experimental approach to the origins of
    structure in human language', *Proceedings of the National Academy
    of Sciences* 105 (2008), pp. 10681–5.

10 Kirby and colleagues removed duplicate labels so that each
    visual scene was associated with a unique label. This was done
    to simulate a communicative pressure to avoid ambiguity. In a
    later study, where people had not only to learn labels but also
    to use them to communicate with someone else – and therefore
    needed to be as specific as possible – they got the same results:
    S. Kirby, M. Tamariz, H. Cornish and K. Smith, 'Compression and
    communication in the cultural evolution of linguistic structure',
    Cognition 141 (2015), pp. 87–102.

11 H. Cornish, R. Dale, S. Kirby and M. H. Christiansen, 'Sequence
    memory constraints give rise to language-like structure through
    iterated learning', *PLOS ONE* 12 (2017): e0168532.

12 T. Dobzhansky, 'Nothing in biology makes sense except in the
    light of evolution', *American Biology Teacher* 35 (1973), pp. 125–9.

13 The original thirty-million-word gap study is B. Hart and
    T. Risley, *Meaningful Differences in the Everyday Experience of
    Young American Children* (Baltimore: Brookes, 1995). It was
    popularized in B. Hart and T. R. Risley, 'The early catastrophe:
    the 30 million word gap by age 3', *American Educator* 27 (2003),
    pp. 4–9. Examples of press coverage: G. Bellafante, 'Before a test,
    a poverty of words', *New York Times*, 5 Oct. 2012, https://www.
    nytimes.com/2012/10/07/nyregion/for-poor-schoolchildren-a-
    poverty-of-words.html; 'Closing the "word gap" between rich and
    poor', NPR, 28 Dec. 2013, https://www.npr.org/2013/12/29/257922222/
    closing-the-word-gap-between-rich-and-poor; J. Ludden,
    'Efforts to close the achievement gap in kids start at home',
    All Things Considered, NPR, 17 March 2014, https://www.npr.
    org/2014/03/17/289799002/efforts-to-close-the-achievement-gap-
    in-kids-start-at-home. Studies on the relationship between input,

vocabulary and language skills: E. Hoff, 'How social contexts support and shape language development', *Developmental Review* 26 (2006), pp. 55–88; M. Burchinal, K. McCartney, L. Steinberg, R. Crosnoe, S. L. Friedman, V. McLoyd et al., 'Examining the black–white achievement gap among low-income children using the NICHD study of early child care and youth development', *Child Development* 82 (2011), pp. 1404–20. Recent discussions of the thirty-million-word gap have been more nuanced: A. Kamenetz, 'Let's stop talking about the "30 million word gap"', *All Things Considered*, NPR, 1 June 2018, https://www.npr.org/sections/ed/2018/06/01/615188051/lets-stop-talking-about-the-30-million-word-gap; R. Pondiscio, 'Don't dismiss that 30 million-word gap quite so fast', *EducationNext*, 6 June 2019, https://www.educationnext.org/dont-dismiss-30-million-word-gap-quite-fast/; R. Michnick Golinkoff, E. Hoff, M. Rowe, C. Tamis-LeMonda and K. Hirsh-Pasek, 'Talking with children matters: defending the 30 million word gap', *Education Plus Development* (blog), Brookings, 21 May 2018, https://www.brookings.edu/blog/education-plus-development/2018/05/21/defending-the-30-million-word-gap-disadvantaged-children-dont-hear-enough-child-directed-words/.

14 The Fix Team, 'Transcript: the third democratic debate', *Washington Post*, 12 Sept. 2019, https://www.washingtonpost.com/politics/2019/09/13/transcript-third-democratic-debate/.

15 Our own quick analysis of the conversational part of the British National Corpus shows that the top one thousand most frequently used words account for 90 per cent of words spoken in everyday conversation (we thank Christoph Rühlemann from Albert-Ludwigs-Universität Freiburg, Germany, for providing us with the relevant word lists). Other analyses show similar results: I. S. P. Nation, 'How large a vocabulary is needed for reading and listening?', *Canadian Modern Language Review* 63 (2006), pp. 59–82; M. P. Rodgers and S. Webb, 'Narrow viewing: the vocabulary in related television programs', *TESOL Quarterly* 45 (2011), pp. 689–717.

16 A. L. Paugh and K. C. Riley, 'Poverty and children's language in anthropological perspective', *Annual Review of Anthropology*, 48 (2019), pp. 297–315.

17 These real-time interactions can be either in person or through videoconferencing, as on apps like Skype or Zoom, as long as they involve the typical well-timed back-and-forth of conversational turn-taking: S. Roseberry, K. Hirsh-Pasek and R. M. Golinkoff, 'Skype me! Socially contingent interactions help toddlers learn language', *Child Development* 85 (2014), pp. 956–70.

18 A. Fernald, V. A. Marchman and A. Weisleder, 'SES differences in language processing skill and vocabulary are evident at 18 months', *Developmental Science* 16 (2013), pp. 234–48; N. Hurtado, V. A. Marchman and A. Fernald, 'Does input influence uptake? Links between maternal talk, processing speed and vocabulary size in Spanish-learning children', *Developmental Science* 11 (2008), pp. F31–F39.

19 R. R. Romeo, J. A. Leonard, S. T. Robinson, M. R. West, A. P. Mackey, M. L. Rowe et al., 'Beyond the 30-million-word gap: children's conversational exposure is associated with language-related brain function', *Psychological Science* 29 (2018), pp. 700–10.

20 More than 90 per cent of recent studies of human psychology and behaviour are based on participants from Western, educated, industrialized, rich, democratic countries, which as a group have come to be labelled by the somewhat self-mocking acronym WEIRD. J. Henrich, S. J. Heine and A. Norenzayan, 'Beyond WEIRD: towards a broad-based behavioral science', *Behavioral and Brain Sciences* 33 (2010), pp. 111–35.

21 For one example of the propagation of the initial claim, see Pinker, *Language Instinct*. For detailed studies, see P. Vogt, J. D. Mastin and D. M. A. Schots, 'Communicative intentions of child-directed speech in three different learning environments: observations from the Netherlands, and rural and urban Mozambique', *First Language* 35 (2015), pp. 341–58; A. Cristia, E. Dupoux, M. Gurven and J. Stieglitz, 'Child-directed speech is infrequent in a forager–farmer population: a time allocation study', *Child Development* 90 (2017), pp. 759–73; L. A. Shneidman and

S. Goldin-Meadow, 'Language input and acquisition in a Mayan village: how important is directed speech?', *Developmental Science* 15 (2012), pp. 659–73.

22 J. P. Bunce, M. Soderstrom, E. Bergelson, C. R. Rosemberg, A. Stein, F. Alam et al., 'A cross-cultural examination of young children's everyday language experiences', *PsyArXiv*, 2 Sept. 2020, https://doi.org/10.31234/osf.io/723pr.

23 M. Casillas, P. Brown and S. C. Levinson, 'Early language experience in a Papuan community', *Journal of Child Language* 48 (2021), pp. 792–814.

24 J. E. Henderson, 'Phonology and grammar of Yele, Papua New Guinea' (monograph, Pacific Linguistics Series B 112, Department of Linguistics, Australian National University, Canberra, 1995), p. 14.

25 Casillas et al., 'Early language experience in a Papuan community'.

26 There is, of course, substantial variation within each industrialized society. This is especially true of the United States, where both ethnic and socio-economic differences may lead to cultural variations that span the gamut of what we've discussed here regarding the relative emphases on schooling and helping out with family activities: E. Ochs and T. Kremer-Sadl, 'Ethical blind spots in ethnographic and developmental approaches to the language gap debate', *Langage et Société* 170 (2020), pp. 39–67.

27 H. R. Waterfall, 'A little change is a good thing: feature theory, language acquisition, and variation sets', unpublished PhD diss., University of Chicago, 2006; J. F. Schwab and C. Lew-Williams, 'Repetition across successive sentences facilitates young children's word learning', *Developmental Psychology* 52 (2016), pp. 879–86.

28 Evidence from corpus analyses suggests that children from low-income families do indeed encounter fewer bursty contexts with repetitions of words across multiple consecutive utterances compared to their high-income peers in both Hebrew and UK English: T. A. L. Shira and I. Arnon, 'SES effects on the use of variation sets in child-directed speech', *Journal of Child Language* 45 (2018), pp. 1423–38.

29 On better language skills with more interaction (see also sources
    in note 18): F. J. Zimmerman, J. Gilkerson, J. A. Richards, D. A.
    Christakis, D. Xu, S. Gray and U. Yapanel, 'Teaching by listening:
    the importance of adult–child conversations to language
    development', *Pediatrics* 124 (2009), pp. 342–9; A. Weisleder
    and A. Fernald, 'Talking to children matters: early language
    experience strengthens processing and builds vocabulary',
    Psychological Science 24 (2013), pp. 2143–52. Talking about what
    children are interested in: M. McGillion, J. M. Pine, J. S. Herbert
    and D. Matthews, 'A randomised controlled trial to test the effect
    of promoting caregiver contingent talk on language development
    in infants from diverse socioeconomic status backgrounds',
    Journal of Child Psychology and Psychiatry 58 (2017), pp. 1122–31.
    Helping children learn abstract concepts: K. Leech, R. Wei, J. R.
    Harring and M. L. Rowe, 'A brief parent-focused intervention to
    improve preschoolers' conversational skills and school readiness',
    Developmental Psychology 54 (2018), pp. 15–28.

7: ENDLESS FORMS MOST BEAUTIFUL

1   Except where noted otherwise, the story of Laura Bridgman is
    based on the following sources: S. G. Howe, *Annual Reports of
    the Perkins Institution* (Boston: John Eastburn, 1838–42); L. E.
    Richards, *Laura Bridgman: The Story of an Opened Door* (New York:
    D. Appleton & Co., 1928); B. L. McGinnity, J. Seymour-Ford and
    K. J. Andries, 'Laura Bridgman', Perkins History Museum, Perkins
    School for the Blind, Watertown, MA, https://www.perkins.org/
    history/people/laura-bridgman; L. Menand, 'Laura's world: what
    a deaf–blind girl taught the nineteenth century', *New Yorker*,
    June 2001, https://www.newyorker.com/magazine/2001/07/02/
    lauras-world; R. Mahoney, 'The education of Laura Bridgman',
    Slate, May 2014, https://slate.com/human-interest/2014/05/
    laura-bridgman-the-first-deaf-blind-person-to-be-successfully-
    educated-before-her-teacher-abandoned-her.html.

2   C. Dickens, *American Notes for General Circulation*, Vol. 1 (London: Chapman & Hall, 1842), p. 73.

3   S. G. Howe, *Ninth Annual Report of the Perkins Institution* (Boston: John Eastburn, 1841), p. 26.

4   Richards, *Laura Bridgman*, p. 36.

5   It is this anchoring in the submerged part of the communication iceberg that allows us still to communicate with one another despite each having a different version of the language of our community. So, having our own language doesn't mean that it is a 'private language', in the sense of Wittgenstein (*Philosophical Investigations*), because the meaning of its terms still originates in language use and interaction, as we outlined in chapter 1.

6   This paragraph is based on several sources: K. Kashefi and D. R. Lovley, 'Extending the upper temperature limit for life', *Science* 301 (2003), p. 934; C. Dalmasso, P. Oger, G. Selva, D. Courtine, S. L'Haridon, A. Garlaschelli et al., '*Thermococcus piezophilus* sp. nov., a novel hyperthermophilic and piezophilic archaeon with a broad pressure range for growth, isolated from a deepest hydrothermal vent at the mid-Cayman rise', *Systematic and Applied Microbiology* 39 (2016), pp. 440–4; M. S. Dodd, D. Papineau, T. Grenne, J. F. Slack, M. Rittner, F. Pirajno et al., 'Evidence for early life in Earth's oldest hydrothermal vent precipitates', *Nature* 543 (2017), pp. 60–4; National Stone Institute, *Stone Testing* (Oberlin, OH: Marble Institute of America, 2016); S. A. Padder, R. Prasad and A. H. Shah, 'Quorum sensing: a less known mode of communication among fungi', *Microbiological Research* 210 (2018), pp. 51–8.

7   A. Kalske, K. Shiojiri, A. Uesugi, Y. Sakata, K. Morrell and A. Kessler, 'Insect herbivory selects for volatile-mediated plant–plant communication', *Current Biology* 29 (2019), pp. 3128–33.

8   This paragraph is based on C. Grüter, 'Communication in social insects: sophisticated problem solving by small brains', in R. Menzel and J. Fischer, eds, *Animal Thinking: Contemporary Issues in Comparative Cognition* (Cambridge, MA: MIT Press, 2011), pp. 163–73.

9 R. T. Hanlon and J. B. Messenger, 'Adaptive coloration in young cuttlefish (*Sepia officinalis L.*): the morphology and development of body patterns and their relation to behaviour', *Philosophical Transactions of the Royal Society of London B, Biological Sciences* 320 (1988), pp. 437–87; P. Karoff, ' "Chameleon of the sea" reveals its secrets', Harvard John A. Paulson School of Engineering and Applied Sciences, 29 Jan. 2014, https://www.seas.harvard.edu/news/2014/01/chameleon-sea-reveals-its-secrets; R. T. Hanlon, M. J. Naud, P. W. Shaw and J. N. Havenhand, 'Transient sexual mimicry leads to fertilization', *Nature* 433 (2005), p. 212.

10 T. Price, P. Wadewitz, D. Cheney, R. Seyfarth, K. Hammerschmidt and J. Fischer, 'Vervets revisited: a quantitative analysis of alarm call structure and context specificity', *Nature Scientific Reports* 5 (2015), 13220.

11 F. Wegdell, K. Hammerschmidt and J. Fischer, 'Conserved alarm calls but rapid auditory learning in monkey responses to novel flying objects', *Nature Ecology & Evolution* 3 (2019), pp. 1039–42.

12 S. Dolotovskaya, J. Torroba Bordallo, T. Haus, A. Noll, M. Hofreiter, D. Zinner et al., 'Comparing mitogenomic timetrees for two African savannah primate genera (*Chlorocebus* and *Papio*)', *Zoological Journal of the Linnean Society* 181 (2017), pp. 471–83.

13 D. C. Dennett, 'Intentional systems in cognitive ethology: the "Panglossian paradigm" defended', *Behavioral & Brain Sciences* 6 (1983), pp. 343–90; R. Dunbar, *Gossip, Grooming and the Evolution of Language* (Cambridge, MA: Harvard University Press, 1996); L. F. Wiener, 'The evolution of language: a primate perspective', *Word* 35 (1984), pp. 255–69.

14 N. Collar and D. A. Christie, 'Common nightingale (*Luscinia megarhynchos*), version 1.0', in J. del Hoyo, A. Elliott, J. Sargatal, D. A. Christie and E. de Juana, eds, *Birds of the World* (Ithaca, NY: Cornell Lab of Ornithology, 2020), https://birdsoftheworld.org/bow/species/comnig1/cur/introduction.

15 A. R. Chandler, 'The nightingale in Greek and Latin poetry', *Classical Journal* 30 (1934), pp. 78–84; C. Maxwell, *The female*

sublime from Milton to Swinburne: bearing blindness (Manchester: Manchester University Press, 2001).

16 Although it's more typical for just males to sing among a number of European and North American songbirds, this picture doesn't hold across the world. In fact, it seems likely that female song is an ancestral trait that has been selected against in northern temperate regions: M. L. Hall, K. Riebel, K. E. Omland, N. E. Langmore and K. J. Odom, 'Female song is widespread and ancestral in songbirds', *Nature Communications* 5 (2014), pp. 1–6; K. Riebel, K. J. Odom, N. E. Langmore and M. L. Hall, 'New insights from female bird song: towards an integrated approach to studying male and female communication roles', *Biology Letters* 15 (2019): 20190059.

17 Many birds do have alarm calls (like the vervet monkeys) that can serve to warn of danger, to communicate location between pairs or members of a flock, or to beg for food – but these calls are largely innate: S. A. Gill and A. M. K. Bierema, 'On the meaning of alarm calls: a review of functional reference in avian alarm calling', *Ethology* 119 (2013), pp. 449–61. There are a few exceptions, including the remarkable vocal learning abilities of parrots, but these do not appear to be observed to the same extent in the wild as they are in the lab: I. M. Pepperberg, 'Acquisition of the same/different concept by an African grey parrot (*Psittacus erithacus*): learning with respect to categories of color, shape, and material', *Animal Learning and Behavior* 15 (1987), pp. 423–32.

18 Example of the song of the (superbly named) superb lyrebird: Zoos South Australia, 'Superb lyrebird imitating construction work', Adelaide Zoo, video, 4:01, 3 Aug. 2009, https://www.youtube.com/watch?v=WeQjkQpeJwY.

19 The rarity of songbird dialects: J. Podos and P. S. Warren, 'The evolution of geographic variation in birdsong', *Advances in the Study of Behavior* 37 (2007), pp. 403–58. Chickadee song variation: D. E. Kroodsma, B. E. Byers, S. L. Halkin, C. Hill, D. Minis, J. R. Bolsinger et al., 'Geographic variation in black-capped chickadee songs and singing behavior', *The Auk* 116 (1999), pp. 387–402.

Dialects associated with genetic variation: E. A. MacDougall-Shackleton and S. A. MacDougall-Shackleton, 'Cultural and genetic evolution in mountain white-crowned sparrows: song dialects are associated with population structure', *Evolution* 55 (2001), pp. 2568–75.

20 This paragraph draws on K. Riebel, R. F. Lachlan and P. J. Slater, 'Learning and cultural transmission in chaffinch song', *Advances in the Study of Behavior* 47 (2015), pp. 181–227; S. Carouso-Peck, O. Menyhart, T. J. DeVoogd and M. H. Goldstein, 'Contingent parental responses are naturally associated with zebra finch song learning', *Animal Behaviour* 165 (2020), pp. 123–32; M. D. Beecher, 'Why are no animal communication systems simple languages?', *Frontiers in Psychology* 12 (2021): 602635.

21 Cultural transmission of vocal learning appears in a few other species as well, such as humpback whales, but they are also subject to the same limitations as birdsong – whale song, too, may be better called 'whale music'. E. Mercado III and C. E. Perazio, 'Similarities in composition and transformations of songs by humpback whales (*Megaptera novaeangliae*) over time and space', *Journal of Comparative Psychology* 135 (2021), pp. 28–50.

22 O. Fehér, H. Wang, S. Saar, P. P. Mitra and O. Tchernichovski, 'De novo establishment of wild-type song culture in the zebra finch', *Nature* 459 (2009), pp. 564–8.

23 A. Diez and S. A. MacDougall-Shackleton, 'Zebra finches go wild! Experimental cultural evolution of birdsong', *Behaviour* 157 (2020), pp. 231–65.

24 We have focused primarily on communication using chemical, visual and auditory signalling, but other sensory modes are also recruited to communicate through tactile, electrical and vibrational means. However, apart from Laura Bridgman's use of touch to communicate, none of these modes of communication affords the kind of adaptable variation seen in human language.

25 This paragraph draws on D. M. Eberhard, G. F. Simons and C. D. Fennig, 'Sign language', in *Ethnologue: Languages of the World*, 23rd

edn (Dallas, TX: SIL International, 2020), online version: http://
www.ethnologue.com; National Institute on Deafness and Other
Communication Disorders, *American Sign Language* (fact sheet),
NIH Publication No. 11-4756 (Bethesda, MD: National Institutes of
Health, March 2019).

26 Relevant sources are T. Daneyko and C. Bentz, 'Click languages
tend to have large phoneme inventories: implications for
language evolution and change', in Y. Sahle, H. Reyes-Centeno
and C. Bentz, eds, *Modern Human Origins and Dispersal* (Tübingen,
Germany: Kerns Verlag, 2019), pp. 315–29; M. Yip, *Tone* (Cambridge:
Cambridge University Press, 2002).

27 J. Meyer, 'Typology and acoustic strategies of whistled languages:
phonetic comparison and perceptual cues of whistled vowels',
Journal of the International Phonetic Association 38 (2008), pp. 69–94;
H. F. Nater, *The Bella Coola Language*, Mercury Series, Canadian
Ethnology Service No. 92 (Ottawa: National Museums of Canada,
1984).

28 This paragraph builds on N. Evans and S. C. Levinson, 'The myth
of language universals: language diversity and its importance
for cognitive science', *Behavioral and Brain Sciences* 32 (2009), pp.
429–48; T. E. Payne, *Describing Morphosyntax: A Guide for Field
Linguists* (Cambridge: Cambridge University Press, 1997); T. Osada,
A Reference Grammar of Mundari (Tokyo: Institute for the Study of
Languages and Cultures of Asia and Africa, Tokyo University of
Foreign Studies, 1992).

29 E. Schultze-Berndt, 'Simple and complex verbs in Jaminjung: a
study of event categorisation in an Australian language', PhD diss.,
Radboud University, Nijmegen, Netherlands, 2000.

30 A. Y. Aikhenvald, *Classifiers: A Typology of Noun Categorization
Devices* (Oxford: Oxford University Press, 2000); P. K. Austin, 'A
grammar of the Diyari language of north-east South Australia',
PhD diss., Australian National University, Canberra, Australia,
1978.

31 This paragraph draws on Evans and Levinson, 'The myth of
language universals'; M. Steedman, 'Foundations of universal

grammar in planned action', in M. H. Christiansen, C. Collins and S. Edelman, eds, *Language Universals* (New York: Oxford University Press, 2009), pp. 174–99; D. L. Everett, 'Cultural constraints on grammar and cognition in Pirahã: another look at the design features of human language', *Current Anthropology* 46 (2005), pp. 621–46.

32   This paragraph draws on: A. Y. Aikhenvald, *Evidentiality* (Oxford: Oxford University Press, 2004); S. McLendon, 'Evidentials in eastern Pomo with a comparative survey of the category in other pomoan languages', in A. Y. Aikhenvald and D. M. V. Dixon, eds, *Studies in Evidentiality* (Philadelphia: John Benjamins, 2003), pp. 101–29.

33   This paragraph is based on the transcript of the Fox News Channel interview with Dick Cheney, 15 Feb. 2006: http://www.nbcnews. com/id/11373634#.XrLbfy-Z3OQ; E. Loeweke and J. May, *General grammar of Fasu (Namo Me)* (Ukarumpa, Papua New Guinea: Summer Institute of Linguistics, 2008).

34   Indeed, entire books are dedicated to such linguistic curiosities, such as G. Dorren, *Babel: around the world in twenty languages* (New York: Atlantic Monthly Press, 2018); G. McCulloch, *Because internet: understanding the new rules of language* (New York: Riverhead Books, 2019); J. McWhorter, *What language is: and what it isn't and what it could be* (New York: Avery, 2012).

35   Quoted in H. Hitchings, *The Language Wars: A History of Proper English* (New York: Farrar, Straus & Giroux, 2011), p. 21.

36   *UNESCO Atlas of the World's Languages in Danger* (Paris: UNESCO, 2010, http://www.unesco.org/languages-atlas/. Europe's endangered languages are indicative of the broader threat of rapid decline and extinction that many smaller languages face across the world because of globalization, with substantial collateral loss of cultural knowledge: A. Kik, M. Adamec, A. Y. Aikhenvald, J. Bajzekova, N. Baro, C. Bowern et al., 'Language and ethnobiological skills decline precipitously in Papua New Guinea, the world's most linguistically diverse nation', *Proceedings of the National Academy of Sciences* 118 (2021): e2100096118.

37 D. Nettle, 'Explaining global patterns of language diversity', *Journal of Anthropological Archaeology* 17 (1998), pp. 354–74.

38 Evans and Levinson, 'The myth of language universals'.

39 R. Molesworth, *An Account of Denmark, as It Was in the Year 1692* (London: Goodwin, (1694), p. 91.

40 K. Tucholsky, 'Eine schöne Dänin', in *Gesammelte Werke in zehn Bänden*, Vol. 5 (1927; repr. Hamburg, Germany: Rowohlt, 1975).

41 The sketch is from the Norwegian comedy show called *Uti Vår Hage* and can be viewed here: https://www.youtube.com/watch?v=s-mOY8VUEBk.

42 Except when explicitly noted otherwise, this section builds on the extensive review of Danish by F. Trecca, K. Tylén, A. Højen and M. H. Christiansen, 'Danish as a window onto language processing and learning', *Language Learning* 71 (2021), pp. 799–833, https://doi.org/10.1111/lang.12450.

43 The transliterations of the examples are rather rough, so for readers familiar with the International Phonetic Alphabet, here are some more precise transcriptions. Danish: *løbe* (to run) [ˈløːu̯ə]; *kniv* (knife) [ˈkʰniu̯ˀ]; *røget ørred* (smoked trout) [ˈʁʌjəðˀˈœ̞ʁʌðˀ]; *Find bilen!* (Find the car!) [ˈfɛnˀ ˈb̥iːʔln̩]; *Her er aben!* (Here's the monkey!) [ˈheˀʌ æʌ ˈɛːb̥m̩]. Norwegian: *røkt ørret* (smoked trout) [rœkt œ̂rːət].

44 E. Kidd, S. Donnelly and M. H. Christiansen, 'Individual differences in language acquisition and processing', *Trends in Cognitive Sciences* 22 (2018), pp. 154–69; E. Dąbrowska, 'Different speakers, different grammars: individual differences in native language attainment', *Linguistic Approaches to Bilingualism* 2 (2012), pp. 219–25; J. Street and E. Dąbrowska, 'More individual differences in language attainment: how much do adult native speakers of English know about passives and quantifiers?', *Lingua* 120 (2010), pp. 2080–94.

45 S. Goudarzi, 'We all speak a language that will go extinct', *New York Times*, 12 Aug. 2020, https://www.nytimes.com/2020/08/12/opinion/language-translation.html.

46 C. Tennie, J. Call and M. Tomasello, 'Ratcheting up the ratchet: on the evolution of cumulative culture', *Philosophical Transactions of the Royal Society B: Biological Sciences* 364 (2009), pp. 2405–15.

8: THE VIRTUOUS CIRCLE: BRAINS, CULTURE AND LANGUAGE

1   H. A. Wisbey Jr, 'The life and death of Edward H. Rulloff', *Crooked Lake Review*, May 1993, https://www.crookedlakereview.com/articl es/34_66/62may1993/62wisbey.html.

2   The entire wiring diagram of the tiny 'brain' of *C. elegans* is known; see, for example, S. J. Cook, T. A. Jarrell, C. A. Brittin, Y. Wang, A. E. Bloniarz, M. A. Yakovlev et al., 'Whole-animal connectomes of both *Caenorhabditis elegans* sexes', *Nature* 571 (2019), pp. 63–71. Trying to link a wiring diagram to behaviour, though, even for this tiny roundworm, remains a difficult challenge: F. Jabr, 'The connectome debate: is mapping the mind of a worm worth it?', *Scientific American*, 2 Oct. 2012.

3   F. De Waal, *Are We Smart Enough to Know How Smart Animals Are?* (New York: W. W. Norton, 2016). The figures given here are for the entire nervous system, not just the brain. Humans are by no means the animal with the largest numbers of neurons (or indeed brain size), being eclipsed by whales and, on some measures, elephants.

4   A. Washburn, 'Helen Hamilton Gardener', in E. T. James, J. Wilson James and P. S. Boyer, eds, *Notable American Women, 1607–1950: A Biographical Dictionary*, Vol. 2 (Cambridge, MA: Harvard University Press, 1974), pp. 11–13.

5   C. Koch, 'Does brain size matter?', *Scientific American Mind*, Jan.– Feb. 2016, pp. 22–5.

6   V. van Ginneken, A. van Meerveld, T. Wijgerde, E. Verheij, E. de Vries and J. van der Greef, 'Hunter–prey correlation between migration routes of African buffaloes and early hominids:

evidence for the "out of Africa" hypothesis', *Annals of Integrative Molecular Medicine* 4 (2017), pp. 1–5.

7   L. C. Aiello and P. Wheeler, 'The expensive-tissue hypothesis: the brain and the digestive system in human and primate evolution', *Current Anthropology* 36 (1995), pp. 199–221. One interesting line of evidence of early food processing, probably including cooking, comes from analysis of the size of molars in the human lineage – molars can be much smaller once there is no longer the need for munching large quantities of non-nutritious raw food: C. Organ, C. L. Nunn, Z. Machanda and R. W. Wrangham, 'Phylogenetic rate shifts in feeding time during the evolution of *Homo*', *Proceedings of the National Academy of Sciences* 108 (2011), pp. 14555–9.

8   This viewpoint is especially associated with the anthropologist Robin Dunbar: for example, R. I. M. Dunbar, *Grooming, Gossip, and the Evolution of Language*. Dunbar suggests that the early function of language may be building, and learning about, social relationships; and, as he points out, this function is still evident today in the gossip and chit-chat that comprise most of our daily conversations, with task-focused information exchanges taking a back seat.

9   The precise sense of smartness that might be relevant to this kind of argument is by no means widely agreed upon but presumably includes the ability to deal in a highly flexible way with a complex environment, to plan, to solve problems, and to understand and collaborate with others. Indeed, outside the narrow domain of intelligence testing, defining smartness 'in the wild', and particularly across species, is very difficult: see e.g. M. Colombo, D. Scarf and T. Zentall, 'The comparative psychology of intelligence: Macphail revisited', *Frontiers in Psychology* 12 (2021): 648782. Thus, smartness (along with cleverness and intelligence) may be yet another familiar term that turns out not to have a common essence.

10 For a similar argument, see Everett, *How Language Began*. It is possible that natural selection for greater intelligence might operate via a small number of so-called *NOTCH2NL* genes, which

appear to control the pace at which neurons are created early in brain development: I. T. Fiddes, G. A. Lodewijk, M. Mooring, C. M. Bosworth, A. D. Ewing, G. Mantalas et al., 'Human-specific *NOTCH2NL* genes affect notch signaling and cortical neurogenesis', *Cell* 173 (2018), pp. 1356–69; I. K. Suzuki, D. Gacquer, R. Van Heurck, D. Kumar, M. Wojno, A. Bilheu et al., 'Human-specific *NOTCH2NL* genes expand cortical neurogenesis through delta/notch regulation', *Cell* 173 (2018), pp. 1370–84. Looking across species, brains change shape as they change size – but these size changes are mostly well predicted by assuming a single underlying factor in neural development. Different brain areas grow at different speeds so that prolonging or shortening brain development automatically reshapes the brain. As an aside, the brain areas that are especially involved in language do not seem to have grown disproportionately: B. L. Finlay and R. B. Darlington, 'Linked regularities in the development and evolution of mammalian brains', *Science* 268 (1995), pp. 1578–84; B. L. Finlay, R. B. Darlington and N. Nicastro, 'Developmental structure in brain evolution', *Behavioral and Brain Sciences* 24 (2001), pp. 263–78.

11   It is interesting to wonder if there are specific cognitive changes that are crucial in underpinning the human ability to play linguistic charades. One suggestion focuses on the possibility of a uniquely human 'interactional engine'; see e.g. S. C. Levinson, 'On the human "interaction engine"', in N. J. Enfield and S. C. Levinson, eds, *Roots of Human Sociality: Culture, Cognition and Interaction* (Oxford: Berg, 2006), pp. 39–69. Another, not necessarily incompatible, viewpoint centres on the perhaps uniquely human ability to form shared understandings and joint plans with others; see e.g. Tomasello, *Origins of Human Communication*. A further component may be a specialized human ability to 'read' the minds of others by attributing to them beliefs, desires and intentions; see e.g. H. M. Wellman, *The Child's Theory of Mind* (Cambridge, MA: MIT Press, 1992). It seems likely, though, that it was the coming together of a constellation of existing traits, rather than the emergence of a single qualitatively new trait, that was critical

to kick-starting the uniquely human trajectory of rich linguistic, social and cultural life: E. L. MacLean, 'Unraveling the evolution of uniquely human cognition', *Proceedings of the National Academy of Sciences* 113 (2016), pp. 6348–54.

12   This viewpoint is a version of the 'cultural brain' hypothesis, which posits that brain size and cultural complexity have mutually reinforced each other, leading to rapid expansions of both; see e.g. M. Muthukrishna, M. Doebeli, M. Chudek and J. Henrich, 'The cultural brain hypothesis: how culture drives brain expansion, sociality, and life history', *PLoS Computational Biology* 14 (2018): e1006504. Here, we put a particular emphasis on the development of the ability to create charades to underpin the cumulative development of language as a critical trigger and amplifier for this process. For related viewpoints, see M. Tomasello, *The Cultural Origins of Human Cognition* (Cambridge, MA: Harvard University Press, 1999).

13   E. M. Scerri, M. G. Thomas, A. Manica, P. Gunz, J. T. Stock, C. Stringer et al., 'Did our species evolve in subdivided populations across Africa, and why does it matter?', *Trends in Ecology & Evolution* 33 (2018), pp. 582–94.

14   A. S. Brooks, J. E. Yellen, R. Potts, A. K. Behrensmeyer, A. L. Deino, D. Leslie et al., 'Long-distance stone transport and pigment use in the earliest middle stone age', *Science* 360 (2018), pp. 90–4.

15   Interestingly, there does seem to be evidence of 'exchange' between individual animals – a sort of positive tit-for-tat, for example, in vervet monkeys: C. Fruteau, B. Voelkl, E. van Damme and R. Noë, 'Supply and demand determine the market value of food providers in wild vervet monkeys', *Proceedings of the National Academy of Sciences* 106 (2009), pp. 12007–12. Indeed, lab experiments with rats seem to show reciprocation between grooming and supplying food: M. K. Schweinfurth and M. Taborsky, 'Reciprocal trading of different commodities in Norway rats', *Current Biology* 28 (2018), pp. 594–9. But this is very different from groups exchanging goods or services with each other, as with the Haush and Cook, and, it is conjectured, between bands of middle Stone Age people trading valuable rocks.

16 This is not to say that non-human animals are not intelligent. Indeed, animals, and apes in particular, are remarkably intelligent when considered on their own terms (for a thorough and impassioned treatment of this topic, see De Waal, *Are We Smart Enough to Know How Smart Animals Are?*). It seems quite likely that subjective experience and even consciousness may not be unique to humans but extend to other animals as well, including octopi and cuttlefish: P. Godfrey-Smith, *Other Minds: The Octopus, the Sea, and the Deep Origins of Consciousness* (New York: Farrar, Straus & Giroux, 2016).

17 M. Tomasello, 'Why don't apes point?', in Enfield and Levinson, eds, *Roots of Human Sociality*, pp. 506–24. Interestingly, chimps do make pointing gestures to humans, using the whole arm and an open hand rather than precise pointing with the fingers, in order to point out the location of food they wish to be given: see e.g. D. A. Leavens and W. D. Hopkins, 'Intentional communication by chimpanzees (*Pan troglodytes*): a cross-sectional study of the use of referential gestures', *Developmental Psychology* 34 (1998), pp. 813–22. But of course this is an instrumental action, aiming to achieve the chimp's own objective. Human infant pointing, by contrast, is often focused on helpfully pointing out something of interest or something that another person would like to have. Although scholars differ concerning the precise significance of apes pointing to humans, there is agreement that apes do not spontaneously point to each other.

18 J. Call, B. A. Hare and M. Tomasello, 'Chimpanzee gaze following in an object-choice task', *Animal Cognition* 1 (1998), pp. 89–99.

19 M. Tomasello, J. Call and A. Gluckman, 'The comprehension of novel communicative signs by apes and human children', *Child Development* 68 (1997), pp. 1067–81. And note that chimps fail when the container is indicated by gaze, even though chimps and other apes can follow gaze successfully – for example, if one chimp looks at an item of food, the other chimps' gaze will follow: M. Tomasello, J. Call and B. Hare, 'Five primate species follow the visual gaze of conspecifics', *Animal Behaviour* 55 (1998), pp. 1063–9.

20 B. Hare and M. Tomasello, 'Chimpanzees are more skillful in competitive than in cooperative cognitive tasks', *Animal Behaviour* 68 (2004), pp. 571–81.

21 It is fascinating that, while competitive chimps fail to understand human pointing, many other species can do so: for reviews, see A. Miklósi and K. Soproni, 'A comparative analysis of animals' understanding of the human pointing gesture', *Animal Cognition* 9 (2006), pp. 81–93; M. A. Krause, M. A. R. Udell, D. A. Leavens and L. Skopos, 'Animal pointing: changing trends and findings from 30 years of research', *Journal of Comparative Psychology* 132 (2018), pp. 326–45. For domesticated animals, such as dogs, goats and horses, it is possible that this ability may have arisen through thousands of years of contact with humans, leading to selective breeding favouring the animal's ability to interact successfully with humans. This explanation does not account for the case of African elephants, which can also use human pointing gestures to locate food. African elephants have never been domesticated, although they have been taken from the wild and tamed to work alongside humans for at least four thousand years: A. F. Smet and R. W. Byrne, 'African elephants can use human pointing cues to find hidden food', *Current Biology* 2 (2013), pp. 2033–7.

22 R. A. Gardner and B. T. Gardner, 'Teaching sign language to a chimpanzee', *Science* 165 (1969), pp. 664–72.

23 E. S. Savage-Rumbaugh, J. Murphy, R. A. Sevcik, K. E. Brakke, S. L. Williams, D. M. Rumbaugh et al., 'Language comprehension in ape and child', *Monographs of the Society for Research in Child Development* 58 (1993), pp. 1–222.

24 I. Schamberg, D. L. Cheney, Z. Clay, G. Hohmann and R. M. Seyfarth, 'Call combinations, vocal exchanges and interparty movement in wild bonobos', *Animal Behaviour* 122 (2016), pp. 109–16.

25 M. Tomasello, J. Call, K. Nagell, R. Olguin and M. Carpenter, 'The learning and use of gestural signals by young chimpanzees: a trans-generational study', *Primates* 37 (1994), pp. 137–54.

26 R. W. Byrne, E. Cartmill, E. Genty, K. E. Graham, C. Hobaiter and J. Tanner, 'Great ape gestures: intentional communication

with a rich set of innate signals', *Animal Cognition* 20 (2017), pp. 755–69.

27 I. Nengo, P. Tafforeau, C. C. Gilbert, J. G. Fleagle, E. R. Miller, C. Feibel et al., 'New infant cranium from the African Miocene sheds light on ape evolution', *Nature* 548 (2017), pp. 169–74.

28 Byrne et al., 'Great ape gestures'. Indeed, considering culture more broadly, it is possible that much or all of the 'cultural' variation between chimpanzee groups can be explained by purely genetic variation between these groups: K. E. Langergraber, C. Boesch, E. Inoue, M. Inoue-Murayama, J. C. Mitani, T. Nishida et al., 'Genetic and "cultural" similarity in wild chimpanzees', *Proceedings of the Royal Society B: Biological Sciences* 278 (2011), pp. 408–16. By contrast, humans exhibit spectacular cultural diversity independent of genetics – such, perhaps, is the catalytic power of language.

29 It used to be thought that fossil evidence concerning the uniquely human 'descended larynx' supposedly required to produce more intelligible vocal speech, and in particular the vowel contrasts present in spoken language, restricted the appearance of spoken language to the last two hundred thousand years: P. Lieberman, 'Primate vocalizations and human linguistic ability', *Journal of the Acoustical Society of America* 44 (1968), pp. 1574–84. But it turns out that almost every aspect of this account is open to debate, which leaves open the possibility that spoken (and, of course, signed) languages may have arisen very much earlier: L. J. Boë, T. R. Sawallis, J. Fagot, P. Badin, G. Barbier, G. Captier et al., 'Which way to the dawn of speech? Reanalyzing half a century of debates and data in light of speech science', *Science Advances* 5 (2019): eaaw3916. Moreover, any putative evolution of speech-related adaptations would in any event require that there was a pre-existing pressure for improved spoken language ability, possibly through the kind of vocal charades discussed in chapter 1.

30 A number of species do show some amount of cultural evolution, such as orcas, apes and even bees, but its extent and complexity pales in comparison with the evolution of human culture; for a

discussion, see A. Whiten, 'Cultural evolution in animals', *Annual Review of Ecology, Evolution, and Systematics* 50 (2019), pp. 27–48.

31 For purpose of experimental design, the researchers also tested the opposite pairing of colours and tastes – tasty pink corn and bitter red corn – and got the same results: E. van de Waal, C. Borgeaud and A. Whiten, 'Potent social learning and conformity shape a wild primate's foraging decisions', *Science* 340 (2013), pp. 483–5.

32 L. V. Luncz and C. Boesch, 'Tradition over trend: neighboring chimpanzee communities maintain differences in cultural behavior despite frequent immigration of adult females', *American Journal of Primatology* 76 (2014), pp. 649–57.

33 Tomasello, *Cultural Origins of Human Cognition*.

34 R. Kaplan, *The Nothing That Is: A Natural History of Zero* (New York: Oxford University Press, 2000); C. Seife, *Zero: The Biography of a Dangerous Idea* (New York: Viking, 2000).

35 P. Gordon, 'Numerical cognition without words: evidence from Amazonia', *Science* 306 (2004), pp. 496–9.

36 P. Brown, 'How and why are women more polite: some evidence from a Mayan Community', in S. McConnell-Ginet, R. Borker and N. Furman, eds, *Women and Language in Literature and Society* (New York: Praeger, 1980), pp. 111–36; S. C. Levinson and P. Brown, 'Immanuel Kant among the Tenejapans: anthropology as empirical philosophy', *Ethos* 22 (1994), pp. 3–41; S. C. Levinson and P. Brown, 'Background to "Immanuel Kant among the Tenejapans"', *Anthropology Newsletter* 34 (1993), pp. 22–3.

37 S. C. Levinson, 'Yélî Dnye and the theory of basic color terms', *Journal of Linguistic Anthropology* 10 (2000), pp. 3–55.

38 See N. B. McNeill, 'Colour and colour terminology', *Journal of Linguistics* 8 (2008), pp. 21–33; T. Regier, C. Kemp and P. Kay, 'Word meanings across languages support efficient communication', in B. MacWhinney and W. O'Grady, eds, *The Handbook of Language Emergence* (Hoboken, NJ: Wiley-Blackwell, 2015), pp. 237–63.

39 G. Thierry, P. Athanasopoulos, A. Wiggett, B. Dering and J. R. Kuipers, 'Unconscious effects of language-specific terminology on

preattentive color perception', *Proceedings of the National Academy of Sciences* 106 (2009), pp. 4567–70.

40 M. Maier and R. Abdel Rahman, 'Native language promotes access to visual consciousness', *Psychological Science* 29 (2018), pp. 1757–72.

41 What is particularly neat about these experiments is that the measure is completely non-linguistic and completely incidental to the task people are given (to report a change in shape, not colour).

42 E. Sapir, 'The status of linguistics as a science', *Language* 5 (1929), pp. 207–14; B. L. Whorf, 'Science and linguistics', in *Language, Thought, and Reality: Selected Writings of Benjamin Lee Whorf*, ed. J. B. Carroll (Cambridge, MA: MIT Press, 1956), pp. 207–19.

43 Sapir and Whorf seem unlikely collaborators. Yale's Edward Sapir was one of the most distinguished linguists of his time. His PhD student, Benjamin Lee Whorf, started out as a chemical engineer and only took up linguistics as a sideline. Remarkably, Whorf carried out his pathbreaking graduate research at Yale while working as a full-time fire prevention officer for the Hartford Fire Insurance Company.

44 Maynard Smith and Szathmáry, *The Origins of Life*.

45 Lots of eukaryotes reproduce asexually, and many sexually reproducing groups of species include some asexually reproducing species (e.g. different species of salamander adopt different strategies). Some rather complex animals – including the Komodo dragon – can reproduce asexually, though this is rare: P. C. Watts, K. R. Buley, S. Sanderson, W. Boardman, C. Ciofi and R. Gibson, 'Parthenogenesis in Komodo dragons', *Nature* 444 (2006), pp. 1021–2.

46 Interestingly, multicellularity appears to have evolved independently at least twenty-five times throughout the evolution of life. Multicelled plants and animals began to take off only over the last seven hundred million years or so: R. K. Grosberg and R. R. Strathmann, 'The evolution of multicellularity: a minor major transition?', *Annual Review of Ecology, Evolution, and Systematics* 38 (2007), pp. 621–54; J. T. Bonner, 'The origins of multicellularity', *Integrative Biology* 1 (1998), pp. 27–36.

47 N. Kutsukake, 'Complexity, dynamics and diversity of sociality in group-living mammals', *Ecological Research* 24 (2009), pp. 521–31.

48 R. I. M. Dunbar, 'The social ecology of gelada baboons', in D. I. Rubenstein and R. W. Wrangham, eds, *Ecological Aspects of Social Evolution: Birds and Mammals* (Princeton, NJ: Princeton University Press, 1986), pp. 332–51.

49 C. N. Waters, J. Zalasiewicz, C. Summerhayes, A. D. Barnosky, C. Poirier, A. Gałuszka et al., 'The Anthropocene is functionally and stratigraphically distinct from the Holocene', *Science* 351 (2016), p. 262; M. Subramanian, 'Anthropocene now: influential panel votes to recognize Earth's new epoch', *Nature* 21 (2019), https://www.nature.com/articles/d41586-019-01641-5.

EPILOGUE: LANGUAGE WILL SAVE US FROM THE SINGULARITY

1   Y. M. Bar-On, R. Phillips and R. Milo, 'The biomass distribution on Earth', *Proceedings of the National Academy of Sciences* 115 (2018), pp. 6506–11.

2   'The size of the World Wide Web (the internet)', World Wide Web Size, accessed 26 July 2021, https://www.worldwidewebsize.com/.

3   J. McCormick, 'Worldwide AI spending to hit $35.8 billion in 2019', *Wall Street Journal*, 13 March 2019, https://www.wsj.com/articles/worldwide-ai-spending-to-hit-35-8-billion-in-2019-11552516291.

4   As reported by S. Ulam, 'John von Neumann 1903–1957', *Bulletin of the American Mathematical Society* 64 (1958), pp. 1–49, https://www.ams.org/journals/bull/1958-64-03/S0002-9904-1958-10189-5/S0002-9904-1958-10189-5.pdf.

5   Musk's actual words, as reported, were: 'I think we should be very careful about artificial intelligence. If I had to guess at what our biggest existential threat is, it's probably that. So we need to be very careful . . . With artificial intelligence we are summoning the demon. In all those stories where there's the guy with the pentagram and the holy water, it's like – yeah, he's sure he can

control the demon. Doesn't work out': 'Elon Musk: artificial intelligence is our biggest existential threat', *Guardian*, 27 Oct. 2014, https://www.theguardian.com/technology/2014/oct/27/elon-musk-artificial-intelligence-ai-biggest-existential-threat.

6   S. Russell, *Human Compatible: Artificial Intelligence and the Problem of Control* (London: Penguin, 2019).

7   'Top 6 best chess engines in the world in 2021', *iChess*, 3 June 2021, https://www.ichess.net/blog/best-chess-engines/.

8   D. Silver, J. Schrittwieser, K. Simonyan, I. Antonoglou, A. Huang, A. Guez et al., 'Mastering the game of Go without human knowledge', *Nature* 550 (2017), pp. 354–9.

9   AlphaStar Team, 'AlphaStar: mastering the real-time strategy game Starcraft II', Research (blog), *DeepMind*, 24 Jan. 2019, https://deepmind.com/blog/article/alphastar-mastering-real-time-strategy-game-starcraft-ii.

10 For a non-technical overview of GPT-3's capabilities, see W. D. Heaven, 'OpenAI's new language generator GPT-3 is shockingly good – and completely mindless', *MIT Technology Review*, 20 July 2020, https://www.technologyreview.com/2020/07/20/1005454/openai-machine-learning-language-generator-gpt-3-nlp/. For a sceptical perspective on earlier generations of AI, from a different perspective from ours, see H. Dreyfus, *What Computers Can't Do: The Limits of Artificial Intelligence* (Cambridge, MA: MIT Press, 1972).

11 T. Brown, B. Mann, N. Ryder, M. Subbiah, J. Kaplan, P. Dhariwal et al., 'Language models are few-shot learners', *OpenAI*, submitted 28 May 2020, updated 22 July 2020, https://arxiv.org/abs/2005.14165v4. The number of synapses in the human brain is far larger still – estimated to be more than two hundred trillion in the cerebral cortex alone: see e.g. C. Koch, *Biophysics of Computation: Information Processing in Single Neurons* (New York: Oxford University Press, 1999), p. 87.

12 The full story is here: https://drive.google.com/file/d/1qtPa1cGgzTCaGHULvZIQMC03bk2G-YVB/view. The more one reads, the more incoherent it begins to seem – a clever knitting

together of stock phrases and word patterns with no hint of a narrative thread or overall point.

13 The interview is, as of 2 June 2021, at: Umais (@Maizek), 'You mention that most of the HENRY prompts are yours', Twitter, 21 July 2020, 9:55 a.m., https://twitter.com/Maizek_/status/ 1285604281761095685.

14 K. Lacker, 'Giving GPT-3 a Turing test', Kevin Lacker's Blog, 6 July 2020, https://lacker.io/ai/2020/07/06/giving-gpt-3-a-turing-test.html.

15 J. C. Wong, '"A white-collar sweatshop": Google Assistant contractors allege wage theft', *Guardian*, 25 June 2019, https://www. theguardian.com/technology/2019/may/28/a-white-collar-sweatshop-google-assistant-contractors-allege-wage-theft.

ACKNOWLEDGEMENTS

We are indebted to so many people who have helped make this book possible that any list will inevitably be incomplete. But we'll do our best!

We'd first like to thank our families, Anita and Sunita, and Louie, Maya and Caitlin, for their kindness and forbearance, and for acting over the past two decades as incredibly valuable sounding boards for our ideas, which gradually coalesced into *The Language Game* (Anita even read through and commented on the whole book) – and in particular for tolerating our long absences and lengthy visits to each other's homes in Ithaca and Oxford. Much of the writing and revising was done during the dark days of the Covid-19 pandemic – thanks especially to our families for putting up with our long hours on the book at such a difficult time.

Our wonderful colleagues and collaborators have also helped inspire and develop many of the ideas described here. Most of them, too, have provided detailed feedback on the academic work that feeds into this book and in some cases on parts of the manuscript itself. In particular, we would like to thank Blair Armstrong, Inbal Arnon, Arash Aryani, Damian Blasi, Dorthe Bleses, Louisa Bogaerts, Pablo Contreras Kallens, Chris Conway, Rick Dale, Christina Dideriksen, Mark Dingemanse, Laurent Dubreuil, Thomas Farmer, Felicity Frinsel, Ram Frost, Rebecca Frost, Riccardo Fusaroli, Anne Hsu, Anders Højen, Erin Isbilen, Byurakn Ishkhanyan, Ethan Jost, Evan Kidd, Maryellen MacDonald,

Stewart McCauley, Alice Milne, Jennifer Misyak, Padraic Monaghan, Luca Onnis, Andreas Roepstorff, Noam Siegelman, Fabio Trecca, Kristian Tylén, Serene Wang and Ben Wilson.

We also owe large intellectual debts to numerous wonderful researchers who have helped create the new approach to understanding language that we outline in this book – though not all of them will agree with everything we say, of course. We have had particularly important and formative conversations over the years with, among many others, Christina Behme, Andy Clark, Herb Clark, Bill Croft, Peter Culicover, Ewa Dąbrowska, Jeff Elman, Nick Enfield, Nick Evans, Adele Goldberg, John Goldsmith, Simon Kirby, Stephen Levinson, Elena Lieven, Brian MacWhinney, Jay McClelland, Martin Pickering, Pete Richerson, Linda Smith, Mark Steedman, Michael Tomasello, Bruce Tomblin and Chris Westbury.

Thanks, too, for the incredibly careful and valuable input to the entire manuscript from Morten's Cornell fall 2020 Topics in Psycholinguistics seminar, from detailed sub-editing to help clarifying, reorganizing and strengthening (and challenging) our key arguments: Mica Carroll, Forrest Davis, Isabella Di Giovanni, Steven Elmlinger, Penelope Rosenstock-Murav, Amrit Singh, Linda Webster – and especially Pablo Contreras Kallens, Katerina Faust, Felicity Frinsel, Severine Hex, Erin Isbilen, Alice Milne, Emma Murrugarra and Serene Wang, who went through multiple versions of several of the chapters. In addition, we've had critical feedback and helpful pointers on specific parts of the book from Marisa Casillas, Marcus Perlman and Fabio Trecca. The book is immeasurably better for this incredibly generous and insightful input. We're also grateful for help with the figures from Pablo Contreras Kallens, Matthias Parchettka and Marcus Perlman; and our special thanks go out to Sunita Christiansen for the five excellent figures she made for us.

We'd like to thank our funders. Morten was supported by the Independent Research Fund Denmark (grant number DFF-7013-00074), the Binational Science Foundation (grant number 2011107), the Economic and Social Research Council, UK (grant number ES/L008955/1) and the Australian Research Council (grant number 74695). Nick was supported by the ESRC Network for Integrated Behavioural Science (grant number ES/P008976/1) and the Leverhulme Trust (grant number RP2012-V-022). We also owe our respective institutions our thanks: Cornell University (especially the Department of Psychology), Aarhus University in Denmark (School of Communication and Culture and the Interacting Minds Centre), the Haskins Laboratories and the University of Warwick (especially the Behavioural Science Group at Warwick Business School), for providing the intellectual environment and practical support to make this work possible. The development of the ideas in this book has also benefited greatly from our visits to the Max Planck Institute for Psycholinguistics in Nijmegen, Netherlands, and the Santa Fe Institute in New Mexico.

Finally, warm thanks to our enthusiastic and insightful editors in the United Kingdom (Susanna Wadeson at Transworld) and the United States (Thomas Kelleher of Basic Books), and our wonderful literary agents, Catherine Clarke, of Felicity Bryan Associates, Oxford, and George Lucas, of Inkwell Management, New York. Thanks also to our production editor Kelly Anne Lenkevich and wonderful copy-editors Christina Palaia and Gillian Somerscales for helping to turn our manuscript into a finished book.

Working on this book and the ideas that underpin it has been terrifically exciting and often rather joyful for both of us. We are truly grateful for the support of so many delightful and talented people who have helped make this possible.

PICTURE ACKNOWLEDGEMENTS

Figure 1.1, 'A view of Endeavour's watering place in the Bay of Good Success', Tierra del Fuego: f.11 – BL Add MS 23920.jpg. Image taken from *A Collection of Drawings made in the Countries visited by Captain Cook in his First Voyage, 1768–1771*, originally published/produced in 1769, held and digitized by the British Library and uploaded to Flickr Commons, Wikimedia Commons, https://commons.wikimedia.org/wiki/File:Endeavour%27s_watering_place_in_the_Bay_of_Good_Success,_Tierra_del_Fuego_-_Drawings_made_in_the_Countries_visited_by_Captain_Cook_in_his_First_Voyage_(1769),_f.11_-_BL_AdD_MS_23920.jpg. The caption reads: 'A view of the Endeavour's watering place in the Bay of Good Success, Tierra del Fuego, with natives. January 1769'.

Figure 2.1: This figure is based on figure 1.C in S. C. Levinson, 'Turn-taking in human communication – origins and implications for language processing', *Trends in Cognitive Sciences* 20 (2016), pp. 6–14.

Figure 3.1: Figure from J. Wilkins, *An Essay Towards a Real Character and a Philosophical Language* (London: Gellibrand, 1668).

Figure 3.2: Image copied from https://upload.wikimedia.org/wikipedia/commons/e/e7/Booba-Kiki.svg.

Table 4.1: Table from H. Diessel, 'Construction grammar and first language acquisition', in T. Hoffmann and G. Trousdale, eds, *The Oxford Handbook of Construction Grammar* (Oxford: Oxford University Press, 2013), pp. 347–64. Original data from M. Tomasello, *First Verbs: A Case Study of Early Grammatical Development* (Cambridge: Cambridge University Press, 1992).

Table 4.2: Table adapted from H. Hammarström, 'Linguistic diversity and language evolution', *Journal of Language Evolution* 1 (2016), pp. 19–29.

Table 4.3: Adapted from Wikipedia, 'Old English Grammar', last modified 25 July 2021, https://en.wikipedia.org/wiki/ Old_English_grammar.

Figure 5.1: Linguistic tree from A. Schleicher, 'Die ersten Spaltungen des indogermanischen Urvolkes', *Allgemeine Monatsschrift für Wissenschaft und Literatur* 3 (1853), pp. 786–7 at p. 787. Tree of life diagram from C. Darwin, *On the Origin of Species by Means of Natural Selection* (London: John Murray, 1859), pp. 116–17.

Figure 5.2: H. Gray, *Anatomy of the Human Body* (New York: Lea & Febiger, 1918), available via Wikimedia Commons.

Figure 7.1: Figure created using data from H. Hammarström, R. Forkel, M. Haspelmath and S. Bank, *Glottolog 4.3* (Jena, Germany: Max Planck Institute for the Science of Human History, 2020), https://doi.org/10.5281/zenodo.4061162.

INDEX

Note: References in *italics* are to figures; references in **bold** are to tables; 'n' refers to note number in 'Notes and Resources' section.

ABOUT THE AUTHORS

Morten H. Christiansen is the William R. Kenan, Jr. Professor of Psychology at Cornell University, Professor in Cognitive Science of Language at the School of Communication and Culture, Aarhus University, Denmark, and Senior Scientist at the Haskins Labs. He was awarded the Cognitive Psychology Section Award from the British Psychological Society in 2013 and a Charles A. Ryskamp Research Fellowship from the American Council of Learned Societies in 2006. He was elected Fellow of the Association for Psychological Science in 2009, made Fellow of the Psychonomic Society in 2013, elected Fellow of the Cognitive Science Society in 2017 and elected as a foreign member of the Royal Danish Academy of Sciences and Letters in 2021. He lives with his family in New York.

Nick Chater is a professor of behavioural science at the University of Warwick. He is the author of the award-winning book *The Mind Is Flat*. He lives in Oxford.